Heath Mathematics

Walter E. Rucker · Clyde A. Dilley · David Lowry

Contributing author: **Earl G. Ockenga**

 D. C. Heath and Company
Lexington, Massachusetts   Toronto

Illustrations   Leo Abbett; Charlie Freeman/Sharon Kurlansky; George Hughes/
Gwen Goldstein; Mark Kelly/Sharon Kurlansky; Andrew Shiff

Design of front matter and Warmup: Verne Bowman

Photography   Arthur d'Arazian/The Image Bank: 276; Jonathan Barkan: 117;
Sharon Beals: 82, 83, 152, 157, 195; Fredrik D. Bodin: 89; Gerald Brimacombe/The
Image Bank: 28; Stuart Cohen: 302; Kevin Galvin: 19; Ellis Herwig/Stock, Boston:
337; J. Irwin/Shostal Assoc.: 53; Mark Kane: 165; Tom Magno: 80, 100, 106, 131,
188, 196, 197, 201, 202, 203, 217, 273, 284, 324, 365, 366, 387, 424, 425; D. McCoy/
Rainbow: 143; Morse Photography, Bernal's Gator Swim Club, Cambridge, Mass.:
Cover; NASA: 20, 22, 45; Julie O'Neil: 49, 74, 213, 269, 286, 323, 330, 331, 384, 385;
Wayne Ruple/Globe Photos, Inc.: 348, 349; Deidra Delano Stead: 191, 260, 280;
Augustus Upitis/Shostal Assoc.: 245; Jerry Wachter/Focus on Sports: 113; Jonathan
Wright/Bruce Coleman, Inc.: 301

Contents

Use the Warmup "magazine" to
- discover whether you need to review some whole number skills
- review and practice whole number skills
- apply your skills on puzzles and brain teasers

THE WHOLE NUMBER REVIEW
WARMUP

DON'T PASS THIS UP!

NO PASSING ZONE

Nine of these signs have 30 sides.

How many of them are No-Passing signs?

BROKEN KEY

37
629
+598
1601

The key for 4 is broken. How many whole numbers less than 100 can-not be printed on the calculator?

SOMETHING FISHY HERE

lure $3   reel $29

rod $15   tackle box $12

Cindy, Tim, and Lance each bought 3 different items. Cindy said she spent $47. Tim said he spent $30. Lance said he spent $45. Who mis-calculated?

NAIL IT DOWN!

If you bought 12 of these boxes of nails, how many boxes would be left?

TEST YOUR SKILLS

Read. Then write in words.

1. 72,000

2. 152,300

3. 5,023,816

4. 593,627,000

5. 23,568,400,000

6. 9,051,007,000

ANY ERRORS? Read the REMINDER, then GRAB A PENCIL!

READING REMINDER

Look at the place-value chart. See how commas help in reading large numbers.

Trillions			Billions			Millions			Thousands			Ones		
Hundreds	Tens	Ones	Hundreds	Tens	Ones	Hundreds	Tens	Ones	Hundreds	Tens	Ones	Hundreds	Tens	Ones
				9	6	1	4	6	0	8	5	2	7	3

Standard numeral: 9, 6, 1 4 6, 0 8 5, 2 7 3

Read as: ninety-six billion, one hundred forty-six million, eighty-five thousand, two hundred seventy-three.

GRAB A PENCIL!

Give the place value of the underlined digit.

1. 1<u>4</u>6,235   *(4 ten thousands)*

2. 7,<u>2</u>16,305

3. 29<u>6</u>,003,165

4. 573,<u>8</u>06

5. <u>3</u>4,872,129

6. <u>7</u>,238,422,000

7. 9<u>5</u>,061

8. 6,291,0<u>8</u>2

9. 8,<u>1</u>52,883,420,000

10. 861,5<u>9</u>7

11. 1,<u>6</u>66,660,000

12. 5<u>6</u>,842,073,000,000

CHECK YOURSELF

You should be able to find each answer in this list:

8 hundreds, 7 billions, 2 hundred thousands, 5 thousands, 1 hundred billion, 6 trillions, 9 tens, 4 ten thousands, 6 millions, 0 hundreds, 3 ten millions, 6 hundred millions

CAN YOU BEAT IT?

An amateur astronomer wrote these numbers in words in 4 minutes. Can you beat that?

1. 272,000

2. 6,892,300

3. 17,426,000

4. 106,350

5. 7,080,010

6. 450,800,000

7. 675,000,000,000

8. 23,500,000,000,000

WORLD'S TALLEST TALE

Crack the code to get the message.

0	1	2	3	4	5	6	7	8	9
A	C	D	E	F	H	I	J	K	L
M	N	O	P	R	S	T	U	W	Y

6 * 5 * 3 * 4 * 3   6 * 5
0   4 * 0 * 4 * 0 * 3 * 4
8 * 5 * 2 * 5 * 3   1 * 2 * 8 * 5
0 * 4 * 3   5 * 2   6 * 0 * 9 * 9
6 * 5 * 0 * 6   5 * 3   5 * 0 * 5
6 * 2   8 * 3 * 3 * 3   6 * 5 * 3 * 0
3 * 3 * 1 * 1 * 3 * 2   6 * 1   6 * 5 * 3
0 * 5 * 6 * 4 * 2 * 2 * 2 * 0 * 3.

Inside Out

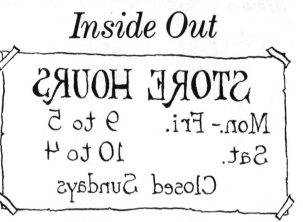

How many hours is the store open each week?

MAP FACTS

Kokomo is as far north of Indianapolis as Ottenbein is west of Kokomo. Indianapolis is in what direction from Ottenbein?

TaKe NoTe

If 2 girls can fill 2 notebooks in 2 weeks and 3 boys can fill 3 notebooks in 3 weeks, how many notebooks can 6 girls and 6 boys fill in 6 weeks?

STRING ALONG

Be a winner! Build the longest string of math words.

Rules
- The last letter of a math word must match the first letter of the next word.
- You cannot use a word more than once.

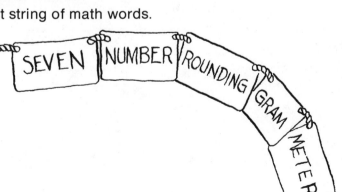

TEST YOUR SKILLS

Round to the nearest hundred.
1. 893   2. 816

3. 3952   4. 14,768

Round to the nearest ten thousand.
5. 78,143   6. 14,463

7. 915,036   8. 198,721

Round to the nearest million.
9. 7,416,000   10. 46,800,050

11. 5,824,000   12. 169,700,000

ANY ERRORS?   Read the RULES, then GRAB A PENCIL!

ROUNDING RULES

1. Find the place to which you are rounding.
2. Look at the digit to the right.
3. If that digit is 5 or greater, round up. If that digit is less than 5, round down.

EXAMPLES: Round to the nearest ten thousand.

418,350
8 is greater than 5.
Round up: 420,000

1,364,291
4 is less than 5.
Round down: 1,360,000

GRAB A PENCIL!

Round to the nearest hundred.
1. 742   2. 616   3. 1846   4. 1395   5. 6982

Round to the nearest ten thousand.
6. 58,342   7. 13,099   8. 715,036   9. 746,428

Round to the nearest million.
10. 45,421,000   11. 46,800,000   12. 29,790,000   13. 15,455,800

CHECK YOURSELF

You should be able to find each answer in this list:
| 600 | 700 | 1400 | 1800 | 7000 | 10,000 | 60,000 | 720,000 | 750,000 |
| 15,000,000 | | | 30,000,000 | | | 45,000,000 | | 47,000,000 |

CAN YOU BEAT IT?

A commercial fisherman rounded these numbers to the nearest thousand in 50 seconds. Can you beat that?

6724 pounds is about 7000 pounds.

1. 1745   2. 2068   3. 7502   4. 995   5. 6440   6. 7270

7. 8801   8. 14,435   9. 2906   10. 8413   11. 39,850   12. 45,550

4

MATH SCRABBLE

Unscramble these math words.

NTE   NILIOML

RDUHNDE   SOUNDTAH

EON   OLIBLIN

WORLD'S MOST ABSURD AD

Crack the code to get the message.
Hint: Use your rounding skills.

A	B	C	D	· · ·	Z
10	20	30	40	· · ·	260

ADVERTISEMENT

FOR SALE   Lawn rake with no teeth.
69 * 149 * 153 * 41   62 * 148 * 184
179 * 8 * 114 * 88 * 142 * 73
251 * 12 * 177 * 44 * 188
234 * 91 * 204 * 76   138 * 153
202 * 179 * 47 * 53 * 193.

Call 555-6888 anytime.

CALENDAR FACTS

A month has 5 Mondays. The month neither begins nor ends on Monday. On what day of the week does the month begin?

TRIANGLE TANGLE

How many triangles can you find in this square? *Hint:* There are more than 40.

Scavenger Hunt

Look on these two pages. Find the smallest number with a 4 in the thousands place. Round the number to the nearest hundred. Did you get 14,400?

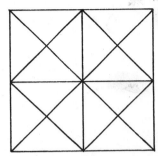

NO FAIR PEEKING

Here are four views of the same cube. The cube has the numbers 1–6. What numbers are on opposite sides of the cube?

TEST YOUR SKILLS

Add.

1.	2.	3.	4.	5.
4	56	754	637	842
8	48	237	67	960
7	+73	+691	+582	637
+8				+295

ANY ERRORS?   Read the ADVICE, then GRAB A PENCIL!

ADDITION ADVICE

Here's how!

	ADD ONES. REGROUP.	ADD TENS. REGROUP.	ADD HUNDREDS. REGROUP.
858	858	858	858
+796	+796	+796	+796
	4	54	1654

GRAB A PENCIL!

Add.

1.	78	2.	529	3.	5173
	+56		+298		+8861

4.	48	5.	392	6.	8476
	21		517		1295
	+68		+636		+863

7.	17	8.	248	9.	831
	23		367		1526
	14		421		395
	+56		+588		+4288

CHECK YOURSELF

You should be able to find each sum in this list:

110	134	137	827	1545	1624
7040	10,634	14,034			

CAN YOU BEAT IT?

Find the 3 errors. It took an Internal Revenue Service agent 1 minute to correct the errors. Can you beat that?

$8274
+1469
~~$10,733~~
$9,743

1.	629	2.	4106
	+498		+3986
	1127		7092

3.	14,261	4.	6926
	+7,559		+629
	21,820		7655

5.	7169	6.	85,326
	+887		+9,099
	8056		94,335

WEIGH-IN TIME

Sonya and Bill weigh 150 kg.

Bill and Rita weigh 140 kg.

Sonya and Rita weigh 130 kg.

How much does each person weigh?

HAVE YOU HEARD THIS ONE?

Crack the code to get the joke.

CODE

a	b	c	d	···	z
2	5	8	11	···	77

What did the jar of mayonnaise say to the refrigerator?

"8 * 35 * 44 * 56 * 14   59 * 23 * 14
11 * 44 * 44 * 53.   26 * 38
11 * 53 * 14 * 56 * 56 * 26 * 41 * 20."

SCAVENGER HUNT

Look on these two pages. Find the largest number less than 1000. Find the smallest number greater than 1000. Add. Did you get a total of 2087?

REFLECT ON THIS

WHAT CAPITAL LETTERS OF THE ALPHABET LOOK LIKE THEIR MIRROR IMAGE?

Who's Keeping Score?

Cristina and Jeff bowled three games. The scores were:
    game 1—152 to 122
    game 2—132 to 112
    game 3—150 to 140
Cristina's total score was 424. Which games did she win?

LOOK BOTH WAYS

Rules	Example
• Use the last four digits of your telephone number. ⟶	6214
• Reverse the digits. ⟶	4126
• Add. ⟶	10340
• Reverse the digits. ⟶	04301
• Add. ⟶	14,641
• Stop when you get a sum that reads the same forward as backward.	

SUBTRACTION SUGGESTIONS

Here's how!

Here's how to handle zeros in subtraction.

	REGROUP A TEN. SUBTRACT ONES.	REGROUP A HUNDRED. SUBTRACT TENS.	SUBTRACT HUNDREDS.
5 6 3 −2 7 8	5 $\overset{5}{\cancel{6}}$ 3 −2 7 8 ___ 5	$\overset{4}{\cancel{5}}\overset{15}{\cancel{6}}$ 3 −2 7 8 __ 8 5	$\overset{4}{\cancel{5}}\overset{15}{\cancel{6}}$ 3 −2 7 8 2 8 5

REGROUP. THEN SUBTRACT.
7 0 0 0 −4 3 7	$\overset{6}{\cancel{7}}\overset{9}{\cancel{0}}\overset{9}{\cancel{0}}\overset{10}{\cancel{0}}$ −4 3 7 6 5 6 3

GRAB A PENCIL!

Subtract.

1.   96
   −58

2.   182
   −67

3.   521
   −496

4.   304
   −142

5.   800
   −417

6.   6735
   −2158

7.   5812
   −4779

8.   6000
   −1591

9.   9004
   −7567

CHECK YOURSELF

You should be able to find each answer in this list:

25   38   115   162   383

1033   1437   4409   4577

CAN YOU BEAT IT?

A bus driver said these differences in 1 minute. Can you beat that? Write only your answers.

48 seats.
13 empty seats.
35 passengers on board.

1. 48 − 21

2. 62 − 40

3. 67 − 55

4. 85 − 43

5. 96 − 72

6. 78 − 15

7. 69 − 36

8. 65 − 34

9. 99 − 78

10. 87 − 16

BROKEN KEY

The key for 4 is broken. How many whole numbers less than 100 cannot be printed on the calculator?

WHERE IN THE WORLD?

Crack the code to name the city.

In what city would you pay 335 markkas for a $90 pair of skis? The city's code name is

GI * DF * KM * RT * HJ * MO * JL * HJ.

HOW TIME FLIES

The sum of the digits shown on the watch is 10. How many minutes before the sum of the digits will be 20?

Stuck On Stickers

> I MAY BE SLOW, BUT I'M
> AHEAD OF YOU.

Carolyn, Brad, Jennifer, and Paul collected a total of 14 bumper stickers. Each had more than one sticker. Jennifer had the most. Carolyn had more than Paul. Brad had the fewest.

How many bumper stickers did each person have?

HORSING AROUND

You bought a horse for $60 on Monday. On Tuesday you sold it for $70. You bought the horse back for $80 on Wednesday. On Thursday you sold the horse again for $90. Did you make or lose money? How much money did you make or lose?

Scavenger Hunt

a b c d ... z
$1 $2 $3 $4 ... $26

Find the most expensive 3-letter word on this page.

TEST YOUR SKILLS

Multiply.

1. 187	2. 308	3. 82	4. 461	5. 826
×4	×7	×37	×25	×476

ANY ERRORS?   Read the MEMO, then GRAB A PENCIL!

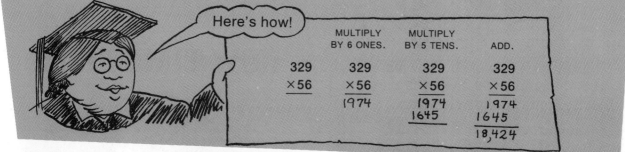

MULTIPLICATION MEMO

Here's how!

	MULTIPLY BY 6 ONES.	MULTIPLY BY 5 TENS.	ADD.
329	329	329	329
×56	×56	×56	×56
	1974	1974	1974
		1645	1645
			18,424

GRAB A PENCIL!

Multiply.

1. 37	2. 448	3. 237
×8	×7	×9

4. 93	5. 44	6. 41
×76	×53	×71

7. 635	8. 301	9. 946
×63	×62	×29

10. 235	11. 730	12. 1046
×462	×349	×78

CHECK YOURSELF
You should be able to find each answer
in this list:

296	2133	2332	2911	3136
7068	18,662	27,434	40,005	
81,588	108,570	254,770		

CAN YOU BEAT iT?

A box-office cashier said these
products in 90 seconds. Can you
beat that? Write only your answers.

$21

1. 4 × 8	2. 7 × 7	3. 9 × 6
4. 3 × 9	5. 5 × 8	6. 4 × 5
7. 2 × 7	8. 0 × 8	9. 9 × 9
10. 4 × 6	11. 6 × 6	12. 8 × 4
13. 70 × 5	14. 50 × 9	15. 90 × 7
16. 80 × 7	17. 60 × 3	18. 40 × 7

HAPPY BIRTHDAY

\ S	M	T	W	T	F	S
APRIL						
	1	2	3	4	5	6
7	8	9	10	11	12	13
14	15	16	17	18	19	20
21	22	23	24	25	26	27
28	29	30				

Add together the dates of the days before Tom's birthday and that number will be four times the date of his birthday. When is Tom's birthday?

FOOL'S GOLD

Jill and Brenda panned for gold. Jill said to Brenda, "Give me one of your nuggets and I'll have as many as you have." Brenda said, "Give me one of your nuggets and I'll have twice as many as you." How many nuggets did each girl have?

FOUL PLAY

Brian scored 10 points more than Dave. Calvin scored 6 points less than Brian. Mike scored 8 points more than Calvin.

Who scored the most points?
Who scored the least points?

World's Worst Guarantee

Crack the code to get the message.

9	9	9	9	9	9	9	9	9
×1	×2	×3	×4	×5	×6	×7	×8	×9
a	b	c	d	e	f	g	i	k
l	m	n	o	r	s	t	u	y

PROFESSIONAL WASTE REMOVAL
For service, call 555-9348.

54 * 9 * 63 * 72 * 54 * 54 * 9 * 27 * 63 * 72 * 36 * 27
63 * 72 * 9 * 45 * 9 * 27 * 63 * 45 * 45 * 36,   36 * 45
36 * 36 * 72 * 18 * 9 * 45   81 * 36 * 72 * 45
63 * 9 * 45 * 18 * 9 * 63 * 45   18 * 9 * 27 * 81.

DON'T PASS THIS UP!

Nine of these signs have 30 sides.

How many of them are No-Passing signs?

TEST YOUR SKILLS

Multiply.

1. 437
×600

2. 592
×380

3. 746
×409

4. 8314
×270

5. 6947
×802

ANY ERRORS?   Read the MEMO, then GRAB A PENCIL!

MULTIPLICATION MEMO

If you know how to do these—

MULTIPLY BY 6 ONES.

329
×6
1974

MULTIPLY BY 8 HUNDREDS.

329
×800
263,200

then you know how to do this:

MULTIPLY BY 6 ONES, THEN BY 8 HUNDREDS.

329
×806
1974
2632
265,174

GRAB A PENCIL!

Multiply.

1. 397
×40

2. 885
×700

3. 629
×800

4. 438
×120

5. 681
×470

6. 926
×380

7. 234
×102

8. 680
×405

9. 702
×904

10. 6225
×420

11. 8341
×602

12. 5876
×130

CHECK YOURSELF
You should be able to find each answer
in this list:

15,880	23,868	52,560	275,400
320,070	351,880	503,200	619,500
634,608	763,880	2,614,500	5,021,282

CAN YOU BEAT IT?

A hobby-store manager counted packages and multiplied to find the number of beads. She said these products in 1 minute. Can you beat that?

3 packages
96
×3
288
beads in all.

1. 120
×5

2. 240
×7

3. 175
×4

4. 325
×9

A PENNY FOR YOUR THOUGHTS

Kevin guessed 450 pennies.
Lance guessed 580 pennies.
Carla guessed 318 pennies.

One guess was off by 91, one was off by 39, and one was off by 171.

How many pennies are in the jar?

Through The Looking Glass

The number 808 looks like its mirror image. What other numbers less than 1000 look like their mirror image?

SCAVENGER HUNT

Look on these two pages. Find the largest 3-digit number. Find the smallest 3-digit number. Multiply. Did you get a product of 94,452?

FOR THE BIRDS

Three times the price is $50 more than two times the price. What is the price of the parrot?

Where In The World?

Crack the code to name the city.
In what city would you pay 15,300 yen for a $64 camera?
The city's code name is GLPBL.

NAIL IT DOWN!

If you bought 12 of these boxes of nails, how many boxes would be left?

TEST YOUR SKILLS

Divide.

1. $7\overline{)453}$ 2. $3\overline{)802}$ 3. $47\overline{)1753}$ 4. $24\overline{)8741}$

ANY ERRORS?   Read the DIRECTIONS, then GRAB A PENCIL!

DIVISION DIRECTIONS

Here's how!

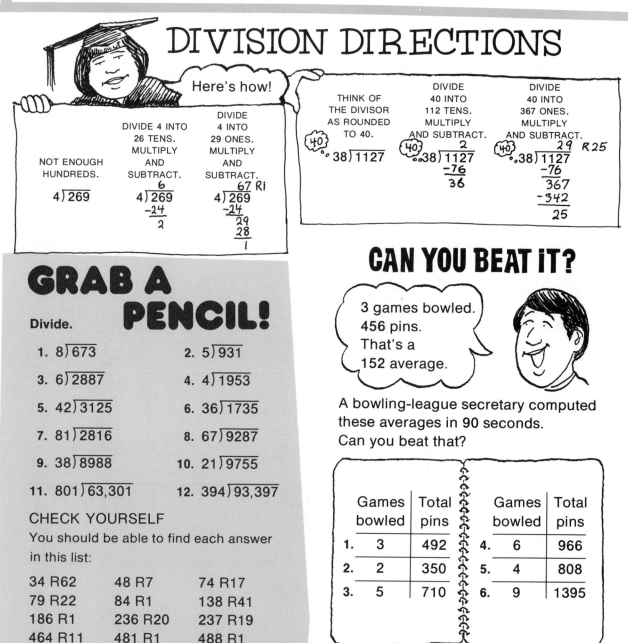

NOT ENOUGH HUNDREDS.

$4\overline{)269}$

DIVIDE 4 INTO 26 TENS. MULTIPLY AND SUBTRACT.

$$\begin{array}{r} 6 \\ 4\overline{)269} \\ -24 \\ \hline 2 \end{array}$$

DIVIDE 4 INTO 29 ONES. MULTIPLY AND SUBTRACT.

$$\begin{array}{r} 67\,R1 \\ 4\overline{)269} \\ -24 \\ \hline 29 \\ 28 \\ \hline 1 \end{array}$$

THINK OF THE DIVISOR AS ROUNDED TO 40.

40
$38\overline{)1127}$

DIVIDE 40 INTO 112 TENS. MULTIPLY AND SUBTRACT.

40
$$\begin{array}{r} 2 \\ 38\overline{)1127} \\ -76 \\ \hline 36 \end{array}$$

DIVIDE 40 INTO 367 ONES. MULTIPLY AND SUBTRACT.

40
$$\begin{array}{r} 29\ R25 \\ 38\overline{)1127} \\ -76 \\ \hline 367 \\ -342 \\ \hline 25 \end{array}$$

GRAB A PENCIL!

Divide.

1. $8\overline{)673}$ 2. $5\overline{)931}$

3. $6\overline{)2887}$ 4. $4\overline{)1953}$

5. $42\overline{)3125}$ 6. $36\overline{)1735}$

7. $81\overline{)2816}$ 8. $67\overline{)9287}$

9. $38\overline{)8988}$ 10. $21\overline{)9755}$

11. $801\overline{)63,301}$ 12. $394\overline{)93,397}$

CHECK YOURSELF

You should be able to find each answer in this list:

34 R62	48 R7	74 R17
79 R22	84 R1	138 R41
186 R1	236 R20	237 R19
464 R11	481 R1	488 R1

CAN YOU BEAT IT?

3 games bowled.
456 pins.
That's a
152 average.

A bowling-league secretary computed these averages in **90 seconds**.
Can you beat that?

	Games bowled	Total pins		Games bowled	Total pins
1.	3	492	4.	6	966
2.	2	350	5.	4	808
3.	5	710	6.	9	1395

PICK OUT THE SQUARES

How many squares do you see?

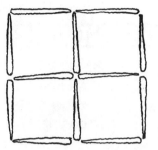

Draw a picture. Show how to move 3 toothpicks to make 3 squares all the same size.

Finders Keepers?

LOST AND FOUND

Found. Man's billfold. Owner must identify contents. Call 555-6262 after 6 p.m.

There are six bills (ones, fives, and tens) in the billfold. There are more fives than tens. There are more tens than ones. How much money is in the billfold?

SCAVENGER HUNT

Look on these two pages to find this mystery number.

CLUES:
- It is a 4-digit number.
- Each digit is odd.
- It is divisible by 5 and 9.

DOGGONE IT!

Lucky is 7 years older than Rover and 4 years older than Fido. Fido is twice Rover's age. How old is Lucky?

Whistling In The Dark

2 whistles and 3 books cost $19.
3 whistles and 2 books cost $16.
How much does one whistle cost?

TaKiNG STocK

Elmer counted 9 pigs and cows.
He counted 10 cows and horses.
He counted 16 animals in all.

How many cows did he count?

TEST YOUR SKILLS

Divide.

1. $27\overline{)8153}$ 2. $53\overline{)37,461}$ 3. $438\overline{)89,404}$ 4. $561\overline{)33,704}$

ANY ERRORS?   Read the DIRECTIONS, then GRAB A PENCIL!

DIVISION DIRECTIONS

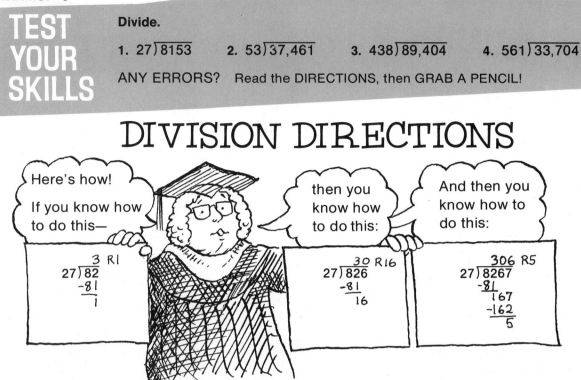

Here's how!

If you know how to do this—

$$\begin{array}{r} 3 \text{ R1} \\ 27\overline{)82} \\ -81 \\ \hline 1 \end{array}$$

then you know how to do this:

$$\begin{array}{r} 30 \text{ R16} \\ 27\overline{)826} \\ -81 \\ \hline 16 \end{array}$$

And then you know how to do this:

$$\begin{array}{r} 306 \text{ R5} \\ 27\overline{)8267} \\ -81 \\ \hline 167 \\ -162 \\ \hline 5 \end{array}$$

GRAB A PENCIL!

Divide.

1. $2\overline{)61}$ 2. $4\overline{)825}$

3. $43\overline{)895}$ 4. $67\overline{)694}$

5. $28\overline{)1703}$ 6. $52\overline{)3671}$

7. $52\overline{)36,714}$ 8. $3\overline{)1226}$

9. $173\overline{)6956}$ 10. $284\overline{)22,721}$

CHECK YOURSELF

You should be able to find each answer in this list:

10 R24	20 R35	30 R1	40 R36	60 R23
70 R31	80 R1	206 R1	408 R2	706 R2

CAN YOU BEAT IT?

A horticulturist said these quotients in 55 seconds. Can you beat that? Write only your answers.

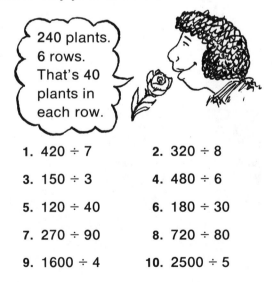

240 plants. 6 rows. That's 40 plants in each row.

1. $420 \div 7$ 2. $320 \div 8$

3. $150 \div 3$ 4. $480 \div 6$

5. $120 \div 40$ 6. $180 \div 30$

7. $270 \div 90$ 8. $720 \div 80$

9. $1600 \div 4$ 10. $2500 \div 5$

Who Cleaned The Brushes?

> **HELP WANTED**
>
> TEENAGERS. Immediate job openings for barn painters. No experience required. Call 555-1162 between 2 and 5 p.m.

A group of teenagers were hired. They were paid a total of $910 in $100 bills and $10 bills. Each got the same number of $100 bills and each got the same number of $10 bills. How many teenagers were there?

WHERE IN THE WORLD?

Crack the code to name the city.

In what city would you pay 2800 pesetas for a $400 moped?

The city's code name is PDGULG.

SOMETHING FISHY HERE

lure $3   reel $29

rod $15   tackle box $12

Cindy, Tim, and Lance each bought 3 different items. Cindy said she spent $47. Tim said he spent $30. Lance said he spent $45. Who miscalculated?

KEEP THE CHANGE

Two dimes, some nickels, one quarter, and seven pennies total 77¢. How many nickels are there?

SCAVENGER HUNT

Look on these two pages. Find the largest 4-digit number. Find the smallest 2-digit number. Divide. Did you get a quotient of 826 R7?

LOOSE CHANGE

Hot dog 49¢   Salad 46¢   Milk 38¢

Karen bought two items. She gave the cashier a $1 bill and got back 3 coins in change. What did she buy?

POSTTEST

A good score on this test means you
are ready to start Chapter 1.

A. Write in words.
1. 207,000
2. 36,400,000
3. 8,050,010

B. Round 327,401,985 to the nearest
1. million.
2. hundred.
3. ten thousand.

C.

1.	2.	3.	4.	5.
6473 +7409	46 93 +85	619 278 +653	827 68 +298	506 948 674 +871

D.

1.	2.	3.	4.	5.
851 −283	9073 −4624	8412 −766	600 −249	7012 −6747

E.

1.	2.	3.	4.	5.
581 ×4	6027 ×8	814 ×74	627 ×481	903 ×397

F.

1.	2.	3.	4.	5.
827 ×800	659 ×460	724 ×209	5816 ×780	2943 ×508

G. 1. 7)4580 2. 38)2328 3. 45)7642 4. 436)36200

H. 1. 26)9107 2. 72)43511 3. 122)61223 4. 387)15486

**Score
with Honors**

0 wrong   1 wrong   2 wrong

Decimals

1

Decimals

The space shuttle *Columbia* roared into orbit for the first time on April 12, 1981. *Columbia* remained in orbit for 54.5 hours before reentering the earth's atmosphere and landing in the southern California desert.

During its descent *Columbia* was traveling 7 times the speed of sound, or about 1.4167 miles each second.

To read this reentry speed, we can use a place-value chart.

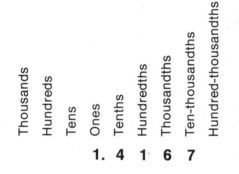

Thousands	Hundreds	Tens	Ones	Tenths	Hundredths	Thousandths	Ten-thousandths	Hundred-thousandths
			1.	4	1	6	7	

1. Read the whole-number part
   "one"   **1.4167**

2. Read the decimal point as "and"
   "and"   **1.4167**

3. Read the decimal part as you would read a whole number
   "four thousand one hundred   **1.4167**
      sixty-seven"

4. Read the value of the last place on the right
   "ten-thousandths"   **1.4167**
      ↑

One and four thousand one hundred sixty-seven ten-thousandths

EXERCISES

For 295.781603, give the digit that is in the

1. tens place
2. tenths place
3. hundreds place
4. hundredths place
5. ten-thousandths place
6. thousandths place
7. millionths place
8. hundred-thousandths place

Read aloud. Then write in words.

9. 0.52
10. 0.036
11. 5.72
12. 0.0591

13. 7.324
14. 6.0938
15. 42.16590
16. 7.28304

17. 6203.149
18. 620.3149
19. 62.03149
20. 6.203149

Write the standard numeral.

21. eight and nine tenths
22. fifteen and six hundredths
23. forty and one hundred twenty-five thousandths
24. ninety-four ten-thousandths
25. two hundred seventy-eight and seven hundred sixty-five thousandths
26. one hundred fifty-two and three hundred eighty-two millionths

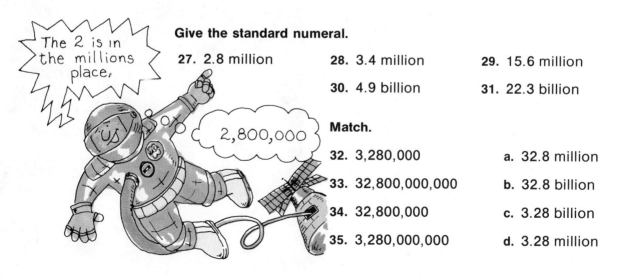

The 2 is in the millions place.

2,800,000

Give the standard numeral.

27. 2.8 million
28. 3.4 million
29. 15.6 million
30. 4.9 billion
31. 22.3 billion

Match.

32. 3,280,000   a. 32.8 million
33. 32,800,000,000   b. 32.8 billion
34. 32,800,000   c. 3.28 billion
35. 3,280,000,000   d. 3.28 million

Rounding decimals

The space shuttle *Columbia* can carry cargo as well as people into space. The cargo bay measures 18.146 meters in length.

To write a rule for rounding decimals, we can use a place-value chart.

Tens	Ones	Tenths	Hundredths	Thousandths
1	8.	1	4	6

Numbers like this can be rounded in several ways. To round to the nearest whole number:

1. Find the digit in the ones place.

   ↓
   18.146

2. a. Look at the digit that is one place to the right. If it is 5 or greater, round up.

   b. If it is less than 5, write the digit in the ones place.

   ↓
   18.146

I is less than 5, so we don't round up.

18 is the nearest whole number.

Rounded to the nearest tenth, 18.146 is 18.1.
Rounded to the nearest hundredth, 18.146 is 18.15.

EXERCISES

Round each decimal to the nearest one (or whole number).

1. 26.3
2. 8.9
3. 35.6
4. 52.5
5. 74.09
6. 24.83
7. 76.45
8. 89.368
9. 99.72
10. 153.495
11. 279.89
12. 399.634

Round to the nearest tenth.

13. 6.73
14. 5.28
15. 12.06
16. 23.029
17. 65.38
18. 51.46
19. 79.82
20. 184.60
21. 196.193
22. 220.095
23. 358.551
24. 296.742

Round to the nearest hundredth.

25. 79.835
26. 16.374
27. 29.182
28. 74.365
29. 32.298
30. 38.409
31. 86.635
32. 72.382
33. 263.1141
34. 591.2963
35. 748.5294
36. 599.6994

Round 369.4278351 to the nearest

37. tenth
38. thousandth
39. hundredth
40. ten-thousandth
41. millionth
42. hundred-thousandth

★ **43.** Study the clues to find this number. ☐.☐☐☐

Clue 1

If you round the number to the nearest whole number, you get 6.

Clue 2

If you round the number to the nearest tenth, you get 6.0.

Clue 3

If you round the number to the nearest hundredth, you get 6.00.

Clue 4

It is the smallest such number.

Comparing decimals

Cascade Junior High School holds a coin-stacking contest each year. The table shows the time it took each of 5 contestants to stack 50 pennies.

Contestant	Time (seconds)
John Bradley	43.53
Bev Dorr	43.17
Vern Eastman	45.39
Charlie Fitch	44.07
Tara Kilby	43.57

Who stacked the coins in a shorter time, John Bradley or Bev Dorr?

To answer the question, compare the decimals by starting at the left and comparing the digits that are in the same place.

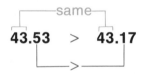

$$43.53 > 43.17$$

So, Bev Dorr stacked the coins in a shorter time.

EXERCISES

1. Who stacked the coins in a shorter time, Vern Eastman or Tara Kilby?

2. Charlie Fitch's time is shorter than only one other person's time. Whose time is that?

3. Is Tara Kilby's time longer or shorter than John Bradley's time?

4. Rank the times from shortest time to longest time. Who had the shortest time?

< or >?

5. 3.8 ● 3.9

6. 5.06 ● 5.02

7. 12.34 ● 12.034

8. 9.09 ● 10

9. 82.05 ● 82.049

10. 75.283 ● 75.29

11. 0.12 ● 0.099

12. 15.03 ● 14.13

13. 8.235 ● 12.68

14. 3.27 ● 0.327

15. 86.73 ● 867.3

16. 2.999 ● 3

In the tallest-stack event, each contestant gets 3 tries to build the tallest stack of pennies. The table shows the time it took contestants to build their tallest stacks.

Use the table to complete.

Contestant	Number of pennies in stack	Time
Juan Amigna	99	2 minutes 1.43 seconds
Bev Dorr	99	2 minutes 1.56 seconds
Jennifer Hartshorn	101	2 minutes 12.13 seconds
Bill McNelly	99	2 minutes 1.46 seconds
John Roberts	101	2 minutes 12.06 seconds

17. Who stacked 101 pennies in a shorter time?

18. Who stacked 99 pennies in the shortest time?

19. A contestant with a taller stack ranks higher than a contestant with a shorter stack. When 2 contestants build stacks with the same number of pennies, the contestant with the shorter time ranks higher. Rank the contestants.

 **PROJECT** Try the coin-stacking events yourself. Each penny must be flat on a table to start and must be picked up (not slid off the edge).

Adding and subtracting decimals

Jane made two runs down the slalom course. Her times were 35.26 seconds and 36.19 seconds. In a slalom race the two times are added and the skier with the fastest total time wins.

$$\begin{array}{r} \overset{1}{3}\overset{1}{5}.26 \\ +36.19 \\ \hline 71.45 \end{array}$$

When adding or subtracting decimals, be sure to line up the decimal points.

Alice had a total time of 74.02 seconds. You can subtract to find out how much better Jane's time was. You can estimate the difference by subtracting 71 from 74.

$$\begin{array}{r} 7\overset{3}{4}.\overset{9}{0}2 \\ -71.45 \\ \hline 2.57 \end{array}$$

EXERCISES
Give each sum.

1. $\begin{array}{r} 3.7 \\ +2.8 \end{array}$

2. $\begin{array}{r} 5.94 \\ +3.8 \end{array}$

3. $\begin{array}{r} 65.4 \\ +78.9 \end{array}$

4. $\begin{array}{r} 6.88 \\ +9.758 \end{array}$

5. $\begin{array}{r} 5.9384 \\ +2.6578 \end{array}$

6.	5.9	7.	9.08	8.	4.3	9.	88.60	10.	0.2735
	6.8		3.65		6.58		5.79		0.9115
	+3.7		+8.17		+9.4		+30.70		+0.2673

Give each difference.

11.	5.3	12.	9.0	13.	1.83	14.	2.834	15.	0.544
	−2.7		−3.5		−0.91		−1.799		−0.270

16.	6.3482	17.	8.07	18.	5.4	19.	4	20.	2.3
	−1.7063		−2.9		−3.68		−2.38		−1.657

Give each sum or difference. Remember to line up the decimal points.

21. 5.63 + 2.84   22. 4.38 − 1.59   23. 7.98 + 3.59

24. 0.084 − 0.009   25. 5.93 + 24.3   26. 15.6 − 8.34

27. 9.06 + 10.4   28. 17 − 9.83   29. 8.4 + 3.9 + 6.2

30. 4 − 1.382   31. 6.84 + 2.056   32. 6.831 − 2.4

Solve.

33. Find each skier's total time.

34. How much less was Franklin's total time than Langley's?

35. What was the difference between the fastest and slowest total times?

36. Rank the six skiers from fastest to slowest. (Use total times.)

37. What time would Davis have had to get on her second run to win the slalom?

Time in seconds

Name	First Run	Second Run
Brown	35.26	36.19
Davis	35.74	38.28
Franklin	36.29	35.48
Jones	38.02	37.54
Langley	36.13	38.29
Manning	37.18	36.42

38. ⭐ **ME OH MY!**

The letters M, E, and Y stand for three digits. Find the digit that each letter stands for.

```
  M.E
+ M.Y
-----
 EY.E
```

Multiplying decimals

Below are two methods for finding the product

$$\begin{array}{r} 13.4 \\ \times 2.8 \\ \hline \end{array}$$

ESTIMATION METHOD

Step 1.
Multiply as whole numbers.

$$\begin{array}{r} 13.4 \\ \times 2.8 \\ \hline 1072 \\ 268 \\ \hline 3752 \end{array}$$

Step 2.
Estimate the product and place the decimal point.

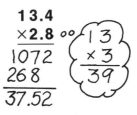

$$\begin{array}{r} 13.4 \\ \times 2.8 \\ \hline 1072 \\ 268 \\ \hline 37.52 \end{array}$$

$$\begin{array}{r} 13 \\ \times 3 \\ \hline 39 \end{array}$$

SHORTCUT METHOD

Step 1.
Multiply as whole numbers.

$$\begin{array}{r} 13.4 \\ \times 2.8 \\ \hline 1072 \\ 268 \\ \hline 3752 \end{array}$$

Step 2.
Count the digits to the right of the decimal points.

$$\begin{array}{r} 13.4 \\ \times 2.8 \\ \hline 1072 \\ 268 \\ \hline 3752 \end{array}$$

1 digit
+1 digit
―――――
2 digits

Step 3.
Count off the same number of digits to place the decimal point in the product.

$$\begin{array}{r} 13.4 \\ \times 2.8 \\ \hline 1072 \\ 268 \\ \hline 37.52 \end{array}$$

EXERCISES

Copy each "product" and place the decimal point.

1.	7.3	2.	9.01	3.	3.4	4.	200	5.	6.9
	×5.8		×5.2		×0.16		×7.1		×0.15
	4234		46852		544		14200		1035

6.	8.6	7.	3.01	8.	0.47	9.	4.7	10.	4.7
	×0.07		×0.23		×1.8		×1.8		×0.18
	602		6923		846		846		846

Multiply.

11.	5.2	12.	9.4	13.	0.78	14.	6.9	15.	4.9
	×2.1		×0.32		×0.43		×0.18		×36

16.	24.2	17.	3.91	18.	46.8	19.	3.29	20.	74.2
	×2.8		×3.5		×0.24		×0.73		×8.5

21.	59.3	22.	8.26	23.	7.52	24.	983	25.	6.54
	×1.65		×1.03		×0.242		×3.11		×42.1

Multiple choice. (*Hint:* Estimate!)

26. Four members of a relay team skated 100 meters each in 10.9 seconds, 11.3 seconds, 11.6 seconds, and 10.8 seconds. What was their total-team time?

    a. 400.8 s   **b.** 11 s

    c. 4.5s   **d.** 44.6 s

27. A four-member relay team skated a 400-meter race. The average time for each skater was 11.2 seconds. What was the team time in seconds?

    a. 4.48   **b.** 4480

    c. 448   **d.** 44.8

28. In the 1500-meter race in the 1980 Winter Olympics, Eric Heiden's time was 1 minute 55.44 seconds. This was 3.84 seconds better than the previous record. What was the previous record?

    a. 1 min 49.38 s   **b.** 1 min 51.60 s

    c. 1 min 59.28 s   **d.** 4 min 3.84 s

29. In the 1000-meter race, Eric Heiden beat the previous record of 1 minute 19.32 seconds by 4.14 seconds. What was his time?

    a. 1 min 15.18 s   **b.** 1 min 23.46 s

    c. 5 min 15.18 s   **d.** 1 min 29.32 s

Zeros in multiplication

Sometimes you have to write some extra zeros before you place the decimal point in the product.

Step 1. Multiply.

Step 2. Need 3 digits to the right of the decimal point. So, write 2 extra zeros.

Step 3. Place the decimal point in the product.

$$\begin{array}{r} 0.04 \\ \times 0.2 \\ \hline 8 \end{array} \qquad \begin{array}{r} 0.04 \\ \times 0.2 \\ \hline 008 \end{array} \qquad \begin{array}{r} 0.04 \\ \times 0.2 \\ \hline 0.008 \end{array}$$

EXERCISES
Give each product.

1. $\begin{array}{r} 0.4 \\ \times 0.2 \\ \hline \end{array}$
2. $\begin{array}{r} 0.4 \\ \times 0.3 \\ \hline \end{array}$
3. $\begin{array}{r} 0.02 \\ \times 0.4 \\ \hline \end{array}$
4. $\begin{array}{r} 0.02 \\ \times 0.5 \\ \hline \end{array}$
5. $\begin{array}{r} 0.02 \\ \times 0.9 \\ \hline \end{array}$

6. $\begin{array}{r} 0.12 \\ \times 0.3 \\ \hline \end{array}$
7. $\begin{array}{r} 0.13 \\ \times 0.4 \\ \hline \end{array}$
8. $\begin{array}{r} 2.8 \\ \times 0.3 \\ \hline \end{array}$
9. $\begin{array}{r} 0.28 \\ \times 0.3 \\ \hline \end{array}$
10. $\begin{array}{r} 0.028 \\ \times 0.3 \\ \hline \end{array}$

11. $\begin{array}{r} 0.004 \\ \times 0.02 \\ \hline \end{array}$
12. $\begin{array}{r} 0.007 \\ \times 0.03 \\ \hline \end{array}$
13. $\begin{array}{r} 0.013 \\ \times 0.14 \\ \hline \end{array}$
14. $\begin{array}{r} 0.029 \\ \times 0.35 \\ \hline \end{array}$
15. $\begin{array}{r} 0.036 \\ \times 0.57 \\ \hline \end{array}$

16. $\begin{array}{r} 3.56 \\ \times 0.42 \\ \hline \end{array}$
17. $\begin{array}{r} 7.04 \\ \times 0.31 \\ \hline \end{array}$
18. $\begin{array}{r} 0.067 \\ \times 0.08 \\ \hline \end{array}$
19. $\begin{array}{r} 4.07 \\ \times 0.28 \\ \hline \end{array}$
20. $\begin{array}{r} 5.13 \\ \times 4.02 \\ \hline \end{array}$

21. $\begin{array}{r} 28.7 \\ \times 8.06 \\ \hline \end{array}$
22. $\begin{array}{r} 51.7 \\ \times 0.0004 \\ \hline \end{array}$
23. $\begin{array}{r} 82.7 \\ \times 50.2 \\ \hline \end{array}$
24. $\begin{array}{r} 6.07 \\ \times 6.07 \\ \hline \end{array}$
25. $\begin{array}{r} 0.412 \\ \times 0.044 \\ \hline \end{array}$

Multiple choice.
Choose the correct answer by estimating.

26. 53.77 + 82.31
    a. 126.28   **b.** 136.08   **c.** 147.08   **d.** 251.28

27. 703.11 − 498.26
    a. 304.85   **b.** 204.85   **c.** 145.85   **d.** 263.85

28. 50 − 7.24
    a. 52.76   **b.** 43.76   **c.** 57.24   **d.** 42.76

29. (25.8 + 36.5) + 41.1 *Work inside parentheses first.*

    a. 103.4   **b.** 92.4   **c.** 123.4   **d.** 96.4

30. (56.2 − 13.9) + 21.7
    a. 64.0   **b.** 56.6   **c.** 54.0   **d.** 60.6

31. 29.7 × 4.2
    a. 96.64   **b.** 132.74   **c.** 124.74   **d.** 112.64

32. (3.1 + 5.3) × 2.7
    a. 35.28   **b.** 22.68   **c.** 16.98   **d.** 43.58

33. (3.14 × 5.1) × 5.1
    a. 81.6714   **b.** 93.2124   **c.** 15.2673   **d.** 60.5134

Solve.

34. I can jump 6 times as high on the moon.

ARTHUR
EARTH JUMP
125 cm

How high can Arthur jump on the moon?

35. I can jump 2.7 times as high on Mars.

ASTRID
EARTH JUMP
138 cm

How high can Astrid jump on Mars?

Dividing a decimal by a whole number

You divide a decimal by a whole number just as you divide a whole number by a whole number. Study these examples.

$$\begin{array}{r} 9.8 \\ 2\overline{)19.6} \\ -18 \\ \hline 16 \\ -16 \\ \hline 0 \end{array}$$

$$\begin{array}{r} 2.125 \\ 8\overline{)17.000} \\ -16 \\ \hline 10 \\ -8 \\ \hline 20 \\ -16 \\ \hline 40 \\ -40 \\ \hline 0 \end{array}$$

I had to write these extra zeros.

EXERCISES
Give each quotient.

1. $2\overline{)5.8}$
2. $3\overline{)9.3}$
3. $5\overline{)0.25}$
4. $7\overline{)1.47}$
5. $6\overline{)0.456}$

6. $4\overline{)16.4}$
7. $2\overline{)1.7}$
8. $4\overline{)2.7}$
9. $8\overline{)2.0}$
10. $5\overline{)32.4}$

11. $24\overline{)55.2}$
12. $45\overline{)283.5}$
13. $36\overline{)27.0}$
14. $25\overline{)82.4}$
15. $81\overline{)52.65}$

Divide. Round each quotient to the nearest hundredth.

16. $3\overline{)94.1}$
17. $7\overline{)9.56}$
18. $6\overline{)42.83}$
19. $9\overline{)6.178}$
20. $6\overline{)59.378}$

21. $19\overline{)58.3}$
22. $32\overline{)5.11}$
23. $42\overline{)17.2}$
24. $183\overline{)26.8}$
25. $205\overline{)396.8}$

Problem solving—using a graph

Ecology is the study of the relation between living things and their surroundings. The way we live can greatly affect our environment. For example, the disposal of trash is a problem for many communities. The graph shows the average amount of trash (metal, glass, paper products, etc.) that each person in the United States produces each day.

Solve.

1. How many kilograms of trash were produced by each person in 1920? In 1970? In 1975?

2. How many more kilograms per person per day were produced in 1980 than in 1970?

3. The population in 1920 was 105,710,620. How many kilograms were produced each day? Round your answer to the nearest million kilograms.

4. The population in 1980 was 226,504,825. Compute the daily amount of trash in 1980. Round your answer to the nearest million kilograms.

5. How many more kilograms of trash were produced in a day in 1980 than in 1920? (See exercises 3 and 4.)

6. Compute the yearly amount of trash produced by a family of 4 in 1980.

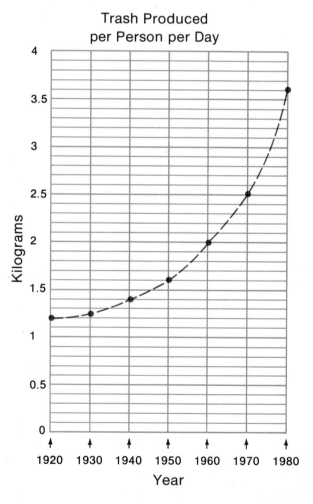

Trash Produced per Person per Day

Dividing by a decimal

Below are two methods for finding this quotient: $5.4\overline{)9.18}$

ESTIMATION METHOD

Step 1.

Divide as whole numbers.

Step 2.

Estimate the quotient and place the decimal point.

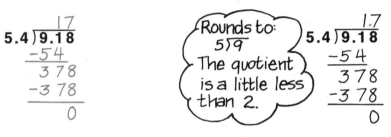

$$
\begin{array}{r}
17 \\
5.4\overline{)9.18} \\
-54 \\
\hline
378 \\
-378 \\
\hline
0
\end{array}
$$

Rounds to: $5\overline{)9}$ The quotient is a little less than 2.

$$
\begin{array}{r}
1.7 \\
5.4\overline{)9.18} \\
-54 \\
\hline
378 \\
-378 \\
\hline
0
\end{array}
$$

SHORTCUT METHOD

You can multiply both the divisor and the dividend by the same number without changing the quotient.

Step 1.

Multiply both divisor and dividend by 10.

Step 2.

Place the decimal point for the quotient directly above the decimal point in the dividend.

Step 3.

Divide.

$5.4\overline{)9.18}$

$5.4\overline{)9.18}$

$$
\begin{array}{r}
1.7 \\
5.4\overline{)9.18} \\
-54 \\
\hline
378 \\
-378 \\
\hline
0
\end{array}
$$

Move both decimal points 1 place to the right.

34

EXERCISES
Divide.

1. $0.06\overline{)0.0912}$ 2. $0.8\overline{)19.68}$ 3. $0.005\overline{)0.412}$

4. $0.04\overline{)1.408}$ 5. $1.2\overline{)3.840}$ 6. $3.4\overline{)53.04}$

7. $0.56\overline{)23.968}$ 8. $0.74\overline{)18.722}$ 9. $3.8\overline{)171.38}$

10. $0.025\overline{)5.0325}$ 11. $0.46\overline{)22.862}$ 12. $0.52\overline{)24.336}$

13. $13.5\overline{)434.7}$ 14. $0.274\overline{)93.434}$ 15. $82.9\overline{)5015.45}$

Divide. Round each quotient to the nearest hundredth.

16. $0.3\overline{)5.5}$ 17. $0.6\overline{)3.61}$ 18. $0.03\overline{)0.287}$

19. $0.09\overline{)0.537}$ 20. $0.47\overline{)5.666}$ 21. $0.035\overline{)63.8}$

22. $2.31\overline{)12.9}$ 23. $4.52\overline{)1.46}$ 24. $53.6\overline{)8.68}$

Solve. Round each answer to the nearest hundredth.

25. Diane scored 263 points in 15 basketball games. How many points did she average per game?

26. Karen ran 9.2 kilometers in 46.92 minutes. What was the average number of kilometers per minute?

27. Jim swam 5.5 laps of the pool in 3.82 minutes. How many minutes per lap did he average?

28. John ran 40 meters in 4.4 seconds. At that rate, how long would it take him to run 100 meters?

29. ★ CHALKBOARD CHALLENGE

Some of the digits were erased in this division problem. Find the missing digits.

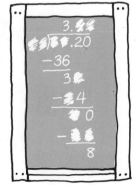

Estimate to find the incorrect answer.

1. a. $47.2 + 7.31 = 54.51$

   b. $102.8 - 54.09 = 48.71$

   c. $39.02 + 111.1 = 150.12$

   d. $60.4 - 3.21 = 28.3$

Add.

2. $\begin{array}{r} 6.73 \\ + 2.98 \\ \hline \end{array}$

3. $\begin{array}{r} 57.4 \\ + 28.8 \\ \hline \end{array}$

4. $\begin{array}{r} 93.17 \\ 46.29 \\ + 5.67 \\ \hline \end{array}$

Subtract.

5. $\begin{array}{r} 60.4 \\ - 21.5 \\ \hline \end{array}$

6. $\begin{array}{r} 77.43 \\ - 28.76 \\ \hline \end{array}$

7. $\begin{array}{r} 50.04 \\ - 26.57 \\ \hline \end{array}$

8. $\begin{array}{r} 6.72 \\ - 1.835 \\ \hline \end{array}$

35

Estimating

Calculator errors can be the result of pressing the wrong buttons or pressing the buttons in the wrong order. You can find calculator errors by estimating.

For example, if you round each number below as shown, you can tell that the calculator answer is wrong.

$$(48.9 \times 2.1) + 58.75 = \underline{\ ?\ }$$

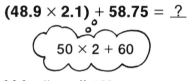

50 × 2 + 60

The answer should be "near" 160.

A calculator was used to complete the following exercises. Estimate to decide whether each answer is reasonable.

1. $9.6 + 13.9 = 23.5$

2. $36.74 - 10.31 = 26.43$

3. $24.2 \times 4 = 9.68$

4. $50 \div 2.5 = 12.5$

5. $75.16 \times 9.7 = 729.052$

6. $153.6 + 72.4 = 81.2$

7. $30.6 \div 4.8 = 6.375$

8. $204.6 - 129.8 = 174.8$

9. $(5.2 + 3.9) \times 8 = 72.8$

10. $(19.8 - 4.9) \times 4 = 9.1$

11. $(60 \div 0.5) + 17.8 = 29.8$

12. $(56 + 3.9) - 14.8 = 45.1$

13. $(2.8 \times 4.2) + 5.9 = 593.84$

14. $(52 \times 3.6) - 25.4 = 161.8$

15. $(12.6 - 3.5) \times 15.6 = 251.16$

16. $(14.6 \div 7.3) \times 9.8 = 196$

17. ⭐ **MAGIC-SQUARE DARTS**

Rob and Carla played a dart game with a dartboard that was a magic square. The player who scored the higher sum with 3 darts was to be the winner. After Rob threw his last dart, he tied the score. Which number did he hit?

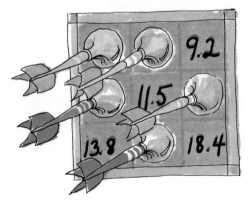

36

The Umpire Strikes Back!

Rules

1. Player X (or O) chooses a baseball and a bat and estimates the product of the two numbers.

2. The player marks the number on the game board that is closest to the estimate.

3. Players take turns until one wins by getting 5 marks in any row, column, or diagonal.

4. One player may challenge the other player's choice by performing the exact multiplication and showing there is a closer choice that could be made. If the challenger is right, he/she gets to mark the square. If the challenger is wrong, he/she loses a turn.

Baseball Game Board

44.37	28.681	115.362	148.77	985.044
407.468	1638.936	710.528	326.716	886.144
3564.288	4596.48	50.439	1370.88	3962.088
5109.48	789.828	1523.88	22.997	261.63
40.443	78.03	2113.56	630.36	202.878

EXAMPLE. Choose 5.1 and 39.78.

To estimate the product:

39.78	Round to	**40**
×5.1	Round to	**×5**
		200

Mark 202.878 on the game board, since it is closest to 200, the estimated product.

Problem solving— too much information

In some problems there are more facts than you need. You have to pick the facts you need to answer the question.

A 4-year-old bloodhound that weighs 60 pounds needs 21 ounces of dry food each day. A 5-pound bag of dry dog food costs 3.2¢ per ounce. How much money does a daily serving cost?

These steps can help you solve the problem.

1. Study the problem until you understand it.

   Find the question.

   Find the information you need to answer the question.

2. Plan what to do and do it.

3. Answer the question and check your answer.

How much money does a daily serving cost?

21 ounces of dry food are required daily. Dry food costs 3.2¢ per ounce.

Multiply 3.2 and 21.

$$\begin{array}{r} 21 \\ \times 3.2 \\ \hline 4\,2 \\ 63 \\ \hline 67.2 \end{array}$$

A daily serving of dry food costs 67.2¢.

The answer seems reasonable because 21 is about 20, 3.2 is about 3, and $20 \times 3 = 60$.

Daily food requirements for adult dogs			
Body weight (in pounds)	Daily servings of dog food		
	Dry (oz)	Semimoist (oz)	Canned (oz)
5	3.5	5	10
10	5.5	9	18
15	7	11	22
20	9	13.5	27
30	12.5	18.5	37
45	17	25	51
60	21	31	62
75	25	37	74

A chart usually has more information than you need. Use this chart to solve the problems.

1. How many more ounces of a dry-type food does a 60-pound dog require than a 30-pound dog per day?

2. Altogether, how many ounces of a semimoist food are required per day for a 75-pound boxer and a 10-pound Pekingese?

3. What is the weight of a 30-inch Welsh terrier that requires 13.5 ounces of semimoist food each day?

4. Two identical 5-year-old bullterriers have a total weight of 60 pounds. How many ounces of dry food should the two dogs be fed each day?

5. A 5-pound bag of dry food costs 3.2¢ an ounce. A 10-pound bag of the same food costs 2.4¢ an ounce.

   a. How much does it cost to feed a 30-pound beagle a day if you buy the food in 5-pound bags?

   b. How much less would it cost per day if you bought the food in 10-pound bags?

6. A 5-pound package of semimoist food costs 4.3¢ an ounce. A 1-pound can of canned food costs 3.1¢ an ounce.

   a. How much does it cost to feed a 15-pound dog each day if you buy the semimoist food?

   b. How much more does it cost per day if you buy the canned food?

Multiplying and dividing by 10, 100, or 1000

If you multiply a number by 10, 100, or 1000, the product is greater than the number.

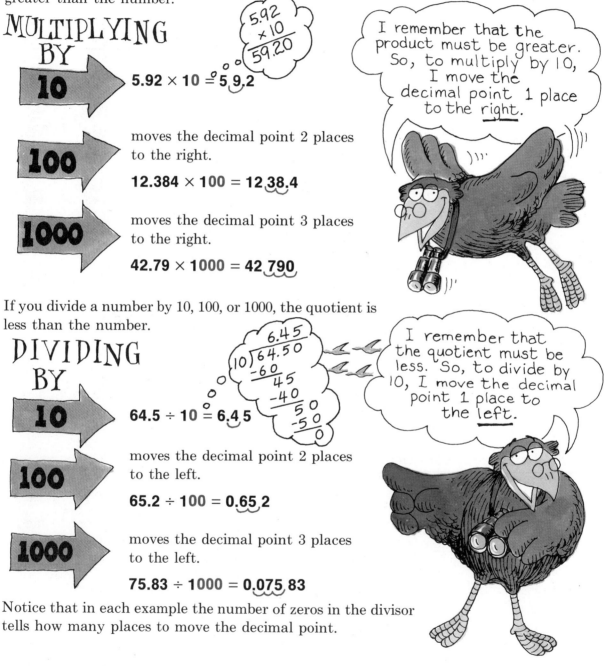

MULTIPLYING BY

10

$$5.92 \times 10 = 59.2$$

$$\begin{array}{r} 5.92 \\ \times 10 \\ \hline 59.20 \end{array}$$

I remember that the product must be greater. So, to multiply by 10, I move the decimal point 1 place to the <u>right</u>.

100

moves the decimal point 2 places to the right.

$$12.384 \times 100 = 1238.4$$

1000

moves the decimal point 3 places to the right.

$$42.79 \times 1000 = 42790$$

If you divide a number by 10, 100, or 1000, the quotient is less than the number.

DIVIDING BY

10

$$64.5 \div 10 = 6.45$$

$$\begin{array}{r} 6.45 \\ 10\overline{)64.50} \\ -60 \\ \hline 45 \\ -40 \\ \hline 50 \\ -50 \\ \hline 0 \end{array}$$

I remember that the quotient must be less. So, to divide by 10, I move the decimal point 1 place to the <u>left</u>.

100

moves the decimal point 2 places to the left.

$$65.2 \div 100 = 0.652$$

1000

moves the decimal point 3 places to the left.

$$75.83 \div 1000 = 0.07583$$

Notice that in each example the number of zeros in the divisor tells how many places to move the decimal point.

Give each product.

1. 67 × 1000
2. 67 × 100
3. 67 × 10

4. 8.63 × 100
5. 5.942 × 1000
6. 7.638 × 10

7. 59.76 × 100
8. 317.4 × 10
9. 29.38 × 1000

10. 0.0356 × 10
11. 0.004 × 100
12. 0.03285 × 1000

Give each quotient.

13. 7594 ÷ 1000
14. 7594 ÷ 100
15. 7594 ÷ 10

16. 5.9 ÷ 10
17. 5.9 ÷ 100
18. 5.9 ÷ 1000

19. 382 ÷ 10
20. 1.6 ÷ 100
21. 7903 ÷ 1000

22. 0.04 ÷ 10
23. 67.93 ÷ 1000
24. 0.8 ÷ 100

Complete.   1 meter (m) = 100 centimeters (cm)

25. 9.62 m = _?_ cm
26. 15.6 m = _?_ cm
27. 28.356 m = _?_ cm

28. 0.827 m = _?_ cm
29. 1.6 cm = _?_ m
30. 592.6 cm = _?_ m

1 meter (m) = 1000 millimeters (mm)

31. 8.342 m = _?_ mm
32. 62.45 m = _?_ mm
33. 25.4 m = _?_ mm

34. 0.35 m = _?_ mm
35. 365 mm = _?_ m
36. 4283 mm = _?_ m

Here is how to write a decimal as an expanded numeral.

823.65

| 800 | + | 20 | + | 3 | + | 0.6 | + | 0.05 |

expanded numeral → **(8 × 100) + (2 × 10) + (3 × 1) + (6 × 0.1) + (5 × 0.01)**

Give the expanded numeral.

37. 9.74
38. 28.653
39. 792.153
40. 946.382

★ 41. 3.6598
★ 42. 3659.8
★ 43. 42.953
★ 44. 4.2953

Multiplying and dividing by powers of 10

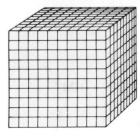

1000 blocks
or
10 × 10 × 10 blocks

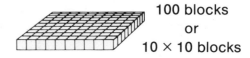

100 blocks
or
10 × 10 blocks

Instead of writing 10 as a factor several times, you can use an exponent with 10 as the base.

$$1000 = 10 \times 10 \times 10 = 10^3$$

Read "10^3" as "10 cubed"
or as "10 to the third power."

3 tells us that 10 was a factor 3 times.

$$100 = 10 \times 10 = 10^2$$

Read "10^2" as "10 squared"
or as "10 to the second power."

$$10 = 10^1$$

Read "10^1" as
"10 to the first power."

When 10 is the base, the exponent tells the number of zeros in the standard numeral.

When you are multiplying by a power of 10, the exponent tells you how far to move the decimal point to the right.

$$5.634 \times 10^2 = ?$$

$$5.634 \times 10^2 = 5\ 63.4$$

Move 2 places.

When you are dividing by a power of 10, the exponent tells you how far to move the decimal point to the left.

$$923.4 \div 10^3 = ?$$

$$923.4 \div 10^3 = 0.923\ 4$$

Move 3 places.

EXERCISES

Give the standard numeral.

1. 10^2 2. 10^4 3. 10^3 4. 10^5 5. 10^6 6. 10^8 7. 10^1

Write as a power of 10.

8. 1000   9. 10,000   10. 1,000,000

11. 100,000   12. 10,000,000   13. 100,000,000

Give each product.

14. 3.56×10

15. 0.758×100

16. 0.08652×1000

17. $0.00825 \times 10,000$

18. 9.62×10^2

19. 17.84×10^1

20. 0.2971×10^2

21. 0.03825×10^3

22. 0.0563×10^5

23. 1.7×10^4

24. 0.816×10^6

25. 0.0936×10^8

26. 0.031×10^4

27. 6.529×10^7

Give each quotient.

28. $29.6 \div 10$

29. $7542 \div 100$

30. $618.3 \div 1000$

31. $51.6 \div 10,000$

32. $2.9 \div 10^1$

33. $74.8 \div 10^3$

34. $319.5 \div 10^2$

35. $764.82 \div 10^5$

36. $5361.7 \div 10^4$

37. $28.14 \div 10^6$

38. $89.6 \div 10^8$

39. $713.4 \div 10^7$

40. **DON'T MISS THIS ONE !**

Look for a pattern.

$2^1 = 2$

$2^2 = 4$

$2^3 = 8$

$2^4 = 16$

$2^5 = 32$

$\vdots$

$2^{40} = 1,099,511,627,77\square$

What is the missing digit?

Estimate to find the incorrect answer.

1. a. $3.67 \times 5.1 = 187.2$

   b. $179.52 \div 3.2 = 56.1$

Multiply.

2. $\begin{array}{r} 924 \\ \times 0.8 \end{array}$

3. $\begin{array}{r} 359 \\ \times 0.06 \end{array}$

4. $\begin{array}{r} 27.4 \\ \times 1.2 \end{array}$

5. $\begin{array}{r} 82.06 \\ \times 0.35 \end{array}$

6. $\begin{array}{r} 6.581 \\ \times 3.04 \end{array}$

Divide. Round the quotient to the nearest hundredth.

7. $0.3\overline{)382}$

8. $0.06\overline{)0.394}$

9. $1.9\overline{)5.29}$

10. $3.8\overline{)89.64}$

11. $0.47\overline{)3}$

43

Large numbers and scientific notation

You can think of the planet Earth as a spinning "spaceship" that takes us around the sun once every year. Each day it travels about 2,570,000 km. Here is that number written in **scientific notation:**

a number
between 1 $\longrightarrow$ **2.57 × 10⁶** $\longleftarrow$ a power
and 10   of 10

Here is how to write a standard numeral in scientific notation.

EXAMPLE 1. 739,000,000

Step 1. Locate the decimal point for a number between 1 and 10.

$$7.39000000$$

Step 2. To find the exponent of 10, count the digits that are to the right of the decimal point.

$$7.39000000$$
$$8$$

Step 3. Write the number in scientific notation.

$$7.39 \times 10^8$$

A number in scientific notation can be written as a standard numeral by multiplying.

EXAMPLE 2. 8.11×10^5

$$8.11 \times 10^5 = 8.11000$$
$$= 811,000$$

Move the decimal point 5 places to the right.

EXERCISES
Write the standard numeral.

1. 5.3×10^2 2. 2.6×10^3 3. 7.4×10^1 4. 9.3×10^5

5. 8.92×10^3 6. 5.66×10^4 7. 4.93×10^5 8. 7.4×10^2

9. 9.31×10^6 10. 1.6×10^5 11. 2.38×10^3 12. 3.02×10^4

13. 5.381×10^7 14. 3.014×10^8 15. 8.342×10^6 16. 5.671×10^9

Write in scientific notation.

17. 89   18. 70   19. 520   20. 880

21. 9600   22. 15,000   23. 362,000   24. 58,000,000

25. 291,000,000   26. 42,800,000,000

27. 4,740,000,000,000   28. 90,000,000,000,000

Write each number in scientific notation.

29. At the equator, the earth is spinning at about 1600 kilometers per hour.

30. The earth stays about 150,000,000 kilometers from the sun.

31. The age of the earth is about 4,500,000,000 years.

32. The earth weighs about 5,990,000,000,000,000,000,000,000 metric tons.

33. The diameter of the sun is about 1,380,000 kilometers.

34. The temperature at the center of the sun is about 20,000,000 degrees Celsius.

35. The earth receives approximately 170,000,000,000,000 kilowatts of power per hour from the sun.

36. The star closest to the earth is about 40,700,000,000,000 kilometers away.

Problem solving—more than one way to solve

1. Study and understand.
2. Plan and do.
3. Answer and check.

Sometimes there is more than one way to solve a problem.

Margo's Deluxe photo album holds 8 photos per page. Her "Slim Jim" album holds 6 photos per page. She has 20 pages of each album filled. How many photos does Margo have?

Jennifer's way to solve

```
  20
 × 8
 160  photos in
         Deluxe album

  20
 × 6
 120  photos in
         "Slim Jim" album

 160
+120
 280  photos altogether
```

Paul's way to solve

```
   8
 + 6
  14  photos on each
        page of both
        albums

  14
 ×20
 280  photos on the
        20 pages of the
        two albums
```

46

EXERCISES

One way to solve each problem is given. Find another way to solve it.

1. Margo bought 3 rolls of 12-exposure film and 3 rolls of 20-exposure film. How many pictures can she take?

$$\begin{array}{r} 12 \\ \times\ 3 \\ \hline 36 \end{array} \quad \begin{array}{r} 20 \\ \times\ 3 \\ \hline 60 \end{array} \quad \begin{array}{r} 36 \\ +60 \\ \hline 96\ \text{pictures} \end{array}$$

2. Tim bought a 12-exposure roll of film for $2.40 and 12 flashbulbs for $3.00. How much will it cost to take one flash picture?

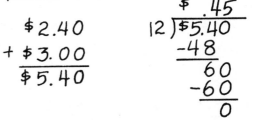

$$\begin{array}{r} \$2.40 \\ +\ \$3.00 \\ \hline \$5.40 \end{array}$$

Solve.

3. A 12-exposure roll of film costs $2.40 and a 20-exposure roll of film costs $3.10. Robin bought 2 rolls of each. How much money did she spend?

4. Jim bought a 20-exposure roll of film for $3.10 and a carton of flash cubes for $4.80. He gave the clerk a $20 bill. How much change should Jim get back?

5. Dana had $50. She bought an Instant Pix camera for $29.89 and a carrying case for $5.29. How much money did she have left?

6. Dana wants to use her new camera to take a picture of each of the 30 students in her homeroom. A 10-picture cartridge of film for the camera costs $7.30. How much money will Dana spend for the film?

7. Juan had 2 rolls of 12-exposure film and 1 roll of 20-exposure film developed and printed. How much change did he get back from a $20 bill?

8. How much less does it cost to develop and print 2 rolls of 24-exposure film than 4 rolls of 12-exposure film?

9. Which is less expensive to develop and print, 2 rolls of 24-exposure film or 1 roll of 12-exposure film and 1 roll of 36-exposure film? How much less expensive?

Price List for Developing and Printing	
Exposures	Cost
12	$3.69
20	$4.89
24	$5.59
36	$7.29

Write the standard numeral. [pages 20–21]

1. eight tenths

2. six and four hundredths

3. one hundred and forty-two thousandths

4. nine and sixteen thousandths

Round 42.9856028 to the nearest [pages 22–23]

5. tenth.

6. ten-thousandth.

7. hundredth.

< **or** >? [pages 24–25]

8. 38.296 ● 38.290

9. 1.536 ● 15.32

10. 0.1 ● 0.098

11. 0.499 ● 0.5

Add or subtract. [pages 26–27]

12. 9.7
     3.62
   + 7.8

13. 19.08
    − 5.63

14. 28.41 + 5.9

15. 182.6 − 13.97

Multiply. [pages 28–31]

16. 6.21
    × 8

17. 72.51
    × 4.3

18. 0.86
    × 5.5

19. 0.04
    × 0.02

Divide. Round quotients to the nearest hundredth.
[pages 32–35]

20. $5\overline{)3.2}$

21. $0.08\overline{)2.3}$

22. $2.4\overline{)52}$

23. $0.58\overline{)3.77}$

Give each product or quotient. [pages 40–43]

24. 5.96 × 10

25. 0.82 × 100

26. 8.86 × 10^3

27. 0.4 × 10^2

28. 95.2 ÷ 10

29. 7.43 ÷ 100

30. 56.7 ÷ 10^3

31. 0.42 ÷ 10^2

Solve. [pages 38–39, 46–47]

32. One of the world's most valuable stamps is an 1856 British Guiana 1¢ stamp. It sold in 1917 for $32,250. The present owner paid $280,000. How much did the price increase from 1917 to the present?

33. A stamp dealer bought 24 stamps for $160. He sold 17 of them for $12.45 each and the remaining stamps for $10.75 each. What was the total profit?

CHAPTER PROJECT

1. How long does it take to walk 50 meters at a normal pace? Give your answer to the nearest tenth second.

2. Compute how long it would take to walk a kilometer. Give your answer in minutes and seconds.

3. Find out how many kilometers it is from Miami, Florida, to Seattle, Washington, and compute how long it would take you to walk from Miami to Seattle.

4. If you walked 8 hours a day, how many days would it take you?

CHAPTER REVIEW

thousandths place
↓
200.016

two ← and → sixteen
hundred   thousandths

Round to the nearest tenth.

tenths place
↓
57.25
       ↖ 5 or greater
         round up
57.3

```
  1 1          3 8
 5.260        4.590
+2.784       -1.782
 -----        -----
 8.044        2.808
```

```
 2.15  ← 2 digits
×3.4   ← 1 digit
-----
 860
645
-----
7.310  ← 3 digits
```

```
        0.27
4.3 )1.1 61
      -8 6
      ----
       3 01
      -3 01
      ----
          0
```

Write in words.

1. 0.4
2. 0.06
3. 0.007
4. 50.123
5. 700.015
6. 85.1375

Round to the nearest tenth.

7. 4.62
8. 20.75
9. 19.97
10. 0.162
11. 1.985
12. 4.4499

Add or subtract.

13.
```
  1.67
+ 3.29
```

14.
```
 14.26
+ 2.984
```

15.
```
  2.58
  3.77
+ 4.81
```

16.
```
  2.35
- 1.462
```

17.
```
 60.04
- 7.56
```

18.
```
 325.106
- 148.15
```

Multiply.

19.
```
  5.7
× 3.4
```

20.
```
 0.62
× 3.4
```

21.
```
 0.04
× 0.3
```

Divide.

22. $0.4\overline{)8.1}$
23. $0.08\overline{)3.3}$
24. $2.5\overline{)74}$

CHAPTER CHALLENGE

Negative exponents are used to write numbers less than 1 in scientific notation.

$$0.1 = 10^{-1}$$
$$0.01 = 10^{-2}$$
$$0.001 = 10^{-3}$$
$$0.0001 = 10^{-4}$$
$$0.00001 = 10^{-5}$$

The thickness of a human hair is about

$$9 \times 10^{-5} \text{ meter}$$

Written as a standard numeral, the thickness in meters is

$$9 \times 10^{-5} = 9 \times 0.00001$$
$$= 0.00009$$

Here is a shortcut:

Move the decimal point to the left the number of places shown by the exponent.

$$9 \times 10^{-5} = 0.00009$$

Give the standard numeral.

1. 3×10^{-4} 2. 2.8×10^{-3} 3. 5.96×10^{-5} 4. 4.3×10^{-6}

5. 6.5×10^{-8} 6. 1.22×10^{-9} 7. 8×10^{-6} 8. 3.758×10^{-9}

Write in scientific notation.

9. 0.052   10. 0.0038   11. 0.436   12. 0.000523

13. 0.000096   14. 0.0001482   15. 0.00000067   16. 0.000000000152

a b c d   a b c d   a b c d   a b c d   a b c d   a b c
| | | | | | | | | | | | | | | | | | | | | | |
      2.   5.   6.

a b c d   a b c d   a b c d   a b c
| | | | | | | | | | | | | | |
      8.   9.   10.   11.   12.

MAJOR CHECKUP
STANDARDIZED FORMAT

Choose the correct letter.

1. The standard numeral for six hundred and fifty-four thousandths is

   a. 0.654
   b. 600.054
   c. 0.0654
   d. none of these

2. 86.5 rounded to the nearest whole number is

   a. 86
   b. 85
   c. 86.5
   d. none of these

3. 3.7249 rounded to the nearest hundredth is

   a. 3.73
   b. 3.725
   c. 3.72
   d. none of these

4. Add.

   $9.28 + 63.975$

   a. 72.155
   b. 63.903
   c. 73.255
   d. none of these

5. Subtract.

   $4.036 - 0.2574$

   a. 3.7786
   b. 1.462
   c. 3.8786
   d. none of these

6. Multiply.

   6.5×2.46

   a. 1.599
   b. 15.99
   c. 16.09
   d. none of these

7. Divide.

   $14.224 \div 2.54$

   a. 56
   b. 5.58
   c. 5.6
   d. none of these

8. Divide and round to the nearest hundredth.

   $26.359 \div 0.021$

   a. 1255.19
   b. 1255.20
   c. 125.52
   d. none of these

9. Divide.

   $601.3 \div 1000$

   a. 601,300
   b. 0.6013
   c. 6.013
   d. none of these

10. $970,000 = \underline{\ ?\ }$

   a. 0.97×10
   b. 9.7×10^4
   c. 9.7×10^5
   d. none of these

11. A 12-ounce box of fish costs $1.62. What is the cost of a 6-ounce serving?

   a. 81¢
   b. 84¢
   c. $9.72
   d. none of these

12. An 8-ounce box of beans costs 84¢. What is the cost of 4 boxes?

   a. 42¢
   b. 44¢
   c. $3.36
   d. none of these

Number Theory
and Equations

2

$V = 9.8t$

Prime numbers and composite numbers

The set of **whole numbers,** *W*, can be described by:

$$W = \{0, 1, 2, 3, \ldots\}$$

The three dots mean that the numbers go on and on in the same manner.

Check the list of numbers and their factors.

2 has two factors
$$1 \times 2 = 2$$

3 has two factors
$$1 \times 3 = 3$$

Whole numbers that have exactly two factors are called **prime numbers.**

4 has three factors
$$1 \times 4 = 4$$
$$2 \times 2 = 4$$

6 and **8** have four factors

Whole numbers (other than 0) that have more than two factors are called **composite numbers.**

The whole numbers 0 and 1 are neither prime nor composite numbers.

Numbers	Factors
1	1
2	1, 2
3	1, 3
4	1, 2, 4
5	1, 5
6	1, 2, 3, 6
7	1, 7
8	1, 2, 4, 8
9	1, 3, 9
10	1, 2, 5, 10
11	1, 11
12	1, 2, 3, 4, 6, 12

EXERCISES

1. The first prime number is 2.
   The tenth prime number is 29.
   List the 10 prime numbers less than 30.

54

2. Copy and complete.

Whole number	Set of all factors	Number of factors	Prime or composite?
30	1, 2, 3, 5, 6, 10, 15, 30	8	composite
31	?	?	?
32	?	?	?
33	?	?	?
34	?	?	?
35	?	?	?
36	?	?	?
37	?	?	?
38	?	?	?
39	?	?	?
40	?	?	?

Prime or composite?

3. 42   **4.** 55   **5.** 41   **6.** 83   **7.** 87   **8.** 63

9. 54   **10.** 57   **11.** 38   **12.** 91   **13.** 69   **14.** 99

Whole numbers that have 2 as a factor are called **even numbers.**

0, 2, 4, 6, . . . are even numbers.

Whole numbers that are not even numbers are called **odd numbers.**

1, 3, 5, 7, . . . are odd numbers.

15. What is the largest even number less than one million?

16. What is the smallest odd number greater than one million?

17. Here are the first four **square numbers:**

a. Give the first ten square numbers.

b. Do square numbers have an even or an odd number of factors?

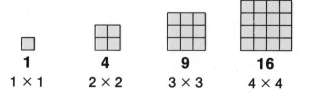

1   **4**   **9**   **16**
1 × 1   2 × 2   3 × 3   4 × 4

Prime factorization

Every composite number can be factored into a product of prime numbers. The numbers in the bottom row of each factor tree are prime numbers.

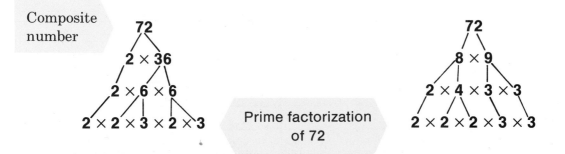

Composite number

Prime factorization of 72

To express a composite number as a product of prime numbers is to give the **prime factorization** of the composite number.

In the prime factorization of 72, the factors 2 and 3 occur more than once. Instead of writing the factors several times, we can use exponents. Read "$2^3 \times 3^2$" as "two cubed times three squared" or as "two to the third power times three to the second power."

$$72 = \overbrace{2 \times 2 \times 2}^{3} \times \overbrace{3 \times 3}^{2}$$
$$= 2^3 \times 3^2$$

The exponent 3 tells us that 2 was used as a factor 3 times.

Here are the prime factorizations of some other composite numbers.

$$45 = 3 \times 15$$
$$= 3 \times 3 \times 5$$
$$= 3^2 \times 5$$

$$400 = 4 \times 100$$
$$= 2 \times 2 \times 10 \times 10$$
$$= 2 \times 2 \times 2 \times 5 \times 2 \times 5$$
$$= 2^4 \times 5^2$$

EXERCISES

Give the prime factorization. Use exponents for factors that occur more than once.

1. 10	**2.** 20	**3.** 24	**4.** 27
5. 32	**6.** 36	**7.** 48	**8.** 54
9. 72	**10.** 84	**11.** 90	**12.** 96
13. 100	**14.** 124	**15.** 144	**16.** 200
17. 240	**18.** 256	**19.** 288	**20.** 300

Give the composite number.

21. 2^3	**22.** $2^2 \times 3$	**23.** $3^2 \times 5$
24. 2^5	**25.** $5^2 \times 7 \times 11$	**26.** $3^2 \times 5 \times 7$
27. $7^3 \times 5$	**28.** $3^4 \times 5$	**29.** $2^4 \times 5^2 \times 13$
30. $5^2 \times 17$	**31.** 3×13^2	**32.** 11×19^2

Solve.

33. What is the smallest composite number that is a square of a prime number? A cube of a prime number?

34. Although there is no largest prime number, the largest prime that is presently known, $2^{21,701} - 1$, was found with the aid of a computer by two 18-year-olds. If you wrote $2^{21,701}$ as a product of 2's, how many 2's would you write?

★ **35.** What is the smallest composite number that is the product of the squares of two different prime numbers?

★ **36.** What is the smallest composite number that is the product of a prime number squared and a different prime number cubed?

Give the prime factorization.
37. 41,160   **38.** 6,126,120

Common factors and common multiples

Common factors

Consider the set of all factors of 12 and the set of all factors of 20.

Factors of 12:   1, 2, 3, 4, 6, 12

Factors of 20:   1, 2, 4, 5, 10, 20

1, 2, and 4 are factors of both 12 and 20. They are called **common factors** of 12 and 20. The **greatest common factor (GCF)** of 12 and 20 is 4.

Here is how to use the prime factorization of the two numbers to find the greatest common factor (GCF).

$$12 = \boxed{2 \times 2} \times 3$$

$$20 = \boxed{2 \times 2} \times 5$$

To find the GCF, multiply the prime numbers that are common to both factorizations.

Each prime factorization contains the factors 2 × 2. So the GCF is 4.

Common multiples

Consider the set of all multiples of 12 and the set of all multiples of 20.

Multiples of 12:   12, 24, 36, 48, 60, . . .

Multiples of 20:   20, 40, 60, 80, . . .

60, 120, 180, . . . are multiples of both 12 and 20. They are called **common multiples** of 12 and 20. The **least common multiple (LCM)** of 12 and 20 is 60.

Here is how to use the prime factorization of the two numbers to find the least common multiple (LCM).

$$12 = \boxed{2 \times 2} \times 3$$

$$20 = \boxed{2 \times 2} \times 5$$

To find the LCM, multiply the GCF by the prime numbers that are not common to both factorizations.

Each common multiple of 12 and 20 contains the factors 2 × 2 and 3 and 5. So the LCM is 60.

58

EXERCISES

Give all of the common factors.

1. 9, 12   2. 12, 16   3. 16, 20   4. 25, 20   5. 36, 24

Give the greatest common factor.

6. 8, 12   7. 16, 24   8. 18, 28   9. 35, 15   10. 16, 42

11. 16, 36   12. 14, 21   13. 48, 36   14. 50, 15   15. 48, 32

Give four common multiples.

16. 2, 3   17. 2, 4   18. 5, 7   19. 9, 6   20. 4, 6

Give the least common multiple.

21. 20, 35   22. 18, 42   23. 10, 12   24. 40, 24   25. 16, 20

26. 18, 24   27. 20, 36   28. 60, 15   29. 12, 20   30. 36, 48

Copy and complete this table.

	Numbers	Product of numbers	GCF	LCM	GCF × LCM
31.	6, 8	?	?	?	?
32.	12, 15	?	?	?	?
33.	16, 36	?	?	?	?
34.	18, 24	?	?	?	?

35. **AGE-OLD PROBLEM**

The least common multiple of our ages is 48. The greatest common factor of our ages is 4. The sum of our ages is 52. How old are we?

Divisibility

Since there is no remainder in this problem, we say that 2538 is **divisible by** 6.

Below, you will find some shortcuts for telling whether a whole number is divisible by certain numbers.

$$
\begin{array}{r}
423 \\
6\overline{)2538} \\
-24 \\
\hline
13 \\
-12 \\
\hline
18 \\
-18 \\
\hline
0
\end{array}
$$

A whole number is divisible by

2 if its last digit is divisible by 2. *Example:* 36,018 is divisible by 2.	**3** if the sum of the digits is divisible by 3. *Example:* 63,501 is divisible by 3. 6 + 3 + 5 + 0 + 1 = 15
4 if its last two digits are divisible by 4. *Example:* 513,732 is divisible by 4.	**5** if its last digit is divisible by 5, that is, if the last digit is 0 or 5. *Example:* 37,145 is divisible by 5.
6 if it is divisible by both 2 and 3. *Example:* 36,702 is divisible by 6.	**8** if its last three digits are divisible by 8. *Example:* 74,112 is divisible by 8.
9 if the sum of its digits is divisible by 9. *Example:* 35,784 is divisible by 9. 3 + 5 + 7 + 8 + 4 = 27	**10** if its last digit is divisible by 10, that is, if the last digit is 0. *Example:* 27,850 is divisible by 10.

EXERCISES

1. Copy and complete.

Whole Number	Divisible by							
	2?	3?	4?	5?	6?	8?	9?	10?
60	*yes*	?	?	?	?	?	?	?
196	?	?	?	?	?	?	?	?
1620	?	?	?	?	?	?	?	?
35,152	?	?	?	?	?	?	?	?
48,394	?	?	?	?	?	?	?	?
56,262	?	?	?	?	?	?	?	?
41,835	?	?	?	?	?	?	?	?
182,394	?	?	?	?	?	?	?	?

Use the divisibility tests to help you decide whether each of the following numbers is prime or composite.

2. 27	**3.** 33	**4.** 39	**5.** 41	**6.** 51	**7.** 57
8. 65	**9.** 81	**10.** 87	**11.** 92	**12.** 111	**13.** 135

True or false?

14. If a number is divisible by 9, then it is divisible by 3.

15. If a number is divisible by 3, then it is divisible by 9.

16. All numbers divisible by 10 are also divisible by 5.

17. All numbers divisible by 2 are even numbers.

18. All numbers divisible by 3 are odd numbers.

19. Some numbers divisible by 5 are odd numbers.

20. A number divisible by 6 is an even number.

★ **21.** What is the largest 4-digit number that is divisible by 6?

★ **22.** What is the smallest 5-digit number that is divisible by 8?

Properties of addition and multiplication

ADDITION

Adding 0 Property
The sum of any number and 0 is the number.
$$279 + 0 = 279$$

Commutative Property of Addition
Changing the order of the addends does not change the sum.
$$258 + 312 = 312 + 258$$

Associative Property of Addition
Changing the grouping of the addends does not change the sum.
$$(82 + 65) + 35 = 82 + (65 + 35)$$

MULTIPLICATION

Multiplying by 1 Property
The product of any number and 1 is the number.
$$374 \times 1 = 374$$

Commutative Property of Multiplication
Changing the order of the factors does not change the product.
$$125 \times 64 = 64 \times 125$$

Associative Property of Multiplication
Changing the grouping of the factors does not change the product.
$$(56 \times 25) \times 4 = 56 \times (25 \times 4)$$

Distributive Property

product   sum   sum of products
$$36 \times (83 + 17) = (36 \times 83) + (36 \times 17)$$

EXERCISES

Give two examples of each of the following properties.

1. commutative property of addition
2. associative property of addition
3. commutative property of multiplication
4. associative property of multiplication
5. distributive property

Use one of the properties above to help you compute each answer in your head.

6. $(39 \times 5) \times 20$
   Hint: $39 \times (5 \times 20)$

7. $(18 \times 7) + (18 \times 3)$
   Hint: $18 \times (7 + 3)$

8. $(186 + 31) + 69$
   Hint: $186 + (31 + 69)$

9. $(65 \times 4) + (65 \times 6)$

10. $(723 + 65) + 35$

11. $(78 \times 25) + (78 \times 75)$

12. $(154 \times 2) \times 500$

13. 758×1

14. $193 + 0$

Mathematics in careers

Meteorologists study and observe the weather. They keep careful records of such things as temperature, humidity, rainfall, and atmospheric pressure. This graph shows the sunrise and sunset times at a certain weather station.

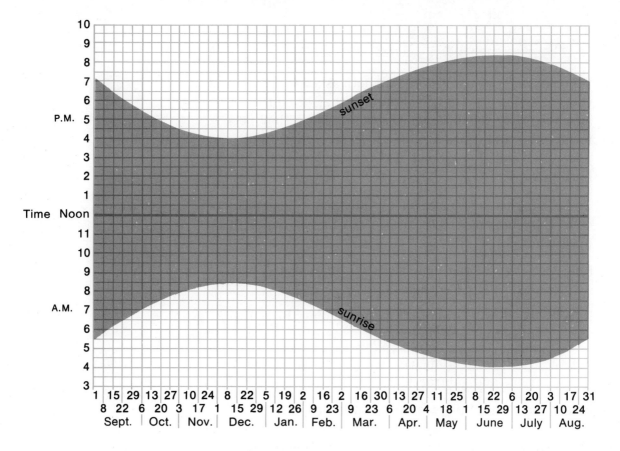

Use the graph to estimate the answers to the following questions.

1. At what time did the sun rise on April 6? On June 1?

2. At what time did the sun set on March 1? On August 1?

3. On what day did the sun set the latest?

4. What day had the most daylight?

5. On what days did the sun rise at 7 o'clock?

6. How much daylight was there on March 1? On June 15?

Order of operations

CARLA'S CALCULATIONS

$6 + 4 \times 7 = 34$

JON'S JOTTINGS

$6 + 4 \times 7 = 70$

Who is right? Carla and Jon were both asked to simplify the expression $6 + 4 \times 7$. Notice that they got different answers. They got different answers because they performed the operations in different orders. Carla multiplied first and then added. Jon added first and then multiplied.

To be sure that an expression has only one value, mathematicians have agreed on these rules for the **order of operations:**

Rule 1. First, do the operations within the grouping symbols (parentheses).

Rule 2. Next, work from left to right doing the multiplications and divisions.

Rule 3. Last, work from left to right doing the additions and subtractions.

Study the rules. Who was right, Carla or Jon?

Here are some examples. The order of operations is shown by the numbered arrows.

$$\overset{1}{\underset{\downarrow}{}} \, \overset{2}{\underset{\downarrow}{}}$$
$$8 \div 4 \times 2 = 4$$

$$\overset{1}{\underset{\downarrow}{}} \, \overset{2}{\underset{\downarrow}{}}$$
$$10 - 6 + 3 = 7$$

$$\overset{2}{\underset{\downarrow}{}} \, \overset{1}{\underset{\downarrow}{}} \, \overset{3}{\underset{\downarrow}{}}$$
$$7 + 3 \times 8 - 4 = 27$$

$$\overset{1}{\underset{\downarrow}{}} \, \overset{3}{\underset{\downarrow}{}} \, \overset{2}{\underset{\downarrow}{}}$$
$$4 \times 2 + 20 \div 2 = 18$$

$$\overset{3}{\underset{\downarrow}{}} \, \overset{1}{\underset{\downarrow}{}} \, \overset{2}{\underset{\downarrow}{}}$$
$$5 + (6 + 2) \div 4 = 7$$

$$\overset{1}{\underset{\downarrow}{}} \, \overset{2}{\underset{\downarrow}{}}$$
$$(7 + 6) \times 2 = 26$$

EXERCISES
Simplify each expression.

1. $5 \times 6 - 4$
2. $16 + 8 \div 4$
3. $20 \div 5 - 3$

4. $18 \div 3 \times 3$
5. $32 - 8 - 6$
6. $16 + 8 \div 4$

7. $15 - 4 + 6$
8. $24 \div 4 \times 2$
9. $36 + 14 - 10$

10. $72 \times (8 - 4)$
11. $(96 + 24) \div 6$
12. $16 \times (15 - 5)$

13. $16 + 8 \div 4 + 4$
14. $(16 + 8) \div 4 + 4$
15. $16 + 8 \div (4 + 4)$

16. $12 + 10 \times 5 - 1$
17. $(12 + 10) \times 5 - 1$
18. $12 + 10 \times (5 - 1)$

19. $6 \times 3 + 4 \times 3$
20. $(6 + 4) \times 3$
21. $6 \times (3 + 4) \times 3$

22. $18 - (15 + 6) \div 3$
23. $18 - 15 + 6 \div 3$
24. $(18 - 15) + 6 \div 3$

★ 25. $36 \div (2 + 4) \times 4 - 5$ ★ 26. $36 \div 2 + 4 \times 4 - 2$ ★ 27. $36 \div 2 + 4 \times (4 - 2)$

★ 28. Four different expressions are described below.

  a. All the operations are additions.

  b. All the operations are subtractions.

  c. All the operations are multiplications.

  d. All the operations are divisions.

  In which of these expressions will you get the same answer
  no matter what order you do the operations in?

29. **HIDDEN PATTERNS**

  Look for the pattern.
  Find the missing numbers.

  $(1 \times 8) + 1 = 9$
  $(12 \times 8) + 2 = 98$
  $(123 \times 8) + 3 = 987$
  $\vdots \qquad \vdots$
  $(? \times ?) + ? = 98,765,432$

  $(1 \times 9) + 2 = 11$
  $(12 \times 9) + 3 = 111$
  $(123 \times 9) + 4 = 1111$
  $\vdots \qquad \vdots$
  $(? \times ?) + ? = 111,111,111$

Variables and expressions

These students are on a walkathon to raise money for a muscular-dystrophy drive. Each student has a sponsor that has agreed to pay a certain amount for each kilometer walked. How much will they raise?

Bill's sponsor is paying him $2 a kilometer. If we let n be the number of kilometers that he walks, the number of dollars that he will raise is given by the expression

$$2n$$

$2n$ is a short way to write $2 \times n$.

The letter n is called a **variable.** To find the number of dollars that he would raise if he walked 15 kilometers, we can **substitute** 15 for n and then simplify the expression.

$$2 \times 15 = 30$$

How many dollars will Bill raise if he walks 18 kilometers? 25 kilometers?

Betty's sponsor is paying her $3 a kilometer. She is also giving $5 of her own money. If m is the number of kilometers she walks, the number of dollars she will raise is given by the expression

$$3m + 5$$

If she walks 11 kilometers, the number of dollars raised will be

$$3 \times 11 + 5 = 38$$

How many dollars will Betty raise if she walks 15 kilometers? 20 kilometers?

EXERCISES

Substitute 12 for n in the expression and simplify.

1. $n + 8$ 2. $n + 15$ 3. $n - 2$

4. $n - 6$ 5. $2n$ 6. $5n$

7. $3n$ 8. $6n$ 9. $2n + 1$

10. $3n + 5$ 11. $4 + 3n$ 12. $5 + 6n$

13. $32 - 2n$ 14. $3n - 4$ 15. $48 - 4n$

To find how many dollars each of the following students raised, substitute the number of kilometers walked in the given expression.

16. Ruth: $n + 18$
kilometers walked: 12

17. Andy: $n + 5$
kilometers walked: 17

18. Robert: $2n + 1$
kilometers walked: 11

19. Marcia: $3n + 6$
kilometers walked: 8

20. David: $4n + 2$
kilometers walked: 6

21. Susan: $3n + 5$
kilometers walked: 9

Let n be the number of kilometers walked. Write an expression for the number of dollars you would raise if your sponsors agreed to pay you

22. $2 a kilometer.

23. $3 a kilometer.

24. $1 a kilometer plus $3 for going on the walkathon.

25. $3 a kilometer plus $1 for going on the walkathon.

26. $2 a kilometer plus $3 for going on the walkathon.

27. $3 a kilometer plus $2 for going on the walkathon.

Estimate to find the incorrect answer.

1. a. $\begin{array}{r} 4.07 \\ \times 2.7 \\ \hline 12.699 \end{array}$

b. $\begin{array}{r} 3.11 \\ \times 2.06 \\ \hline 6.4066 \end{array}$

Multiply.

2. $\begin{array}{r} 3.67 \\ \times 3.6 \end{array}$

3. $\begin{array}{r} 4.98 \\ \times 4.5 \end{array}$

4. $\begin{array}{r} 62.1 \\ \times 5.3 \end{array}$

5. $\begin{array}{r} 3.06 \\ \times 0.82 \end{array}$

6. $\begin{array}{r} 784 \\ \times 5.5 \end{array}$

7. $\begin{array}{r} 96.3 \\ \times 0.73 \end{array}$

8. $\begin{array}{r} 8.17 \\ \times 90 \end{array}$

Formulas

Think about riding a bicycle at a constant speed of 20 kilometers an hour for 5 hours. This table gives the distance you would have traveled at the end of each hour. Notice that the distance traveled in kilometers is 20 times the number of hours.

Distance (kilometers)	Time (hours)
20	1
40	2
60	3
80	4
100	5

We can use this **formula** to show the relationship:

$$d = 20t,$$

where d is the distance in kilometers and t is the time in hours. To find how many kilometers are traveled in 3.2 hours, we can **substitute** 3.2 for t.

$$d = 20 \times 3.2$$
$$= 64$$

EXERCISES

Use the formula $d = 20t$ to compute the distance in kilometers for each of the following times.

1. 1.5 hours   **2.** 3.6 hours   **3.** 4.3 hours   **4.** 2.9 hours

Sound travels at about 335 meters per second. The formula
$d = 335t$ gives the distance (d) in meters that sound travels in t
seconds.

**Use the formula to compute the distance that sound travels for
each of the following times.**

5. 2 seconds

6. 8 seconds

7. 10 seconds

8. 8.2 seconds

9. 5.4 seconds

10. 9.5 seconds

11. 1 minute

12. 2.5 minutes

13. Suppose that 5.2 seconds after you observe a flash of lightning you hear the thunder. How far away was the lightning?

14. Suppose that you are 1 kilometer away from a fireworks show. Will it take more or less than 3 seconds for you to hear a boom?

The formula $d = 4.88t^2$ gives the approximate distance (d) in
meters that an object will fall in t seconds.

**Use the formula to compute how far an object will fall in the
following times.**

15. 10 seconds

16. 5 seconds

17. 3 seconds

18. 1.5 seconds

19. Does an object fall exactly twice the distance in twice the time?

20. Suppose that you dropped a pebble from a bridge and saw the splash 3.5 seconds later. How high above the water is the bridge?

Did you know that you can determine the temperature by counting the chirps of a cricket? This formula tells the temperature (T) in degrees Celsius for the number of chirps (n) in one minute.

$$T = \frac{n}{8} + 5$$

**Find the temperature for the following
number of chirps.**

21. 80

22. 64

23. 92

★ **24.** How many times should a cricket chirp at a temperature of 25°C?

69

Computers in careers

Today we live in the age of computers. A computation that would take hours with paper and pencil can be done on a computer in a few seconds. Even so, computers are not "intelligent." They must be told exactly what to do. The detailed set of instructions given to a computer is called a **program.** It is written by a person called a **programmer.**

Before writing a complicated program, a programmer may write a general plan called a **flow chart.** Below is a flow chart that tells how to open a three-number combination lock. Notice the shapes used for instructions, questions, and Start and Stop.

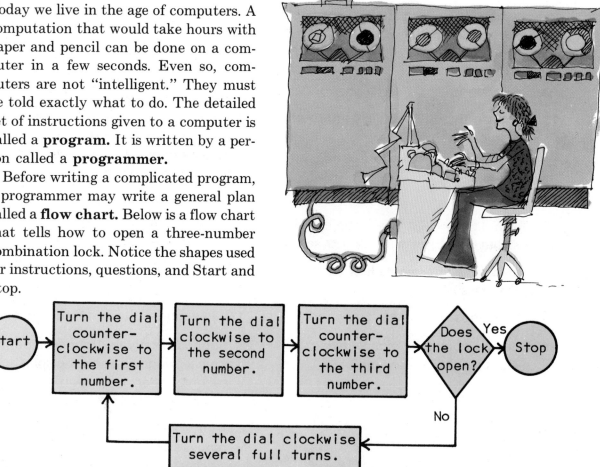

Notice that this flow chart has a question that can be answered Yes or No. Your path through the flow chart depends on your answer to the question. Notice, too, that there is a **loop** in the flow chart. If your answer to the question is No, you go back and start the combination over again. According to this flow chart, you keep trying the combination over and over until the lock opens.

Here is a flow chart for printing the first 5 multiples of 2. Notice the loop in the flow chart. If your answer to the question is *Yes*, you increase A by 1 and go back to the instruction

LET

C = 2A

If your answer is *No*, you stop. Work through the flow chart to see if you get the first 5 multiples of 2.

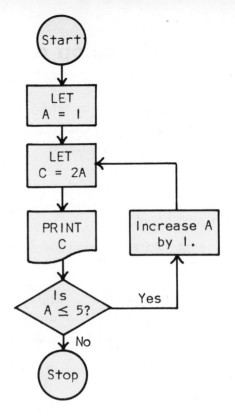

List the numbers you get when you work through these flow charts.

1.

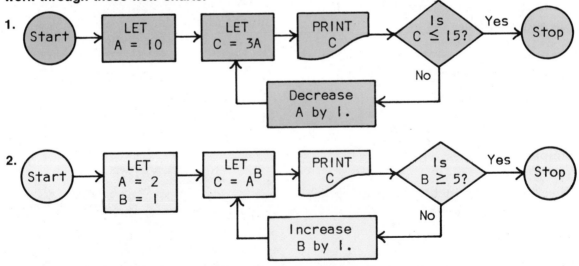

2.

★ **3.** Write a flow chart that tells you to print the first 6 multiples of 5.

★ **4.** Write a flow chart that tells you to print the first power through the sixth power of 3.

Solving addition and subtraction equations

Robert has 57 more matchbooks than David. Robert has 511 matchbooks in all. How many does David have?

Let n be the number of David's matchbooks. Then $n + 57$ is the number of Robert's matchbooks.

We next write an equation for the problem:

$$\overset{\text{Robert's number}}{\overbrace{n + 57}} = \overset{\text{Robert's number}}{511}$$

David's number

Solve the equation by finding the number that can be substituted for n to make the equation true.

Here is how to solve the equation.

Subtract 57 from both sides:

$$n + 57 - 57 = 511 - 57$$

Simplify both sides: $n = 454$

Check the solution by substituting 454 for n in the first equation.

Check: $454 + 57 = 511$

(Does the solution also check in the problem?)

So, David has 454 matchbooks.

Jan has 109 fewer matchbooks than Carl. She has 358 matchbooks in all. How many matchbooks does Carl have?

Let n be the number of Carl's matchbooks. Then $n - 109$ is the number of Jan's matchbooks.

Equation:

$$\overset{\text{Jan's number}}{\overbrace{n - 109}} = \overset{\text{Jan's number}}{358}$$

Carl's number

Add 109 to both sides:
$$n - 109 + 109 = 358 + 109$$

Simplify both sides:
$$n = 467$$

Check: $467 - 109 = 358$

So, Carl has 467 matchbooks.

EXERCISES

Solve each equation by subtracting the same number from both sides. Check the solution.

Same as
$n + 53 = 117$

1. $n + 54 = 79$
2. $n + 38 = 109$
3. $117 = n + 53$
4. $134 = x + 118$
5. $y + 56 = 158$
6. $z + 74 = 206$
7. $40 + n = 125$
8. $58 + n = 174$
9. $139 = 92 + n$
10. $36 + t = 74$
11. $62 + r = 139$
12. $83 + s = 216$

Solve each equation by adding the same number to both sides. Check the solution.

13. $n - 15 = 38$
14. $n - 23 = 49$
15. $76 = n - 42$
16. $x - 65 = 61$
17. $75 = z - 39$
18. $w - 71 = 90$
19. $g - 58 = 102$
20. $s - 67 = 126$
21. $158 = r - 85$
22. $t - 97 = 164$
23. $u - 83 = 253$
24. $v - 75 = 260$

Decide whether Equation A or Equation B would be used to solve each problem. Then solve the problem.

Equation A: $n + 19 = 75$

Equation B: $n - 19 = 75$

25. 19 less than a number n is 75. What is the number?

26. 19 more than a number n is 75. What is the number?

27. The sum of a number n and 19 is 75. What is the number?

28. A number n decreased by 19 is 75. What is the number?

29. Phil gave 19 matchbooks to a friend. He then had 75 matchbooks. How many did he have before he gave the matchbooks away?

30. Susan added 19 matchbooks to her collection in June. She then had 75 matchbooks. How many did she have at the end of May?

Solving multiplication and division equations

Jan bought 3 identical fish for $4.50. How much did she pay for each fish?

Let p be the price of 1 fish. Then $3p$ is the price of 3 fish.

Equation:

$$3\overset{\downarrow}{p} = \overset{\underset{\text{price of 3}}{\downarrow}}{4.50}$$

Divide both sides by 3:

$$\frac{3p}{3} = \frac{4.50}{3}$$

The bars indicate division.

Simplify:

$$p = 1.50$$

Check: $3 \times 1.50 = 4.50$

She paid $1.50 for each fish.

There were 8 fish tanks in the pet shop. The average number of fish in a tank was 35. How many fish were there in all?

Let f be the number of fish there were in all. Then $\frac{f}{8}$ is the average number of fish in a tank.

Equation:

$$\overset{\underset{\substack{\text{average number} \\ \text{of fish in a tank}}}{\downarrow}}{\frac{f}{8}} = 35$$

Multiply both sides by 8:

$$8 \times \frac{f}{8} = 8 \times 35$$

Simplify:

$$f = 280$$

Check: $\frac{280}{8} = 35$

There were 280 fish in all.

74

EXERCISES

Solve each equation by dividing both sides by the same number. Check the solution.

Same as 5r=85

1. $2a = 28$
2. $3b = 57$
3. $85 = 5r$
4. $108 = 9s$

5. $4t = 64$
6. $3x = 81$
7. $5m = 470$
8. $12g = 132$

9. $53y = 954$
10. $228 = 4d$
11. $5n = 245$
12. $2x = 356$

13. $6a = 1.92$
14. $34g = 91.8$
15. $3r = 22.8$
16. $2.24 = 7c$

Solve each equation by multiplying both sides by the same number. Check the solution.

17. $\frac{a}{3} = 5$
18. $\frac{b}{3} = 6$
19. $15 = \frac{x}{2}$
20. $20 = \frac{g}{4}$

21. $\frac{y}{5} = 20$
22. $\frac{m}{12} = 24$
23. $\frac{r}{20} = 6$
24. $\frac{r}{6} = 20$

25. $\frac{c}{9} = 81$
26. $\frac{d}{4} = 25$
27. $32 = \frac{y}{5}$
28. $\frac{m}{3} = 15$

29. $\frac{n}{7} = 1.2$
30. $\frac{x}{15} = 3.2$
31. $\frac{a}{18} = 0.16$
32. $\frac{b}{16} = 0.18$

Decide whether Equation A or Equation B would be used to solve each problem. Then solve the problem.

Equation A: $6n = 84$

Equation B: $\frac{n}{6} = 84$

33. 6 times a number n is 84. What is the number?

34. A number n divided by 6 is 84. What is the number?

35. If you multiply a number n by 6, you get 84. What is the number?

36. The product of a number n and 6 is 84. What is the number?

37. Bill spent $84 for 6 identical rabbits. How much did 1 rabbit cost?

38. Doris bought 6 dogs. The average cost of a dog was $84. How much did all 6 dogs cost?

Problem solving

To solve each problem:
- Write an equation.
- Solve the equation.
- Check the solution in the problem.

Grace hiked all of Raccoon Trail in the morning and 7 miles along another trail in the afternoon. She hiked a total of 22 miles. How many miles long was Raccoon Trail?

Let m be the length of Raccoon Trail. Then $m + 7$ is the total number of miles hiked.

	total miles	total miles
	↓	↓
Equation:	$m + 7 =$	22

Subtract 7 from each side: $m + 7 - 7 = 22 - 7$

Simplify: $m = 15$

Check: $15 + 7 = 22$

So, Raccoon Trail was 15 miles long.

The weight of Ann's pack was $\frac{1}{4}$ her own weight. Her pack weighed 27 pounds. How much did Ann weigh?

Let w be Ann's weight.

Then $\frac{w}{4}$ is the weight of Ann's pack.

weight of Ann's pack in pounds	•	weight of Ann's pack in pounds
↓		↓

Equation: $\quad \dfrac{w}{4} = 27$

Multiply both sides by 4: $\quad 4 \times \dfrac{w}{4} = 4 \times 27$

Simplify: $\quad w = 108$

Check: $\dfrac{108}{4} = 27$

So, Ann weighed 108 pounds.

EXERCISES

Use an equation to solve each problem.

1. Grace bought some packages of Quick Freeze Hiking Food. She sold 12 of them to Ann. She had 24 packages left. How many packages did she buy?

2. The first rest area for hikers on Red Mountain was $\frac{1}{2}$ the way up the mountain. If they had hiked 6 miles when they reached the rest area, what was the total hiking distance up Red Mountain?

3. Grace's pack weighed 6 more pounds than Ann's pack. Grace's pack weighed 22 pounds. How many pounds did Ann's weigh?

4. Today there are 8200 more pine trees in the forest than there were 5 years ago. There are 23,100 trees today. How many were there 5 years ago?

5. On last year's trip, the highest pass the hikers crossed had an altitude of 3025 meters. The highest pass on this year's trip was 54 meters lower. What was the altitude of the lower pass?

6. The hikers passed a Forest Service tree farm. It had 52 rows of white pines, with the same number of trees in each row. There were 5512 white pines in all. How many trees were there in each row?

7. Roberta bought all the food for the weekend camping trip with 3 friends. She paid $55.00. How much money should her friends each give Roberta to pay for their share of the food?

8. Maria drove Roberta and their two friends on the camping trip. If she used 11 gallons of gas and paid $15.00, how much did 1 gallon of gas cost? Round your answer to the nearest cent.

77

Solving two-step equations

In this lesson you will use what you have learned about solving simple equations to solve two-step equations. Study the examples.

EXAMPLE 1.

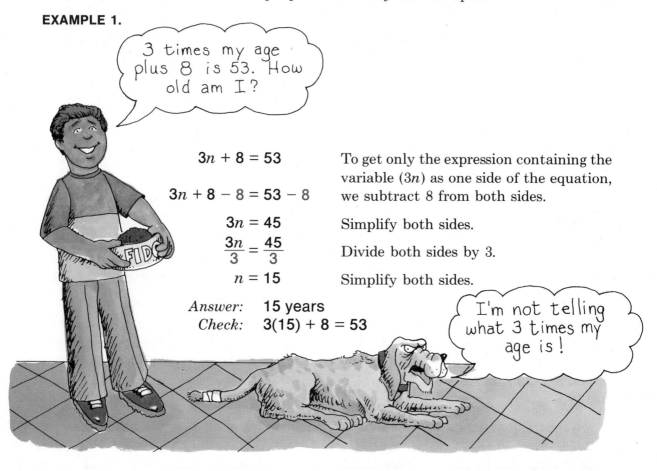

3 times my age plus 8 is 53. How old am I?

$$3n + 8 = 53$$

To get only the expression containing the variable ($3n$) as one side of the equation, we subtract 8 from both sides.

$$3n + 8 - 8 = 53 - 8$$

$$3n = 45$$

Simplify both sides.

$$\frac{3n}{3} = \frac{45}{3}$$

Divide both sides by 3.

$$n = 15$$

Simplify both sides.

Answer: **15 years**
Check: **3(15) + 8 = 53**

I'm not telling what 3 times my age is!

EXAMPLE 2.

$$27 = 5n - 3$$

$$27 + 3 = 5n - 3 + 3$$

$$30 = 5n$$

$$\frac{30}{5} = \frac{5n}{5}$$

$$6 = n$$

Check: $27 = 5(6) - 3$

EXAMPLE 3.

$$16 + 7n = 44$$

$$16 + 7n - 16 = 44 - 16$$

$$7n = 28$$

$$\frac{7n}{7} = \frac{28}{7}$$

$$n = 4$$

Check: $16 + 7(4) = 44$

EXERCISES

Solve and check.

1. $3n + 4 = 22$
2. $5n - 9 = 6$
3. $6n + 8 = 38$
4. $4n - 10 = 2$
5. $7m + 6 = 6$
6. $8n - 12 = 36$
7. $12 = 9a - 15$
8. $4c + 5 = 9$
9. $15 + 2d = 31$
10. $52 = 12 + 4x$
11. $25 + 4w = 49$
12. $38 + 5y = 38$
13. $9b - 36 = 0$
14. $7k - 45 = 4$
15. $23 = 13 + 2a$
16. $7 + 5d = 42$
17. $12 + 4x = 40$
18. $35 = 3a + 8$
19. $6x - 2 = 40$
20. $15a - 25 = 20$
21. $19 + 3c = 40$
22. $4h - 42 = 18$
23. $12r - 48 = 12$
24. $4j - 36 = 0$
25. $25 = 25 + 9r$
26. $12s - 24 = 0$
27. $53 + 7a = 60$
28. $63 = 10t - 27$
29. $9m + 18 = 90$
30. $11s - 37 = 40$

Solve each problem by solving an equation.

★ 31. 3 more than 6 times a number n is 45. What is the number?

★ 32. 5 less than 4 times a number n is 31. What is the number?

★ 33. If you multiply a number n by 8 and subtract 15 from the product, you get 65. What is the number?

★ 34. The sum of 12 times a number n and 47 is 167. What is the number?

Estimate to find the incorrect answer.

1. a. $8.82 \div 4.3 = 2.05$
   b. $19.15 \div 6.3 = 0.304$

Divide.

2. $2.1 \overline{)20.223}$

3. $1.1 \overline{)3.916}$

4. $0.03 \overline{)16.110}$

5. $3.2 \overline{)2.1312}$

6. $50 \overline{)458.50}$

7. $6.3 \overline{)505.89}$

8. $78.4 \overline{)337.12}$

9. $9.21 \overline{)66.312}$

10. $0.803 \overline{)39.347}$

11. $6.25 \overline{)331.25}$

12. $3.08 \overline{)5.0512}$

13. $0.246 \overline{)7.3062}$

79

More on two-step equations

Be a winner!
How many marbles?
Hint: The number of marbles divided by seven, minus 21, is 50.

Solve a two-step equation to find the number of marbles.

Equation: $\frac{n}{7} - 21 = 50$

Add 21: $\frac{n}{7} - 21 + 21 = 50 + 21$

Simplify: $\frac{n}{7} = 71$

Multiply by 7: $7 \times \frac{n}{7} = 7 \times 71$

Simplify: $n = 497$

Answer: 497 marbles

Check: $\frac{497}{7} - 21 = 50$

How many marbles would you have guessed were in the jar?

Study these examples:

EXAMPLE 1. $\frac{n}{9} + 6 = 14$

Subtract 6: $\frac{n}{9} + 6 - 6 = 14 - 6$

Simplify: $\frac{n}{9} = 8$

Multiply by 9: $9 \times \frac{n}{9} = 9 \times 8$

Simplify: $n = 72$

Check: $\frac{72}{9} + 6 = 14$

EXAMPLE 2. $5n - 8 = 37$

Add 8: $5n - 8 + 8 = 37 + 8$

Simplify: $5n = 45$

Divide by 5: $\frac{5n}{5} = \frac{45}{5}$

Simplify: $n = 9$

Check: $5(9) - 8 = 37$

EXERCISES

Solve and check.

1. $5n + 9 = 49$
2. $6c - 3 = 15$
3. $\frac{n}{2} + 8 = 12$

4. $\frac{n}{3} - 5 = 2$
5. $\frac{s}{3} + 14 = 30$
6. $9n + 8 = 89$

7. $12n + 1 = 37$
8. $8r - 8 = 48$
9. $\frac{x}{2} - 8 = 7$

10. $\frac{x}{4} + 5 = 12$
11. $\frac{n}{3} + 7 = 19$
12. $15n + 4 = 79$

13. $6r - 8 = 46$
14. $6a + 8 = 50$
15. $\frac{c}{5} - 3 = 4$

16. $\frac{d}{3} - 8 = 6$
17. $\frac{a}{3} + 16 = 33$
18. $9d - 10 = 26$

19. $20n + 7 = 67$
20. $\frac{r}{4} - 3 = 5$
21. $\frac{w}{5} + 2 = 3$

22. $\frac{x}{3} - 7 = 2$
23. $9y - 16 = 92$
24. $\frac{b}{5} + 6 = 13$

25. $15n - 17 = 73$
26. $\frac{k}{2} - 8 = 6$
27. $3n + 11 = 23$

28. $5c + 10 = 45$
29. $12c - 4 = 68$
30. $\frac{c}{4} + 16 = 28$

31. $\frac{r}{2} - 4 = 12$
32. $10t - 20 = 100$
33. $\frac{r}{8} - 3 = 15$

34. $11c - 17 = 60$
35. $\frac{r}{4} + 11 = 31$
36. $13n + 4 = 30$

Solve each problem by using an equation.

★ 37. If a number is divided by 6 and then 5 is subtracted, the result is 4. What is the number?

★ 38. 3 more than 8 times a number is 107. What is the number?

★ 39. If you divide a number by 4 and add 3 to the result, you get 7. What is the number?

★ 40. If you multiply a number by 7 and subtract 9 from the result, you get 68. What is the number?

41. **KEEP YOUR THUMB OFF THE SCALE!**

One of these eight marbles is heavier than the other seven. Tell how to find the heavy marble by using a balance and making only two weighings.

81

Problem solving

To solve each problem:
- Write an equation.
- Solve the equation.
- Check the solution in the problem.

A produce manager accepted delivery of 15 bushels of apples. The delivery charge was $8. The total bill was $79.25. What was the cost of each bushel?

Let c be the cost of each bushel. Then $15c$ is the cost of 15 bushels. So, the cost of 15 bushels and the delivery charge equals the total bill.

	total bill in dollars		total bill in dollars
Equation:	$15c + 8$	$=$	79.25
Subtract 8:	$15c + 8 - 8 = 79.25 - 8$		
Simplify:	$15c = 71.25$		
Divide by 15:	$\dfrac{15c}{15} = \dfrac{71.25}{15}$		
Simplify:	$c = 4.75$		

Check: $\quad 15(4.75) + 8 = 79.25$

The cost of each bushel was $4.75.

EXERCISES
Use an equation to solve each problem.

1. Last year an apple orchard yielded 475 bushels per acre. That was 38 bushels per acre less than it yielded this year. How many bushels per acre did it yield this year?

2. One particular apple tree yielded 20 bushels of apples. The average number of apples per bushel is about 160. About how many apples were on this tree?

3. The owner of an apple orchard paid a beekeeper $130 for 7 hives of bees to pollinate the apple blossoms on his trees. The owner was charged $15 a day and a $40 delivery-and-pick-up fee. How many days did the owner have the bees?

4. Each tree in an apple orchard was expected to yield 15 bushels of apples. At harvest the total yield was found to be 47,200 bushels, which was 80 bushels short of what was expected. How many trees were in the orchard?

5. An apple orchard has 421 trees. That is 54 trees more than it had 5 years ago. How many trees did it have 5 years ago?

6. The Ruiz family went to a pick-your-own apple orchard. They picked 8 bushels of apples and were charged $25.60. What was the cost of each bushel?

7. One morning insecticide was sprayed on 420 trees in an apple orchard. This number was $\frac{1}{2}$ of the number of trees sprayed in the afternoon. How many trees were sprayed in the afternoon?

★ 8. Sarah was paid 75¢ a bushel for picking apples. After she spent $2 of what she had earned, she had $25 left. How many bushels did she pick?

Give the prime factorization. Use exponents for factors that occur more than once. [pages 54–57]

1. 48   2. 75   3. 72   4. 116   5. 240   6. 300

Give the greatest common factor and the least common multiple. [pages 58–59]

7. 12, 16   8. 18, 36   9. 20, 35   10. 6, 15   11. 14, 21   12. 24, 36

Copy and complete. [pages 60–61]

	Whole number	Divisible by							
		2?	3?	4?	5?	6?	8?	9?	10?
13.	258	?	?	?	?	?	?	?	?
14.	475	?	?	?	?	?	?	?	?
15.	42,196	?	?	?	?	?	?	?	?
16.	30,270	?	?	?	?	?	?	?	?

Solve. [pages 72–75, 78–81]

17. $x + 37 = 95$ 18. $y - 19 = 74$ 19. $58 + w = 117$

20. $5x = 85$ 21. $\frac{t}{2} = 2$ 22. $\frac{r}{4} = 20$

23. $3t + 18 = 57$ 24. $5n - 13 = 87$ 25. $\frac{w}{3} + 9 = 13$

First write an equation. Then solve. [pages 76–77, 82–83]

26. 23 less than a number is 55. What is the number?

27. A number increased by 47 is 139. What is the number?

28. Bill has 4 times as many stamps as Maria. If Bill has 228 stamps, how many stamps does Maria have?

29. Anne jogged 2 kilometers more than 3 times as far as Jill. If Anne jogged 11 kilometers, how many kilometers did Jill jog?

CHAPTER PROJECT

1. Copy and extend the table through 50.

2. One is the only number that has exactly 1 factor. What kind of number has exactly 2 factors?

3. **a.** List the numbers that have an odd number of factors. What kind of number are they?
   b. The square of a prime number has how many factors?
   c. Do the squares of all composite numbers have the same number of factors?

4. **a.** List the numbers that have exactly 4 factors.
   b. Give the prime factorization of each number in your list.
   c. How could you classify numbers having exactly 4 factors? (*Hint:* What about the prime factorization of each number?)

5. See if you can classify numbers having exactly 6 factors.

6. What is the smallest number having exactly 7 factors?

Number	Factors	Number of Factors
1	1	1
2	1,2	2
3	1,3	2
4	1,2,4	3
5	1,5	2
6	1,2,3,6	4
7	1,7	2
8	1,2,4,8	4

Whole numbers with exactly two factors are called **prime numbers.**
Whole numbers (other than 0) with more than two factors are called **composite numbers.**

Prime or composite?

1. 2   2. 3   3. 9   4. 11

5. 15   6. 21   7. 27   8. 29

9. 41   10. 46   11. 57   12. 69

$$56 = 8 \times 7$$
$$= 2 \times 4 \times 7$$
$$= 2 \times 2 \times 2 \times 7 \leftarrow \text{factorization}$$

prime

Give the prime factorization.

13. 10   14. 12   15. 16   16. 20

17. 28   18. 48   19. 64   20. 72

Factors of 12:   1, 2, 3, 4, 6, 12
Factors of 18:   1, 2, 3, 6, 9, 18

The greatest common factor is 6.

Multiples of 12:   12, 24, 36, . . .
Multiples of 18:   18, 36, 54, . . .

The least common multiple is 36.

Give the greatest common factor and the least common multiple.

21. 12, 20   22. 15, 25   23. 16, 24

24. 24, 36   25. 25, 30   26. 18, 24

$$3a - 7 = 20$$
$$3a - 7 + 7 = 20 + 7$$
$$3a = 27$$
$$\frac{3a}{3} = \frac{27}{3}$$
$$a = 9$$

Solve.

27. $x + 7 = 18$ 28. $y + 29 = 63$

29. $w - 12 = 43$ 30. $z - 29 = 82$

31. $3x = 27$ 32. $5x = 65$

33. $9y = 108$ 34. $11w = 143$

35. $3a + 5 = 32$ 36. $6c + 10 = 64$

37. $\frac{b}{4} - 6 = 2$ 38. $\frac{d}{3} + 4 = 9$

The ancient Greeks classified whole numbers in many ways. One way was by the sum of the factors of the whole number.

If the sum is less than the number, the number is **defective;** if the sum is equal to the number, the number is **perfect;** and if the sum is greater than the number, the number is **abundant.**

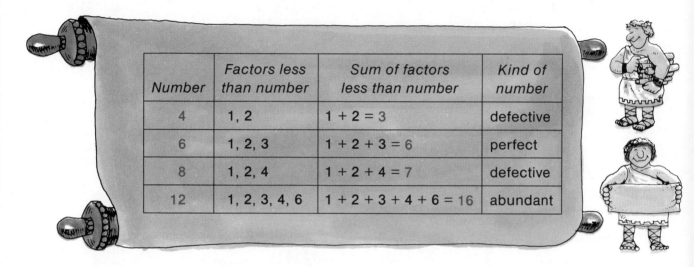

Number	Factors less than number	Sum of factors less than number	Kind of number
4	1, 2	$1 + 2 = 3$	defective
6	1, 2, 3	$1 + 2 + 3 = 6$	perfect
8	1, 2, 4	$1 + 2 + 4 = 7$	defective
12	1, 2, 3, 4, 6	$1 + 2 + 3 + 4 + 6 = 16$	abundant

1. Classify the whole numbers 1 through 30 as defective, perfect, or abundant.

2. Which two numbers less than 30 are perfect numbers?

Euclid (an ancient Greek) discovered the following fact about prime numbers and perfect numbers:

If $2^n - 1$ is a prime number, then $(2^n - 1)2^{n-1}$ is a perfect number.

Example: Let $n = 5$.

Since $2^5 - 1$ is prime, we know that $(2^5 - 1)2^{5-1}$ is perfect.

3. For $n = 5$, what perfect number do you get?

4. What is the next perfect number that can be found this way?

a b c d   a b c d   a b c d   a b c d   a b c d   a b c

1. ▯ ▯ ▯ ▯ 2. ▯ ▯ ▯ ▯

MAJOR CHECKUP
STANDARDIZED FORMAT

5. ▯ ▯ ▯ ▯ 6. ▯ ▯ ▯

a b c d   a b c d   a b c d

7. ▯ ▯ ▯ ▯ 8. ▯ ▯ ▯ ▯ 9. ▯ ▯ ▯ ▯ 10. ▯ ▯ ▯ ▯ 11. ▯ ▯ ▯ ▯ 12. ▯ ▯ ▯

Choose the correct letter.

1. 5.0349 rounded to the nearest hundredth is

    a. 5.03
    b. 5.04
    c. 5.035
    d. none of these

2. Which of these numbers is greater than 0.2?

    a. 0.09
    b. 0.10
    c. 0.199
    d. none of these

3. Add.

$$48.3 + 7.91$$

    a. 56.21
    b. 127.4
    c. 12.74
    d. none of these

4. Subtract.

$$72.4 - 3.77$$

    a. 34.7
    b. 3.47
    c. 68.63
    d. none of these

5. Multiply.

$$4.21 \times 0.07$$

    a. 0.2947
    b. 2.947
    c. 0.02947
    d. none of these

6. Divide.

$$5.6\overline{)11.368}$$

    a. 20.3
    b. 2.3
    c. 2.03
    d. none of these

7. The prime factorization of 144 is

    a. $2^2 \times 3^4$
    b. $2^3 \times 3^2$
    c. $2^4 \times 3^2$
    d. none of these

8. The least common multiple of 12 and 16 is

    a. 32
    b. 48
    c. 96
    d. none of these

9. The solution of $y - 18 = 34$ is

    a. 16
    b. 24
    c. 52
    d. none of these

10. The solution of $6w + 18 = 48$ is

    a. 30
    b. 5
    c. 11
    d. none of these

11. Ellen had 3 times as many records as Frank. Ellen had 12 records. How many records did Frank have?

    a. 4   **b.** 9
    c. 36   **d.** none of these

12. Alan bought some $8 records and one $12 tape. He spent $68. How many records did he buy?

    a. 5   **b.** 6
    c. 7   **d.** none of these

Measurement

Measuring length

The **meter** (m) is the basic unit for measuring length in the metric system. The length of the leather strip is about 1 meter.

These units are used to measure length in the metric system:

1 kilometer (km) = 1000 meters
1 hectometer (hm)* = 100 meters
1 dekameter (dam)* = 10 meters
1 meter (m) = 1 meter
1 decimeter (dm)* = 0.1 meter
1 centimeter (cm) = 0.01 meter
1 millimeter (mm) = 0.001 meter

* These units are seldom used.

Notice that both the metric system and our place-value system are based on the number 10. Because of this, we use decimals to write metric measurements.

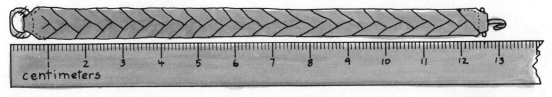

The length of the bracelet is 1 dm + 3 cm + 2 mm. Here are three ways that we can write the length of the bracelet:

1.32 dm
13.2 cm
132 mm

EXERCISES

Draw segments of these lengths.

1. 1 cm   2. 5.2 cm   3. 11.4 cm   4. 19 mm   5. 50 mm

6. 123 mm   7. 1.5 dm   8. 1.43 dm   9. 14.3 cm   10. 143 mm

11. a. Draw a segment 1.46 dm long.
    b. How many cm long is the segment?
    c. How many mm long is it?

12. a. Draw a segment 12.5 cm long.
    b. How many dm long is the segment?
    c. How many mm long is it?

13. a. Draw a segment that is 165 mm long.
    b. How many cm long is the segment?
    c. How many dm long is it?

14. a. On a chalkboard draw a segment that is 1.35 m long.
    b. How many dm long is the segment?
    c. How many cm long is it?
    d. How many mm long is it?

Multiple choice. Pick the answer that seems reasonable.

15. The thickness of a dime is   a. 1 cm   b. 1 m   c. 1 mm   d. 1 dm

16. The diameter (length across) of a nickel is
    a. 2.1 mm   b. 2.1 m   c. 2.1 dm   d. 2.1 cm

17. The length of a new pencil is   a. 1.89 dm   b. 18.9 mm   c. 1.89 m   d. 189 cm

18. The height above the floor of a basketball hoop is
    a. 3.05 dm   b. 3.05 cm   c. 3.05 m   d. 3.05 km

Copy and complete this table. Estimate first!

	Length	Estimate of length	Measurement of length	Difference between estimate and measurement
19.	width of desk	?	?	?
20.	height of desk	?	?	?
21.	length of room	?	?	?
22.	width of room	?	?	?
23.	height of ceiling	?	?	?
24.	width of door	?	?	?

Changing units in the metric system

Since the metric system is based on the number 10, we can easily change from one unit to another by multiplying or dividing by a power of 10.

Study these examples.

EXAMPLE 1. Change 12.6 cm to mm.

Step 1. Recall: 1 cm = 10 mm

Step 2. Think: Since we are changing to a smaller unit, we should get a larger number. So, we should multiply.

Step 3. Compute: 12.6 × 10 = 126
So, 12.6 cm = 126 mm.

EXAMPLE 2. Change 15.6 dm to m.

Step 1. Recall: 10 dm = 1 m

Step 2. Think: Since we are changing to a larger unit, we should get a smaller number. So, we should divide.

Step 3. Compute: 15.6 ÷ 10 = 1.56
So, 15.6 dm = 1.56 m.

EXAMPLE 3. Change 215 cm to m.

Step 1. Recall: 100 cm = 1 m

Step 2. Think: We should get a smaller number, so we divide.

Step 3. Compute: 215 ÷ 100 = 2.15
So, 215 cm = 2.15 m.

EXAMPLE 4. Change 14 km to m.

Step 1. Recall: 1 km = 1000 m

Step 2. Think: We should get a larger number, so we multiply.

Step 3. Compute: 14 × 1000 = 14,000
So, 14 km = 14,000 m.

EXERCISES

1. Change 4.2 cm to mm.

2. Change 397 mm to m.

3. Change 7563.2 m to km.

4. Change 14.2 m to cm.

Copy and complete.

	km	hm	dam	m	dm	cm	mm
5.	0.1	1	10	100	1000		
6.	3.2						
7.							3962
8.					4281		

Copy and complete.

9. 7 m = $\underline{?}$ dm

10. 3 m = $\underline{?}$ cm

11. 5 m = $\underline{?}$ mm

12. 8 km = $\underline{?}$ m

13. 3.9 km = $\underline{?}$ m

14. 563 m = $\underline{?}$ km

15. 672 cm = $\underline{?}$ m

16. 43.2 cm = $\underline{?}$ m

17. 8452 mm = $\underline{?}$ m

18. 57.3 mm = $\underline{?}$ cm

19. 3.9 m = $\underline{?}$ mm

20. 3.9 mm = $\underline{?}$ m

21. 349.4 cm = $\underline{?}$ m

22. 583.1 dm = $\underline{?}$ m

23. 42.71 km = $\underline{?}$ m

24. 35.7 cm = $\underline{?}$ m

25. 426 mm = $\underline{?}$ m

26. 53.2 m = $\underline{?}$ mm

27. 8 km = $\underline{?}$ mm

28. 476.3 mm = $\underline{?}$ km

29. 9 mm = $\underline{?}$ km

Solve.

30. A distance record for throwing a fresh egg was 964.6 decimeters. How many meters was that?

31. One distance record for throwing a Frisbee was 128 meters. How many centimeters was that?

32. A height record for kite flying was 10.830 kilometers. How many meters was that?

33. The longest paper chain (made in less than a day) was made by 75 high school students in San Jose, California. It measured 21,762 meters. How many kilometers was that?

Error of measurement

A measurement is never exact. There is always an error of measurement.

Measured to the nearest cm, both arrowheads are 3 cm long. In each case there is a difference between the true length and the measurement. This difference is called the **error of measurement**. Notice that when we measure to the nearest cm, the **greatest possible error (g.p.e.)** is 0.5 cm. For the length of the arrowheads we can write

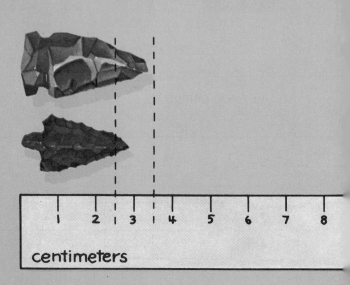

$$3 \text{ cm} \pm 0.5 \text{ cm}$$

(Read as "3 cm plus or minus 0.5 cm.")

This means that the true length is somewhere between 2.5 cm and 3.5 cm.

The greatest possible error is always 0.5 of the unit to which the measurement is made.

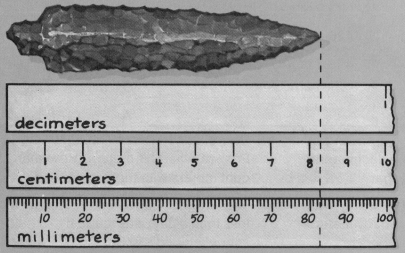

Measurement of the arrowhead	g.p.e.
1 dm to the nearest dm	0.5 dm
8 cm to the nearest cm	0.5 cm
83 mm to the nearest mm	0.5 mm

Notice that as the unit gets smaller, the g.p.e. gets smaller—that is, the measurements are more **precise**.

EXERCISES

Complete this table.

Measurement	Greatest possible error	Range of true length
1. 6 cm to the nearest cm	?	6 cm±0.5 cm
2. 35 cm to the nearest cm	?	?±?
3. 25 m to the nearest m	?	?±?
4. 208 km to the nearest km	?	?±?
5. 4.5 cm to the nearest 0.1 cm	?	?±?
6. 9.8 m to the nearest 0.1 m	?	?±?
7. 6.52 m to the nearest 0.01 m	?	?±?
8. 7.52 km to the nearest 0.01 km	?	?±?

First measure each segment to the nearest cm.
Then give the range of the true length.

9. _____

10. _____

11. _____

12. _____

Pick the unit that gives the most precise measurement.

13. kilometer, meter, millimeter

14. meter, centimeter, decimeter

15. meter, 0.1 meter, 0.01 meter

16. centimeter, 0.1 meter, 0.001 km

17. ⭐ STRETCHING THE TRUTH

Three estimates of the height of a giraffe were 350 cm, 370 cm, and 340 cm. The estimates were off by 6 cm, 4 cm, and 24 cm. How tall was the giraffe?

Estimate to find the incorrect answer.

1. a. 0.64
   ×0.5
   0.320

   b. 4.2
   ×0.3
   0.126

Multiply.

2. 5.7
   ×8

3. 0.64
   ×0.4

4. 29
   ×0.5

5. 6.8
   ×0.5

6. 0.4
   ×0.2

7. 5.2
   ×1.6

8. 78.3
   ×2.9

9. 5.86
   ×3.2

Perimeter

The **perimeter** of a figure is the distance around it.

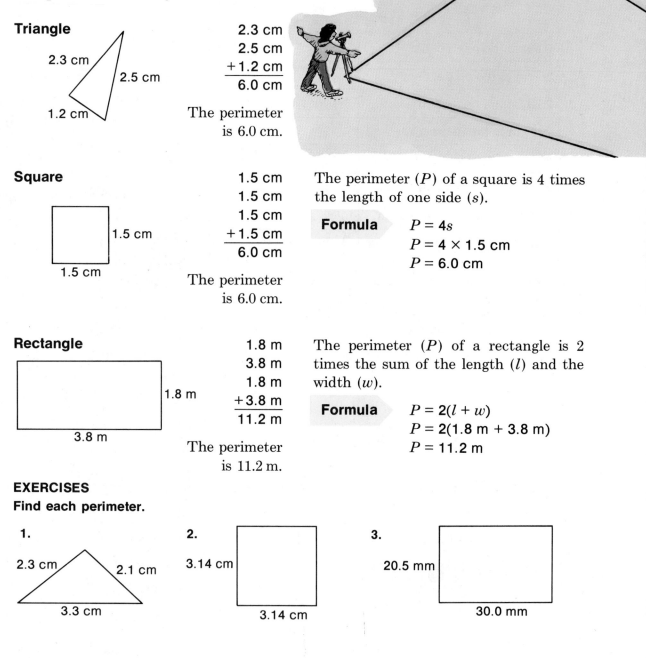

Triangle

2.3 cm
2.5 cm
+1.2 cm
6.0 cm

The perimeter
is 6.0 cm.

Square

1.5 cm
1.5 cm
1.5 cm
+1.5 cm
6.0 cm

The perimeter
is 6.0 cm.

The perimeter (P) of a square is 4 times
the length of one side (s).

Formula

$P = 4s$
$P = 4 \times 1.5$ cm
$P = 6.0$ cm

Rectangle

1.8 m
3.8 m
1.8 m
+3.8 m
11.2 m

The perimeter
is 11.2 m.

The perimeter (P) of a rectangle is 2
times the sum of the length (l) and the
width (w).

Formula

$P = 2(l + w)$
$P = 2(1.8$ m $+ 3.8$ m$)$
$P = 11.2$ m

EXERCISES
Find each perimeter.

1.

2.3 cm   2.1 cm
3.3 cm

2.

3.14 cm
3.14 cm

3.

20.5 mm
30.0 mm

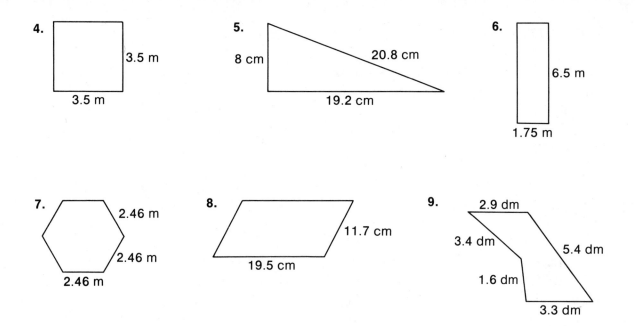

4. 3.5 m, 3.5 m

5. 8 cm, 20.8 cm, 19.2 cm

6. 6.5 m, 1.75 m

7. 2.46 m, 2.46 m, 2.46 m

8. 11.7 cm, 19.5 cm

9. 2.9 dm, 3.4 dm, 5.4 dm, 1.6 dm, 3.3 dm

First measure each side to the nearest millimeter. Then compute the perimeter.

10.   **11.**   **12.**

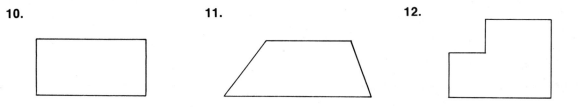

Solve.

13. A patio 6.3 m by 9.6 m is to be edged with brick. If each brick is to be 1.5 dm long, how many bricks will be needed?

14. A rectangular lot that measures 56 m by 120 m is to be fenced in with fencing that costs $4.30 a running meter. How much will the fencing cost?

15. The perimeter of a rectangular parking lot is 580 m. The lot is 150 m long. What is its width?

★ **16.** Each side of a square measured to the nearest cm is 12 cm. What is the g.p.e. of the measurement of each side? What is the perimeter? What is the g.p.e. of the perimeter?

Circumference

The distance around a circle is called its **circumference.** The circumference of this bicycle wheel is about 205.73 cm.

The circumference (C) can be found by multiplying the diameter (d) by π (read as "pi").

Formula $C = \pi d$

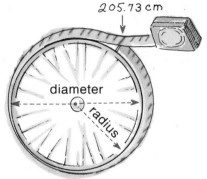

205.73 cm

diameter

radius

π is a number a little greater than 3. We will use 3.14 as an approximate value for π.

The **diameter** of a circle is twice the **radius** of the circle.

EXAMPLE. Find the circumference.

3 m

$C = \pi d$

$C \approx 3.14 \times 3 \text{ m}$ ($\approx$ means *is approximately equal to*)

$C \approx 9.42 \text{ m}$

EXERCISES
Find each circumference to the nearest tenth.

1.
10 cm

2.
4 m

3.
2.3 dm

4.
6 cm

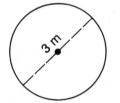

The diameter is 12 cm.

5.
8 cm

6.
4.1 cm

Measure each diameter to the nearest millimeter and compute the circumference.

7.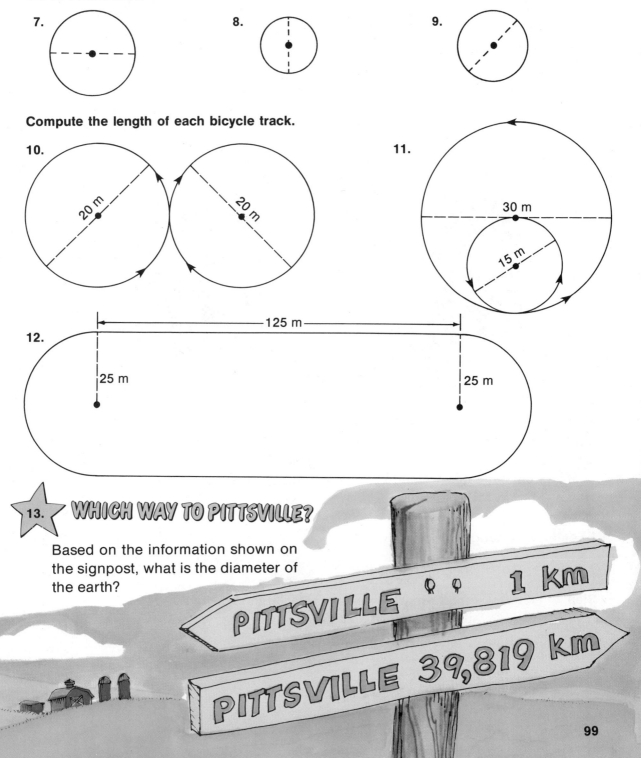

8.

9.

Compute the length of each bicycle track.

10.

20 m

20 m

11.

30 m

15 m

125 m

12.

25 m

25 m

13. **WHICH WAY TO PITTSVILLE?**

Based on the information shown on the signpost, what is the diameter of the earth?

PITTSVILLE 1 KM

PITTSVILLE 39,819 KM

99

Liquid volume

The **liter (L)** is a unit for measuring liquid volume in the metric system.

1000 milliliters (mL) = 1 liter (L)   1 L = 1000 cubic centimeters

¨1 milliliter = 0.001 liter   1 mL = 1 cubic centimeter

1 liter

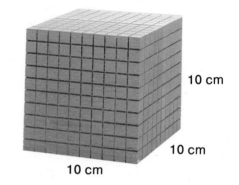

10 cm

10 cm

10 cm

The units for measuring liquid volume are related in the same way as the units for measuring length. Therefore, you can change from one unit of liquid volume to another in the same way as you do with units of length.

EXAMPLE.   Change 325 mL to L.

Step 1.   Recall: 1000 mL = 1 L

Step 2.   Think: Since we are changing to a larger unit, we should get a smaller number. So we divide.

Step 3.   Compute: 325 ÷ 1000 = 0.325

So, 325 mL = 0.325 L.

EXERCISES
Complete.

1. 456 mL = ? L
2. 925 mL = ? L
3. 3625 mL = ? L
4. 8 L = ? mL
5. 0.375 L = ? mL
6. 2.5 L = ? mL
7. 382 L = ? mL
8. 8000 mL = ? L
9. 500 mL = ? L
10. 250 mL = ? L

Liter or milliliter? Which unit would most likely be used to measure the liquid volume of

11. a small milk carton?
12. a drinking glass?
13. a large milk carton?
14. a soft-drink can?
15. an eyedropper?
16. a soup spoon?

Choose the most reasonable liquid volume.

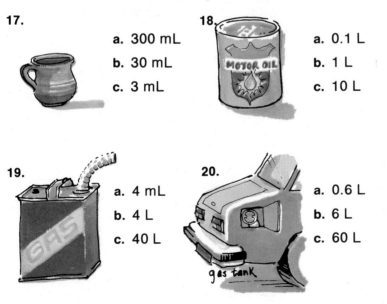

17.
a. 300 mL
b. 30 mL
c. 3 mL

18.
a. 0.1 L
b. 1 L
c. 10 L

19.
a. 4 mL
b. 4 L
c. 40 L

20.
a. 0.6 L
b. 6 L
c. 60 L

gas tank

Give each product.

1. 23 × 100
2. 8.6 × 10
3. 0.53 × 100
4. 4.6 × 1000
5. 0.074 × 1000
6. 9.1 × 100
7. 2.62 × 1000
8. 59.3 × 10
9. 0.745 × 100
10. 83.5 × 1000

Give each quotient.

11. 68 ÷ 10
12. 12.6 ÷ 100
13. 32.18 ÷ 1000
14. 594.6 ÷ 100
15. 38.72 ÷ 10
16. 74.12 ÷ 1000
17. 83.4 ÷ 100
18. 0.86 ÷ 10
19. 52.3 ÷ 100
20. 9.54 ÷ 1000

Measuring weight (mass)

The **gram (g)** is a unit for measuring weight (mass) in the metric system.

 1 kilogram (kg) = 1000 grams (g)

 1 milligram (mg) = 0.001 gram

50 milligrams   400 grams   2 kilograms

EXERCISES
Complete.

1. 1 g = _?_ mg

2. 3 g = _?_ mg

3. 22 g = _?_ mg

4. 0.4 g = _?_ mg

5. 3.2 g = _?_ mg

6. 3000 mg = _?_ g

7. 1500 mg = _?_ g

8. 750 mg = _?_ g

9. 1 kg = _?_ g

10. 3.5 kg = _?_ g

11. 0.43 kg = _?_ g

12. 5000 g = _?_ kg

13. 4500 g = _?_ kg

14. 250 g = _?_ kg

15. 426.5 g = _?_ kg

Milligram, gram, or kilogram? Which unit would most likely be used to measure the weight of

16. a baseball?

17. a desk?

18. a straight pin?

19. a small pill?

20. a large piece of chalk?

21. an orange?

22. a bicycle?

23. an apple seed?

24. a sandwich?

25. your body?

Choose the most reasonable weight.

26.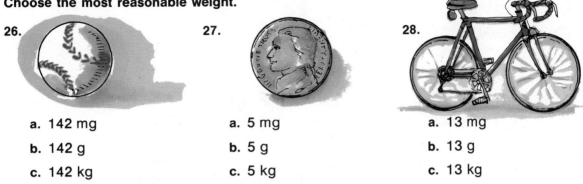

a. 142 mg
b. 142 g
c. 142 kg

27.

a. 5 mg
b. 5 g
c. 5 kg

28.

a. 13 mg
b. 13 g
c. 13 kg

29. Estimate the weight of this textbook. Then weigh it. How close was your estimate?

30. Estimate the weights of some objects in your classroom. Then weigh them. How close was each estimate?

In the metric system, the **Celsius** thermometer is used to measure temperature.

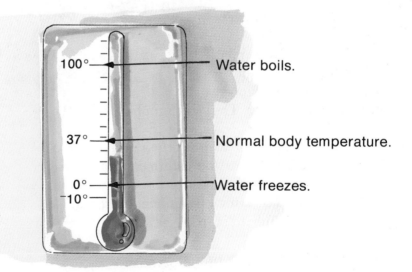

100° — Water boils.

37° — Normal body temperature.

0° — Water freezes.
⁻10°

Choose the most reasonable temperature for

31. a very cold day.   a. ⁻10°C   b. 20°C   c. 30°C

32. your classroom.   a. 2°C   b. 15°C   c. 52°C

33. hot soup.   a. 20°C   b. 40°C   c. 80°C

Computers in careers

Earlier you learned that a programmer often writes a flow chart before writing a program. Here is an example.

Once a flow chart is written for a computer, a detailed set of instructions, a program, must be written in a language that the computer understands. One simple computer language is called BASIC. Here is a program for the flow chart.

In this program there are 5 statements; each is on a separate line. The last statement must be "END."

Each line is numbered. Any number between 0 and 9999 may be used. As you can see, numbers may be skipped,

```
10  LET A = 8
20  LET B = 9
70  LET C = A + B
80  PRINT C
90  END
```

but the numbers must be in order. The same number cannot be used more than once.

This program tells the computer to store the number 8 in a location in its memory referred to as A, to store 9 in a location referred to as B, and to store the sum in location C. Finally, in line 80, the computer is told to print the number stored in C. The last line tells the computer to stop.

These symbols can be used in BASIC programs:

+	(Add)	/	(Divide)
−	(Subtract)	↑	(Raise to a power)
*	(Multiply)	( )	(grouping symbols)

The computer also recognizes the words LET, PRINT, and END. You will learn other words later.

Here are some sample program statements. Notice that the line number can be any number you choose.

$$15 \quad \text{LET X} = \text{A} * \text{B} - 5$$

(Multiply A and B and then subtract 5.)

$$483 \quad \text{LET G} = (\text{A} - \text{B})/\text{D}$$

(Subtract B from A and divide that answer by D.)

$$37 \quad \text{LET R} = \text{M} \uparrow 3 - \text{K}$$

(Raise M to the third power and then subtract K.)

EXERCISES

Follow each program. Tell what the computer would print.

1. 10   LET G = 10
    20   LET H = 7
    30   LET I = 2
    40   LET K = G * H + I
    50   PRINT K
    60   END

2. 200   LET A = 7
    300   LET B = 1
    400   LET C = A ↑ 2 + B
    500   PRINT C
    600   END

3. 1000   LET X = 56
    2000   LET Y = 2
    3000   LET Z = (X − Y)/6
    4000   PRINT Z
    5000   END

4. 110   LET A = 5
    120   LET B = 4
    125   LET C = (A + B) * 2
    130   PRINT C
    140   END

5. 300   LET A = 3
    400   LET B = 2
    500   LET C = (A + B) ↑ 3
    600   PRINT C
    700   END

6. 4000   LET A = 8
    5000   LET B = 4
    6000   LET C = A ↑ 2 − B ↑ 2
    7000   PRINT C
    8000   END

7. Here is a flow chart for computing the circumference of a circle having a diameter of 3.

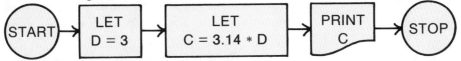

Write a program for the flow chart.

8. Write a program for computing the circumference of a circle having a radius of 8.

Customary units—length

12 inches (in. or ") = 1 foot (ft or ')   1760 yards = 1 mile (mi)

3 feet = 1 yard (yd)   5280 feet = 1 mile

36 inches = 1 yard

These examples show how to change from one customary unit
of length to another.

EXAMPLE 1.   Change 16 ft to in.

Step 1.   Recall: 1 ft = 12 in.

Step 2.   Think: Since we are changing
from a larger unit to a
smaller one, we should
get a larger number.
So, we should multiply.

Step 3.   Compute:
$$\begin{array}{r} 16 \\ \times 12 \\ \hline 32 \\ 16 \\ \hline 192 \end{array}$$

So, 16 ft = 192 in.

EXAMPLE 2.   Change 76 ft to yd.

Step 1.   Recall: 3 ft = 1 yd

Step 2.   Think: Since we are changing
to a larger unit, we
should get a smaller
number. So, we should
divide.

Step 3.   Compute:
$$\begin{array}{r} 25 \\ 3\overline{)76} \\ -6 \\ \hline 16 \\ -15 \\ \hline 1 \end{array}$$

So, 76 ft is $25\frac{1}{3}$ yd.
It is also **25 yd 1 ft.**

106

EXERCISES

Copy and complete.

1. 8 yd = _?_ ft

2. 108 in. = _?_ ft

3. 3 yd = _?_ in.

4. 27 ft = _?_ yd

5. 4 ft = _?_ in.

6. 108 in. = _?_ yd

7. 1 yd 5 in. = _?_ in.

8. 51 ft = _?_ yd

9. 15 yd = _?_ ft

10. 4 mi = _?_ yd

11. 3 ft 4 in. = _?_ in.

12. 19 in. = _?_ ft 7 in.

13. 9 yd 2 ft = _?_ ft

14. 32 ft = _?_ yd 2 ft

15. 3 mi = _?_ yd

16. 117 in. = _?_ ft 9 in.

17. 1 mi 440 ft = _?_ ft

18. 12 yd 1 ft = _?_ ft

19. 6 ft 5 in. = _?_ in.

20. 104 ft = _?_ yd 2 ft

21. 127 in. = _?_ ft 7 in.

Solve.

22. A **fathom** is used to measure the depth of water.
　　　1 fathom = 6 ft
How many fathoms deep is water that is 282 feet deep?

23. The deepest spot in any of the oceans is the Mariana Trench in the Pacific Ocean. It is 6033 fathoms deep. How many feet deep is it?

24. A **furlong** is a measure of length used in horse racing.
　　　1 furlong = 220 yd
How many furlongs are in 1 mile?

25. A **hand** is a unit for measuring the height of a horse.
　　　1 hand = 4 in.
How many inches tall is a horse whose height is 17 hands?

26. Sea distances are usually measured in **nautical miles.**
　　　1 nautical mile is about 6076.1 feet.
A **knot** is a measure of speed at sea.
　　　1 knot is 1 nautical mile per hour.
How many miles per hour is 1 knot?

Liquid volume and weight— customary units

2 cups (c) = 1 pint (pt)

2 pints = 1 quart (qt)

2 quarts = 1 half-gallon

2 half-gallons = 1 gallon (gal)

1 quart · 1 gallon · 1 pint · 1 half-gallon · 1 cup

EXERCISES

Complete.

1. 10 c = _?_ pt
2. 18 pt = _?_ qt
3. 8 qt = _?_ gal

4. 5 qt = _?_ c
5. 14 pt = _?_ c
6. 3 gal = _?_ qt

7. 1 gal = _?_ pt
8. 4 qt = _?_ half-gallons
9. 16 c = _?_ qt

10. 20 pt = _?_ qt
11. 3 qt = _?_ c
12. 5 gal = _?_ half-gallons

13. 2 pt 1 c = _?_ c
14. 3 qt 1 pt = _?_ pt
15. 2 gal 3 qt = _?_ qt

16. 15 pt = _?_ qt 1 pt
17. 19 qt = _?_ gal 3 qt
18. 34 pt = _?_ gal 1 qt

In the metric system, dry material such as grain is measured with the same units used for liquids. In the customary system, different units are used for dry measure.

| 2 pints (pt) = 1 quart (qt) |
| 8 quarts = 1 peck (pk) |
| 4 pecks = 1 bushel (bu) |

Complete.

19. 10 pt = _?_ qt
20. 48 qt = _?_ pk

21. 24 pk = _?_ bu
22. 1 bu = _?_ qt

23. 3 bu = _?_ pk
24. 27 pk = _?_ bu 3 pk

Here are some units for measuring weight.

16 ounces (oz) = 1 pound (lb)

2000 pounds (lb) = 1 ton (T)

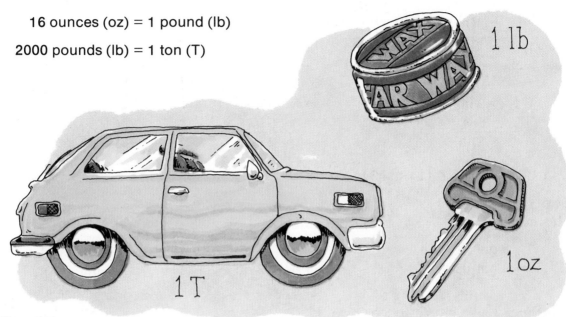

Complete.

25. 5 lb = _?_ oz

26. 2 T = _?_ lb

27. 144 oz = _?_ lb

28. 27 lb = _?_ oz

29. 10,000 lb = _?_ T

30. 384 oz = _?_ lb

31. 1 lb 8 oz = _?_ oz

32. 2 lb 5 oz = _?_ oz

33. 3 lb 11 oz = _?_ oz

34. 20 oz = _?_ lb 4 oz

35. 50 oz = _?_ lb 2 oz

36. 108 oz = _?_ lb 12 oz

37. A bread recipe calls for 2 lb of whole-wheat flour. If you have 1 lb 8 oz of flour, how much more do you need?

38. An empty truck weighs 11,000 lb. When full, it weighs 8 tons. What is the weight of its cargo in pounds?

39. ⭐ BRAIN DRAIN

How can you get exactly 6 gallons of water using these buckets?

Computing with customary units

EXAMPLE 1. Add 1 ft 9 in. and 2 ft 5 in.

Step 1.
Add inches and regroup.

```
     1 ft
     1 ft   9 in.
   + 2 ft   5 in.
   ──────────────
             2 in.
```

Step 2.
Add feet.

```
     1 ft
     1 ft   9 in.
   + 2 ft   5 in.
   ──────────────
     4 ft   2 in.
```

EXAMPLE 2. Subtract 1 gal 3 qt from 3 gal 1 qt.

Step 1.
Regroup.

```
      2      5
      3̸ gal  1̸ qt
    − 1 gal  3 qt
    ─────────────
```

Step 2.
Subtract quarts.

```
      2      5
      3̸ gal  1̸ qt
    − 1 gal  3 qt
    ─────────────
               2 qt
```

Step 3.
Subtract gallons.

```
      2      5
      3̸ gal  1̸ qt
    − 1 gal  3 qt
    ─────────────
      1 gal  2 qt
```

EXAMPLE 3. Multiply 1 lb 8 oz by 3.

Step 1.
Multiply ounces and regroup.

```
     1 lb
     1 lb   8 oz
            × 3
   ──────────────
             8 oz
```

Step 2.
Multiply pounds and add.

```
     1 lb
     1 lb   8 oz
            × 3
   ──────────────
     4 lb   8 oz
```

EXAMPLE 4. Divide 38 yd 2 ft by 4.

Step 1.
Divide yards.

```
        9 yd
     4)38 yd   2 ft
      −36 yd
     ──────────
        2 yd
```

Step 2.
Regroup.

```
        9 yd
     4)38 yd   2̸ f̸t̸
      −36 yd
     ──────────
        2̸ y̸d̸
                 8 ft
```

Step 3.
Divide feet.

```
        9 yd   2 ft
     4)38 yd   2̸ f̸t̸
      −36 yd
     ──────────
        2̸ y̸d̸
                 8 ft
               − 8 ft
               ──────
                   0
```

EXERCISES
Complete.

1. 3 ft 4 in. = <u>40</u> in.
2. 8 yd 2 ft = ? ft
3. 3 qt 1 pt = ? pt
4. 2 gal 3 qt = ? qt
5. 8 pt 1 c = ? c
6. 5 lb 2 oz = ? oz
7. 29 in. = 2 ft ? in.
8. 29 ft = ? yd 2 ft

Add.

9. 2 ft 8 in.
   +1 ft 10 in.

10. 2 yd 2 ft
    +5 yd 2 ft

11. 2 yd 2 ft 7 in.
    +1 yd 1 ft 6 in.

12. 3 gal 3 qt
    +1 gal 3 qt

Subtract.

13. 2 ft 3 in.
    −1 ft 8 in.

14. 6 yd 1 ft
    −3 yd 2 ft

15. 6 yd
    −3 yd 1 ft

16. 4 gal 1 qt
    −1 gal 2 qt

Multiply.

17. 1 ft 7 in.
         ×2

18. 4 qt 1 pt
         ×6

19. 7 lb 6 oz
         ×4

Divide.

20. 4)9 ft 4 in.
21. 2)7 yd 1 ft
22. 2)15 gal 2 qt

Find each perimeter or circumference.

23.
4 ft 5 in. [square]
4 ft 5 in.

24.
[rectangle] 1′ 3″
3′ 2″

25.
[circle 7 yd diameter]

★ 26. The perimeter of a rectangular patio is 36 yd. The width is 6 yd 2 ft. What is its length?

KEEPING SKILLS SHARP

Estimate to find the incorrect answer.

1. a.   5.6
       ×4.5
       ‾‾‾‾‾
       25.2

   b. 16.8
       ×3.5
       ‾‾‾‾‾
       5.88

Multiply.

2. 5.8
   ×2.9

3. 0.26
   ×1.4

4.   7.4
   ×0.35

5. 9.3
   ×6.4

6. 0.52
   ×18

7.   45
   ×2.5

8. 3.81
   ×16

9. 25.3
   ×0.33

CHAPTER CHECKUP

Copy and complete. [pages 90–93, 100–103]

1. 38.6 m = _?_ dm

2. 2.43 km = _?_ m

3. 5620 m = _?_ km

4. 56 cm = _?_ mm

5. 384 mm = _?_ m

6. 43.2 m = _?_ mm

7. 5.1 L = _?_ mL

8. 357.2 mL = _?_ L

9. 63.2 kg = _?_ g

10. 350 g = _?_ kg

11. 750 mg = _?_ g

12. 45 g = _?_ mg

Find the perimeter or circumference of each figure. Use 3.14 as an approximation for π. [pages 96–99]

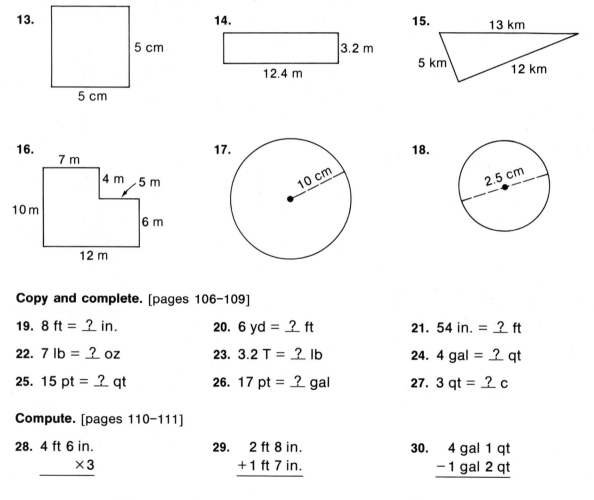

13.
5 cm
5 cm

14.
12.4 m
3.2 m

15.
13 km
5 km
12 km

16.
7 m
4 m
5 m
10 m
6 m
12 m

17.
10 cm

18.
2.5 cm

Copy and complete. [pages 106–109]

19. 8 ft = _?_ in.

20. 6 yd = _?_ ft

21. 54 in. = _?_ ft

22. 7 lb = _?_ oz

23. 3.2 T = _?_ lb

24. 4 gal = _?_ qt

25. 15 pt = _?_ qt

26. 17 pt = _?_ gal

27. 3 qt = _?_ c

Compute. [pages 110–111]

28. 4 ft 6 in.
    ×3

29. 2 ft 8 in.
    +1 ft 7 in.

30. 4 gal 1 qt
    −1 gal 2 qt

Think about the diameter of a basketball and a basketball hoop.

The diameter of the basketball hoop is clearly greater than the diameter of the basketball.

Guess: How many times the diameter of the ball is the diameter of the hoop?

1.5 times?   1.7 times?   2 times?   2.4 times?

Measure: Find a way to measure the diameter of a basketball and the diameter of a basketball hoop.

Compute: How many times the diameter of the ball is the diameter of the hoop?

Was your guess reasonably close?

smaller unit
↓
13.4 m = _?_ mm
↑
larger number
So, multiply by 1000.

13.4 m = 13,400 mm

Complete.

1. 536 mm = _?_ m

2. 4.2 km = _?_ m

3. 17.3 cm = _?_ mm

4. 750 mL = _?_ L

5. 0.4 L = _?_ mL

6. 20 kg = _?_ g

7. 450 g = _?_ kg

8. 1230 mg = _?_ g

The perimeter of a figure is the distance around it.

The circumference of a circle is the distance around it.

$$C = \pi d$$

Give each perimeter (or circumference).
Use 3.14 as an approximation for π.

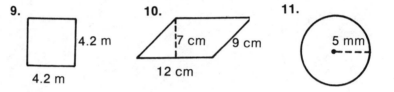

9. 4.2 m, 4.2 m

10. 7 cm, 9 cm, 12 cm

11. 5 mm

larger unit
↓
48 in. = _?_ ft
↑
smaller number
So, divide by 12.

48 in. = 4 ft

Copy and complete.

12. 8 ft = _?_ in.

13. 6 yd = _?_ ft

14. 1 mi = _?_ yd

15. 6 ft 3 in. = _?_ in.

16. 3 gal = _?_ qt

17. 4 qt = _?_ pt

18. 12 c = _?_ pt

19. 8 lb = _?_ oz

2   19
3̶ ft 7̶ in.
−1 ft   8 in.
‾‾‾‾‾‾‾‾‾‾
1 ft 11 in.

1 pt 1 c
    ×3
‾‾‾‾‾‾‾
4 pt 1 c

Compute.

20.   1 ft 8 in.
   +2 ft 9 in.

21.   6 ft
   −2 ft 7 in.

22. 4 pt 1 c
       ×2

23. 2)3 yd 8 in.

Relative error

The length of the shorter piece of mac-ramé is 12 cm to the nearest centimeter. The length of the longer one is 180 cm to the nearest centimeter.
In both cases the greatest possible error is 0.5 cm.

When compared to 12 cm (the shorter length) the g.p.e. is quite large.
When compared to 180 cm (the longer length) the g.p.e. is quite small.

To find the **relative error** of a measurement, we can divide the greatest possible error by the measurement.

Relative error of 12-cm measurement

$$12 \overline{)0.5000} \quad \begin{array}{c} 0.0417 \end{array}$$

Relative error of 180-cm measurement

$$180 \overline{)0.5000} \quad \begin{array}{c} 0.0028 \end{array}$$

Notice that the smaller measurement has the greater relative error.

For each of these measurements, compute the relative error to the nearest hundredth.

1. 15 cm to the nearest centimeter

2. 18 m to the nearest meter

3. 6.3 m to the nearest 0.1 m

4. 43.5 km to the nearest 0.1 km

5. 2.54 kg to the nearest 0.01 kg

6. 3.80 L to the nearest 0.01 L

7. Measure your handspan to the nearest centimeter. Find the relative error of your measurement.

8. Measure your height to the nearest centimeter. Find the relative error of your measurement.

Choose the correct letter.

1. Add.

   5.77 + 3.2

- **a.** 5.45
- **b.** 8.97
- **c.** 6.09
- **d.** none of these

2. Subtract.

   2.001 − 0.693

- **a.** 1.308
- **b.** 1.408
- **c.** 1.418
- **d.** none of these

3. Multiply.

$$\begin{array}{r} 0.04 \\ \times\,0.03 \\ \hline \end{array}$$

- **a.** 0.12
- **b.** 0.012
- **c.** 0.0012
- **d.** none of these

---

4. Divide.

   $4.2\overline{)13.02}$

- **a.** 3.01
- **b.** 3.1
- **c.** 0.31
- **d.** none of these

5. What is the greatest common factor of 16 and 8?

- **a.** 8
- **b.** 16
- **c.** 4
- **d.** none of these

6. Which of these numbers is prime?

- **a.** 1
- **b.** 12
- **c.** 33
- **d.** none of these

---

7. $25 - (4 + 2) \times 3 = \underline{?}$

- **a.** 69
- **b.** 7
- **c.** 57
- **d.** none of these

8. Solve.

$$\frac{a}{2} + 6 = 44$$

- **a.** 76
- **b.** 25
- **c.** 19
- **d.** none of these

9. $47.2 \text{ m} = \underline{?} \text{ cm}$

- **a.** 47,200
- **b.** 4720
- **c.** 0.472
- **d.** none of these

---

10. What is the perimeter?

   3.6 m

   11 m

- **a.** 29.2 m
- **b.** 39.6 m
- **c.** 14.6 m
- **d.** none of these

11. Steve earned $34 for working 5 hours. How much did he earn per hour?

- **a.** $7
- **b.** $6.40
- **c.** $170
- **d.** none of these

12. A dime weighs 2.26 g. A penny weighs 3.1 g. How many more g does the penny weigh than the dime?

- **a.** 0.84
- **b.** 0.96
- **c.** 19.5
- **d.** none of these

Adding and Subtracting Fractions

4

What fraction is colored?

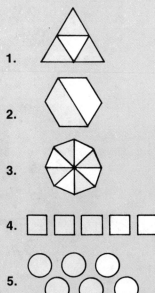

1.

2.

3.

4.

5.

Give two fractions for each colored region.

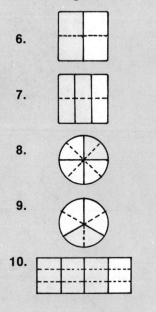

6.

7.

8.

9.

10.

118

Equivalent fractions

The **numerator** and **denominator** of a fraction are the **terms** of the fraction.

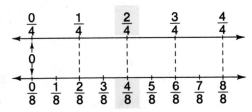

terms $\begin{cases} \dfrac{2}{4} & \leftarrow \text{numerator} \\ & \leftarrow \text{denominator} \end{cases}$

Equivalent fractions stand for the same number.

From the number lines we see that

$$\frac{2}{4} = \frac{4}{8}$$

You can get an equivalent fraction in **higher terms** by multiplying both numerator and denominator by the same whole number (greater than 1).

You can get an equivalent fraction in **lower terms** by dividing both numerator and denominator by the same whole number (greater than 1).

When you divide both terms of a fraction by their greatest common factor (GCF), you get the equivalent fraction in **lowest terms.**

The GCF of 8 and 12 is 4.

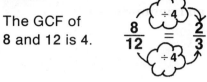

Here is how to find the fraction that is equivalent to $\frac{3}{6}$ and has a denominator of 12.

$$\frac{3}{6} = \frac{?}{12}$$

Step 1. The denominator was multiplied by 2.

Step 2. So, multiply the numerator by 2.

EXERCISES
Copy and complete.

1. $\frac{1}{2} = \frac{?}{6}$ 2. $\frac{1}{3} = \frac{?}{6}$ 3. $\frac{1}{4} = \frac{?}{16}$ 4. $\frac{3}{2} = \frac{6}{?}$ 5. $\frac{2}{7} = \frac{?}{21}$

6. $\frac{5}{8} = \frac{?}{40}$ 7. $\frac{4}{3} = \frac{12}{?}$ 8. $\frac{5}{2} = \frac{10}{?}$ 9. $\frac{5}{6} = \frac{?}{30}$ 10. $\frac{4}{3} = \frac{?}{15}$

11. $\frac{3}{5} = \frac{15}{?}$ 12. $\frac{3}{4} = \frac{18}{?}$ 13. $\frac{2}{9} = \frac{?}{36}$ 14. $\frac{3}{2} = \frac{12}{?}$ 15. $\frac{5}{3} = \frac{?}{15}$

Write in lowest terms.

16. $\frac{6}{8}$ 17. $\frac{4}{16}$ 18. $\frac{9}{12}$ 19. $\frac{16}{14}$ 20. $\frac{24}{30}$ 21. $\frac{14}{18}$ 22. $\frac{18}{32}$

23. $\frac{8}{12}$ 24. $\frac{27}{36}$ 25. $\frac{25}{15}$ 26. $\frac{16}{24}$ 27. $\frac{14}{21}$ 28. $\frac{14}{12}$ 29. $\frac{36}{45}$

30. $\frac{42}{36}$ 31. $\frac{48}{64}$ 32. $\frac{48}{96}$ 33. $\frac{55}{100}$ 34. $\frac{45}{70}$ 35. $\frac{72}{80}$ 36. $\frac{72}{81}$

Write in lowest terms.

37. $\frac{180}{630}$ 38. $\frac{210}{576}$ 39. $\frac{315}{1050}$ 40. $\frac{2475}{8085}$

119

Fractions and decimals

Every fraction is equivalent to a decimal. A fraction can be changed to a decimal by dividing its numerator by its denominator.

EXAMPLE 1. $\frac{7}{8} = ?$

$$
\begin{array}{r}
0.875 \\
8\overline{)7.000} \\
-64 \\
\hline
60 \\
-56 \\
\hline
40 \\
-40 \\
\hline
0
\end{array}
$$

So, $\frac{7}{8} = 0.875$

Since the decimal above terminates (comes to an end), it is called a **terminating decimal.**

Some fractions are equivalent to decimals that do not terminate. They are called **repeating decimals.**

EXAMPLE 2. $\frac{7}{11} = ?$

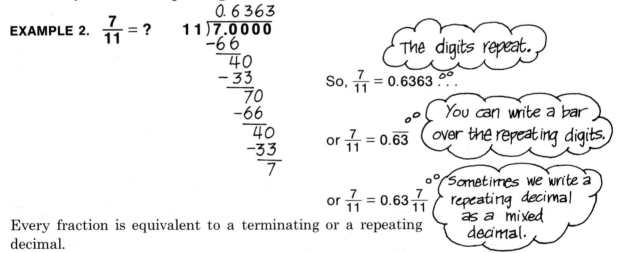

$$
\begin{array}{r}
0.6363 \\
11\overline{)7.0000} \\
-66 \\
\hline
40 \\
-33 \\
\hline
70 \\
-66 \\
\hline
40 \\
-33 \\
\hline
7
\end{array}
$$

So, $\frac{7}{11} = 0.6363\ldots$

The digits repeat.

or $\frac{7}{11} = 0.\overline{63}$

You can write a bar over the repeating digits.

or $\frac{7}{11} = 0.63\frac{7}{11}$

Sometimes we write a repeating decimal as a mixed decimal.

Every fraction is equivalent to a terminating or a repeating decimal.

These examples show how to change a terminating decimal to a fraction.

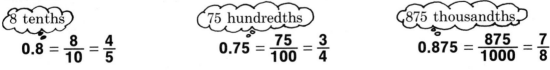

8 tenths

$0.8 = \frac{8}{10} = \frac{4}{5}$

75 hundredths

$0.75 = \frac{75}{100} = \frac{3}{4}$

875 thousandths

$0.875 = \frac{875}{1000} = \frac{7}{8}$

EXERCISES

Change each fraction to a decimal. Tell whether the decimal is terminating or repeating.

1. $\frac{1}{2}$
2. $\frac{1}{6}$
3. $\frac{1}{8}$
4. $\frac{5}{3}$
5. $\frac{3}{5}$
6. $\frac{2}{3}$

7. $\frac{5}{8}$
8. $\frac{5}{4}$
9. $\frac{1}{3}$
10. $\frac{4}{9}$
11. $\frac{3}{8}$
12. $\frac{3}{2}$

Complete.

13. If $\frac{1}{5} = 0.2$ then $\frac{2}{5} = \underline{?}$ $\frac{3}{5} = \underline{?}$ $\frac{4}{5} = \underline{?}$ $\frac{5}{5} = \underline{?}$ $\frac{6}{5} = \underline{?}$

14. If $\frac{1}{4} = 0.25$ then $\frac{2}{4} = \underline{?}$ $\frac{3}{4} = \underline{?}$ $\frac{4}{4} = \underline{?}$ $\frac{5}{4} = \underline{?}$ $\frac{6}{4} = \underline{?}$

Change each decimal to its equivalent fraction in lowest terms.

15. 0.28
16. 0.35
17. 0.6
18. 0.06
19. 0.006

20. 0.375
21. 1.3
22. 4.2
23. 1.25
24. 0.625

<, =, or >?

25. $0.3 \bullet \frac{1}{3}$
26. $\frac{5}{9} \bullet 0.56$
27. $\frac{9}{4} \bullet 2.25$
28. $\frac{7}{9} \bullet 0.77$

29. $1.6 \bullet \frac{8}{5}$
30. $0.875 \bullet \frac{7}{8}$
31. $\frac{1}{6} \bullet 0.16$
32. $\frac{5}{3} \bullet 1.67$

Change each fraction to a decimal.

33. $\frac{2}{13}$
34. $\frac{4}{17}$
35. $\frac{5}{19}$
36. $\frac{5}{21}$

Change to decimals.

37. $\frac{3}{8}$
38. $\frac{1}{60}$
39. $\frac{3}{200}$
40. $\frac{4}{11}$

★ 41. Try to do exercises 33–36 with your calculator.
Why doesn't your calculator always give you the answer?

Comparing fractions

You can compare fractions that have the same denominator by comparing their numerators.

$$\frac{3}{8} < \frac{5}{8}$$

To compare fractions that have different denominators, find equivalent fractions with the same denominator **(common denominator).** A common multiple of the denominators of two fractions is a common denominator. The least common multiple of the denominators is the **least common denominator** (LCD).

EXAMPLE 1. Compare $\frac{2}{3}$ and $\frac{1}{2}$.

Step 1.
Find the least common denominator.

$$\frac{2}{3} \qquad \frac{1}{2}$$

The LCD is 6.

Step 2.
Change to equivalent fractions.

$$\frac{2}{3} \qquad \frac{1}{2}$$
$$\downarrow \qquad \downarrow$$
$$\frac{4}{6} \qquad \frac{3}{6}$$

Step 3.
Compare. Since $\frac{4}{6}$ is greater than $\frac{3}{6}$, $\frac{2}{3}$ is greater than $\frac{1}{2}$.

$$\frac{2}{3} \quad > \quad \frac{1}{2}$$

Greater

$$\frac{4}{6} \qquad \frac{3}{6}$$

Another way to compare two fractions is to change the fractions to equivalent decimals.

EXAMPLE 2. Compare $\frac{1}{4}$ and $\frac{3}{11}$.

Step 1.
Change to equivalent decimals.

$$\frac{1}{4} \qquad \frac{3}{11}$$
$$\downarrow \qquad \downarrow$$
$$0.25 \qquad 0.\overline{27}$$

Step 2.
Compare. Since 0.25 is less than $0.\overline{27}$, $\frac{1}{4}$ is less than $\frac{3}{11}$.

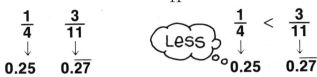

Less

$$\frac{1}{4} \quad < \quad \frac{3}{11}$$
$$\downarrow \qquad \downarrow$$
$$0.25 \qquad 0.\overline{27}$$

EXERCISES

Give the least common denominator.

1. $\frac{1}{2}$ $\frac{3}{4}$ 2. $\frac{5}{6}$ $\frac{1}{3}$ 3. $\frac{3}{8}$ $\frac{1}{4}$

4. $\frac{1}{3}$ $\frac{1}{2}$ 5. $\frac{5}{3}$ $\frac{1}{2}$ 6. $\frac{1}{6}$ $\frac{1}{5}$

7. $\frac{3}{4}$ $\frac{5}{6}$ 8. $\frac{2}{5}$ $\frac{3}{4}$ 9. $\frac{1}{7}$ $\frac{3}{8}$

<, =, or >? Use the equivalent-fraction method.

10. $\frac{3}{8}$ ⬤ $\frac{1}{2}$ 11. $\frac{1}{2}$ ⬤ $\frac{4}{7}$ 12. $\frac{2}{3}$ ⬤ $\frac{4}{6}$

13. $\frac{3}{2}$ ⬤ $\frac{7}{4}$ 14. $\frac{6}{7}$ ⬤ $\frac{5}{6}$ 15. $\frac{5}{8}$ ⬤ $\frac{2}{3}$

16. $\frac{4}{12}$ ⬤ $\frac{1}{3}$ 17. $\frac{3}{2}$ ⬤ $\frac{4}{3}$ 18. $\frac{4}{7}$ ⬤ $\frac{3}{5}$

< or >? Use the decimal method.

19. $\frac{3}{5}$ ⬤ $\frac{1}{2}$ 20. $\frac{4}{5}$ ⬤ $\frac{9}{13}$ 21. $\frac{5}{7}$ ⬤ $\frac{8}{11}$

22. $\frac{4}{9}$ ⬤ $\frac{3}{7}$ 23. $\frac{5}{11}$ ⬤ $\frac{1}{2}$ 24. $\frac{4}{7}$ ⬤ $\frac{7}{13}$

Solve.

25. Will a bolt that is $\frac{7}{8}$ of an inch long go through a sheet of steel that is $\frac{9}{32}$ of an inch thick?

26. Will a bolt that is $\frac{3}{8}$ of an inch in diameter go through a $\frac{5}{16}$-inch hole?

27. Is a $\frac{5}{8}$-inch wrench too large or too small for a $\frac{3}{4}$-inch nut?

★ 28. A certain set of wrenches contains the following sizes in inches:

$\frac{3}{4}$ $\frac{1}{2}$ $\frac{5}{16}$ $\frac{1}{4}$ $\frac{7}{16}$ $\frac{13}{16}$ $\frac{9}{16}$ $\frac{5}{8}$ $\frac{3}{8}$ $\frac{11}{16}$

Order the sizes from smallest to largest.

Estimate to find the two incorrect answers.

1. a. $2.89 \div 0.96 = 30.1$

   b. $35.8 \div 4.02 = 0.89$

   c. $39.2 \div 1.4 = 28$

   d. $355.3 \div 3.23 = 110$

Divide.

2. $0.3\overline{)57.3}$

3. $10\overline{)98.4}$

4. $15\overline{)351}$

5. $2.6\overline{)16.38}$

6. $0.08\overline{)0.1624}$

7. $5.7\overline{)548.91}$

8. $103\overline{)5356}$

9. $21.6\overline{)20.736}$

10. $12.4\overline{)47.12}$

11. $2.65\overline{)7.9765}$

Adding fractions

To add fractions having the same denominator, add the numerators to get the numerator of the sum and use the common denominator for the denominator of the sum.

$$\frac{1}{8} + \frac{3}{8} = \frac{4}{8}$$
$$= \frac{1}{2} \leftarrow \text{lowest terms}$$

When the fractions have different denominators, change to equivalent fractions with common denominators.

Step 1.
Find the least common denominator.

$$\frac{5}{12} + \frac{1}{4} = \frac{}{12} + \frac{}{12}$$

Step 2.
Change to equivalent fractions.

$$\frac{5}{12} + \frac{1}{4} = \frac{5}{12} + \frac{3}{12}$$

Step 3.
Add, and change to lowest terms.

$$\frac{5}{12} + \frac{1}{4} = \frac{5}{12} + \frac{3}{12}$$
$$= \frac{8}{12}$$
$$= \frac{2}{3}$$

EXERCISES
Give each sum in lowest terms.

1. $\frac{1}{3} + \frac{1}{6}$

2. $\frac{1}{3} + \frac{1}{3}$

3. $\frac{1}{2} + \frac{1}{4}$

4. $\frac{1}{6} + \frac{1}{6}$

5. $\frac{1}{10} + \frac{3}{10}$

6. $\frac{3}{8} + \frac{1}{2}$

7. $\frac{2}{5} + \frac{1}{2}$

8. $\frac{1}{3} + \frac{1}{4}$

9. $\frac{1}{5} + \frac{1}{6}$

10. $\frac{1}{2} + \frac{1}{3}$

11. $\frac{5}{9} + \frac{2}{9}$

12. $\frac{1}{6} + \frac{1}{2}$

13. $\frac{3}{8} + \frac{3}{8}$

14. $\frac{3}{4} + \frac{1}{6}$

15. $\frac{1}{8} + \frac{2}{3}$

16. $\frac{3}{8} + \frac{1}{8}$

17. $\frac{1}{10} + \frac{3}{5}$

18. $\frac{1}{9} + \frac{2}{3}$

19. $\frac{1}{2} + \frac{0}{4}$

20. $\frac{1}{2} + \frac{1}{5}$

124

Add. Give each sum in lowest terms.

21. $\frac{1}{3}$
    $+\frac{3}{5}$

22. $\frac{1}{6}$
    $+\frac{3}{5}$

23. $\frac{1}{3}$
    $+\frac{5}{9}$

24. $\frac{1}{3}$
    $+\frac{3}{9}$

25. $\frac{1}{8}$
    $+\frac{3}{4}$

26. $\frac{1}{4}$
    $+\frac{2}{5}$

27. $\frac{1}{8}$
    $+\frac{1}{4}$

28. $\frac{2}{3}$
    $+\frac{1}{6}$

29. $\frac{2}{3}$
    $+\frac{1}{10}$

30. $\frac{3}{10}$
    $+\frac{3}{10}$

31. $\frac{1}{3}$
    $+\frac{5}{12}$

32. $\frac{1}{4}$
    $+\frac{5}{8}$

33. $\frac{5}{9}$
    $+\frac{1}{4}$

34. $\frac{3}{8}$
    $+\frac{2}{5}$

35. $\frac{2}{3}$
    $+\frac{1}{4}$

36. $\frac{1}{10}$
    $+\frac{1}{10}$

37. $\frac{1}{10}$
    $+\frac{3}{4}$

38. $\frac{1}{2}$
    $+\frac{1}{3}$

Solve.

39. Dolores bought $\frac{3}{4}$ of a pound of dates and $\frac{1}{2}$ of a pound of figs. How many pounds of fruit did she buy?

40. Alvin wrote $\frac{1}{3}$ of his English theme on Tuesday and $\frac{1}{2}$ of it on Wednesday. What fraction of his theme did he write during those two days?

41. Andrew read $\frac{1}{8}$ of a book on Monday, $\frac{1}{4}$ of the book on Tuesday, and $\frac{1}{2}$ of the book on Wednesday. What fraction of the book did he read during the three days?

42. A youth group held a car wash to raise money for a camp-out. They earned $\frac{3}{5}$ of the money needed. What fraction of the money did they still need to earn?

43. ⭐ **SUM SMALL WORDS**

Find the four-letter word on these two pages that has the smallest sum. Use the code below.

Code:

a	b	c	d	...	z
$\frac{1}{32}$	$\frac{1}{16}$	$\frac{3}{32}$	$\frac{1}{8}$	...	$\frac{13}{16}$

Example:

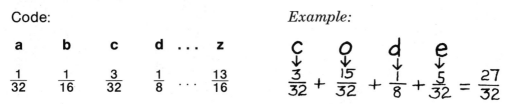

$$\underset{\underset{\frac{3}{32}}{\downarrow}}{c} + \underset{\underset{\frac{15}{32}}{\downarrow}}{o} + \underset{\underset{\frac{1}{8}}{\downarrow}}{d} + \underset{\underset{\frac{5}{32}}{\downarrow}}{e} = \frac{27}{32}$$

Subtracting fractions

To subtract fractions having the same denominator, subtract the numerators to get the numerator of the difference and use the common denominator for the denominator of the difference.

$$\frac{5}{8} - \frac{3}{8} = \frac{2}{8}$$
$$= \frac{1}{4} \leftarrow \text{lowest terms}$$

When the fractions have different denominators, change to equivalent fractions with a common denominator.

Step 1.
Find the least common denominator.

$$\frac{5}{6} - \frac{5}{9} = \frac{}{18} - \frac{}{18}$$

Step 2.
Change to equivalent fractions.

$$\frac{5}{6} - \frac{5}{9} = \frac{15}{18} - \frac{10}{18}$$

Step 3.
Subtract.

$$\frac{5}{6} - \frac{5}{9} = \frac{15}{18} - \frac{10}{18}$$
$$= \frac{5}{18}$$

EXERCISES
Give each difference in lowest terms.

1. $\frac{2}{3} - \frac{1}{3}$

2. $\frac{3}{8} - \frac{1}{4}$

3. $\frac{2}{3} - \frac{1}{6}$

4. $\frac{5}{6} - \frac{1}{3}$

5. $\frac{2}{3} - \frac{1}{2}$

6. $\frac{3}{4} - \frac{2}{3}$

7. $\frac{1}{2} - \frac{1}{6}$

8. $\frac{5}{3} - \frac{4}{3}$

9. $\frac{3}{4} - \frac{5}{8}$

10. $\frac{5}{6} - \frac{2}{3}$

11. $\frac{5}{8} - \frac{1}{8}$

12. $\frac{1}{3} - \frac{2}{9}$

13. $\frac{3}{4} - \frac{1}{3}$

14. $\frac{3}{5} - \frac{1}{5}$

15. $\frac{7}{8} - \frac{3}{4}$

16. $\frac{7}{9} - \frac{2}{3}$

17. $\frac{5}{8} - \frac{1}{4}$

18. $\frac{9}{10} - \frac{1}{2}$

19. $\frac{7}{5} - \frac{3}{5}$

20. $\frac{5}{6} - \frac{5}{9}$

Subtract. Give each difference in lowest terms.

21. $\dfrac{3}{4}$
    $-\dfrac{1}{2}$

22. $\dfrac{2}{3}$
    $-\dfrac{1}{4}$

23. $\dfrac{3}{4}$
    $-\dfrac{5}{8}$

24. $\dfrac{5}{9}$
    $-\dfrac{1}{2}$

25. $\dfrac{5}{6}$
    $-\dfrac{3}{8}$

26. $\dfrac{8}{9}$
    $-\dfrac{3}{4}$

27. $\dfrac{5}{6}$
    $-\dfrac{0}{2}$

28. $\dfrac{5}{8}$
    $-\dfrac{0}{4}$

29. $\dfrac{5}{9}$
    $-\dfrac{2}{9}$

30. $\dfrac{2}{5}$
    $-\dfrac{3}{8}$

31. $\dfrac{3}{4}$
    $-\dfrac{3}{10}$

32. $\dfrac{8}{9}$
    $-\dfrac{2}{3}$

33. $\dfrac{5}{8}$
    $-\dfrac{1}{3}$

34. $\dfrac{9}{10}$
    $-\dfrac{3}{10}$

35. $\dfrac{7}{8}$
    $-\dfrac{1}{3}$

36. $\dfrac{3}{4}$
    $-\dfrac{5}{8}$

37. $\dfrac{7}{10}$
    $-\dfrac{1}{5}$

38. $\dfrac{3}{4}$
    $-\dfrac{1}{6}$

Solve.

39. Don and Dale are twins. They both play basketball. Don scored $\dfrac{3}{8}$ of the team's points and Dale scored $\dfrac{1}{3}$. Who scored more points? What fraction of the team's points more?

40. Their father took a roll of film to the game. He used $\dfrac{1}{2}$ of the roll for Don and $\dfrac{3}{8}$ of the roll for Dale. How much more of the roll did he use for Don?

41. Don and Dale bought a pizza. Don ate $\dfrac{3}{8}$ of it and Dale ate $\dfrac{3}{8}$ of it. How much of the pizza did they eat altogether?

42. If Don scored $\dfrac{3}{8}$ of the team's points and Dale scored $\dfrac{1}{3}$, what fraction of the points did the rest of the team score?

43. **GET THE POINT?**

Dale scored 8 more than $\dfrac{1}{2}$ as many points as I did. How many points did we each score?

DON AND DALE SCORE 47 POINTS

127

Writing whole numbers and mixed numbers as fractions

Look at the pies. They show that there are 12 sixths in 2.

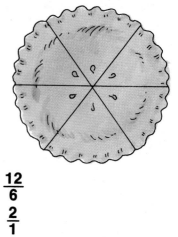

To write a whole number as a fraction, you can write the whole number over a denominator of 1. Then, to change to an equivalent fraction, you multiply both numerator and denominator by the same whole number (not zero).

$$2 = \frac{12}{6}$$

$$2 = \frac{2}{1}$$

$$\frac{2}{1} \overset{\times 6}{\underset{\times 6}{=}} \frac{12}{6}$$

A **mixed number** has a whole-number part and a fraction part.

$2\frac{5}{6}$ is a mixed number.

It means $2 + \frac{5}{6}$.

To write a mixed number as a fraction, you can write the whole-number part as a fraction and then add.

$$2\frac{5}{6} = 2 + \frac{5}{6}$$
$$= \frac{2}{1} + \frac{5}{6}$$
$$= \frac{12}{6} + \frac{5}{6}$$
$$= \frac{17}{6}$$

$$2\frac{5}{6} = \frac{17}{6}$$

$$(6 \times 2) + 5 = 17$$

I multiply 6 by 2 to find how many sixths in 2. Then I add 5 to find how many sixths in $2\frac{5}{6}$.

EXERCISES

Copy and complete.

1. $3 = \frac{?}{2}$
2. $2 = \frac{?}{8}$
3. $5 = \frac{?}{3}$
4. $4 = \frac{?}{5}$
5. $1 = \frac{?}{6}$

6. $8 = \frac{?}{9}$
7. $6 = \frac{?}{4}$
8. $4 = \frac{?}{7}$
9. $3 = \frac{?}{6}$
10. $5 = \frac{?}{10}$

11. $7 = \frac{?}{2}$
12. $7 = \frac{?}{3}$
13. $7 = \frac{?}{5}$
14. $7 = \frac{?}{6}$
15. $7 = \frac{?}{8}$

Write each mixed number as a fraction.

16. $4\frac{1}{5}$
17. $2\frac{3}{8}$
18. $7\frac{2}{3}$
19. $5\frac{1}{2}$
20. $3\frac{1}{4}$
21. $2\frac{5}{6}$

22. $1\frac{7}{10}$
23. $5\frac{3}{4}$
24. $2\frac{7}{9}$
25. $6\frac{2}{5}$
26. $2\frac{1}{3}$
27. $9\frac{1}{2}$

28. $3\frac{1}{8}$
29. $1\frac{3}{5}$
30. $4\frac{1}{6}$
31. $6\frac{3}{10}$
32. $2\frac{4}{5}$
33. $5\frac{1}{8}$

Write each mixed number as a decimal. *Hint:* Change the fraction to a decimal.

$$\frac{1}{4} = 0.25$$

$$3\frac{1}{4} = 3.25$$

34. $1\frac{1}{2}$
35. $2\frac{3}{4}$
36. $4\frac{3}{8}$

37. $2\frac{7}{10}$
38. $3\frac{1}{8}$
39. $2\frac{3}{5}$

40. $1\frac{5}{8}$
41. $6\frac{1}{10}$
42. $3\frac{2}{5}$

Complete.

	43.	44.	45.	46.	47.	48.	49.	50.	51.
Fraction	$\frac{5}{2}$	$\frac{7}{4}$	$\frac{11}{8}$	?	?	?	?	?	?
Mixed number	?	?	?	$2\frac{1}{4}$	$3\frac{2}{5}$	$1\frac{7}{8}$	?	?	?
Decimal	?	?	?	?	?	?	1.6	2.75	2.125

Complete.

	52.	53.	54.	55.	56.	57.
Fraction	$\frac{83}{3}$	$\frac{193}{6}$	$\frac{123}{9}$	?	?	?
Mixed number	?	?	?	$18\frac{1}{3}$	$12\frac{5}{16}$	$25\frac{4}{9}$
Decimal	?	?	?	?	?	?

Writing fractions as whole numbers or as mixed numbers

When the numerator is greater than or equal to the denominator, the fraction is greater than or equal to 1. You can write the fraction as either a whole number or a mixed number by dividing the numerator by the denominator.

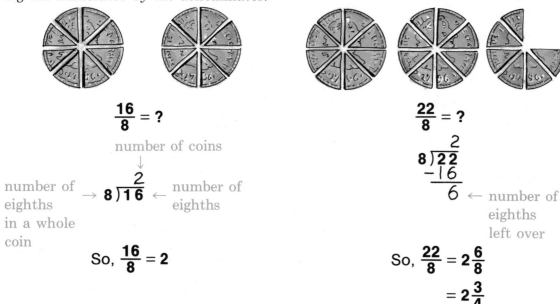

$$\frac{16}{8} = ?$$

number of coins
↓

number of
eighths
in a whole
coin → $8\overline{)16}^{\;2}$ ← number of
eighths

So, $\frac{16}{8} = 2$

$$\frac{22}{8} = ?$$

$$8\overline{)22}^{\;2}$$
$$\underline{-16}$$
$$6 \leftarrow \text{number of eighths left over}$$

So, $\frac{22}{8} = 2\frac{6}{8}$

$\phantom{So, \frac{22}{8}} = 2\frac{3}{4}$

SIMPLEST FORM
* AGREEMENT *

Here is how to write your answers in **simplest form.**

Write a fraction that is less than 1 in lowest terms.

$$\frac{12}{20} = \frac{3}{5}$$

Write a mixed number so that its fraction part is less than 1 and is in lowest terms.

$$2\frac{10}{15} = 2\frac{2}{3}$$

Write a fraction that is greater than or equal to 1 as a whole number or as a mixed number in simplest form.

$$\frac{12}{4} = 3$$

$$\frac{14}{8} = 1\frac{6}{8} = 1\frac{3}{4}$$

Write in simplest form.

1. $\frac{7}{3}$ 2. $\frac{19}{5}$ 3. $\frac{12}{4}$ 4. $\frac{18}{8}$ 5. $\frac{8}{20}$ 6. $\frac{15}{2}$ 7. $\frac{21}{12}$ 8. $\frac{18}{3}$

9. $\frac{14}{20}$ 10. $1\frac{8}{12}$ 11. $\frac{15}{10}$ 12. $3\frac{2}{10}$ 13. $\frac{9}{4}$ 14. $\frac{30}{6}$ 15. $1\frac{10}{12}$ 16. $\frac{12}{18}$

Add or subtract. Give each answer in simplest form.

17. $\frac{1}{2} + \frac{5}{6}$ 18. $\frac{3}{2} - \frac{1}{8}$ 19. $\frac{1}{6} + \frac{5}{6}$ 20. $\frac{7}{3} - \frac{5}{6}$ 21. $\frac{11}{4} - \frac{3}{4}$

22. $\frac{3}{2} + \frac{2}{3}$ 23. $\frac{3}{4} + \frac{2}{5}$ 24. $\frac{5}{4} - \frac{1}{6}$ 25. $\frac{1}{10} + \frac{2}{5}$ 26. $\frac{5}{3} - \frac{2}{5}$

27. $\frac{9}{8} + \frac{7}{8}$ 28. $\frac{5}{6} - \frac{4}{9}$ 29. $\frac{5}{3} + \frac{3}{4}$ 30. $\frac{7}{10} + \frac{1}{2}$ 31. $\frac{8}{3} - \frac{1}{2}$

Solve.

32. In her coin album, Linda had $\frac{3}{4}$ of a page filled with Indian Head pennies and $\frac{7}{8}$ of a page filled with old Lincoln pennies. How many pages were filled with pennies?

33. She had $\frac{1}{2}$ of a page of Carson City dollars and $\frac{5}{8}$ of a page of Walking Liberty halves. How much more of a page was filled with Walking Liberty halves than was filled with Carson City dollars?

34. The nickel section of her album had $\frac{3}{4}$ of a page filled with Buffalo nickels, $\frac{1}{2}$ of a page filled with Jefferson nickels, and $\frac{3}{8}$ of a page filled with Liberty nickels. How many pages of nickels were there in her album?

35. On a page for foreign coins, $\frac{1}{4}$ of the page was filled with French coins and $\frac{1}{8}$ of the page with German coins. How much of the page was *not* filled with coins?

36. ⭐ **DOLLARS AND SENSE**

How many of each coin do I have?

Clue 1: I have only nickels, dimes, and silver dollars.

Clue 2: $\frac{1}{3}$ of my coins are nickels.

Clue 3: $\frac{4}{9}$ of my coins are dimes.

Clue 4: I have $5.10 in all.

Adding mixed numbers

Here is how to add mixed numbers.

EXAMPLE 1. **Step 1.** Change to fractions with a common denominator.

Step 2. Add fractions.

Step 3. Add whole numbers.

$$3\frac{3}{8} = \quad 3\frac{3}{8}$$
$$+2\frac{1}{2} = +2\frac{4}{8}$$
$$\overline{\qquad} \qquad \overline{5\frac{7}{8}}$$

EXAMPLE 2. **Step 1.** Change to fractions with a common denominator.

Step 2. Add fractions.

Step 3. Add whole numbers.

Step 4. Regroup to write the sum as a mixed number in simplest form.

$$2\frac{3}{4} = \quad 2\frac{9}{12}$$
$$+4\frac{1}{3} = +4\frac{4}{12}$$
$$\overline{\qquad} \qquad \overline{6\frac{13}{12}} = 7\frac{1}{12}$$

You can add and regroup in your head as you do with whole numbers.

$$2\overset{1}{\underset{}{\frac{3}{5}}}$$
$$+1\frac{4}{5}$$
$$\overline{4\frac{2}{5}}$$

$$\frac{7}{5} = 1\frac{2}{5}$$

EXERCISES
Add. Write each sum in simplest form.

1. $3\frac{1}{2}$
   $+2\frac{1}{4}$

2. $9\frac{3}{8}$
   $+6\frac{1}{2}$

3. $11\frac{1}{6}$
   $+3\frac{3}{4}$

4. $8\frac{3}{5}$
   $+7\frac{1}{4}$

5. $5\frac{3}{8}$
   $+18\frac{3}{4}$

6. $8\frac{2}{3}$
   $+6\frac{1}{2}$

7. $2\frac{1}{2}$
$+3\frac{5}{6}$

8. $6\frac{2}{5}$
$+5\frac{3}{4}$

9. $7\frac{5}{8}$
$+6\frac{3}{4}$

10. $12\frac{3}{7}$
$+2\frac{1}{3}$

11. $9\frac{3}{4}$
$+1\frac{3}{8}$

12. $4\frac{1}{2}$
$+\frac{7}{8}$

13. $6\frac{7}{8}$
$+\frac{3}{4}$

14. $3\frac{3}{4}$
$+1\frac{1}{4}$

15. $6\frac{1}{2}$
$+7\frac{1}{2}$

16. $9\frac{2}{5}$
$+7\frac{3}{10}$

17. $5\frac{3}{8}$
$+6$

18. $2\frac{5}{8}$
$+10\frac{3}{8}$

19. $16\frac{4}{7}$
$+4\frac{1}{2}$

20. $15\frac{4}{5}$
$+2\frac{1}{5}$

21. $3\frac{7}{8}$
$+\frac{1}{8}$

22. $\frac{6}{7}$
$+8\frac{3}{4}$

23. $\frac{2}{3}$
$+5\frac{4}{5}$

24. $6\frac{7}{8}$
$+2\frac{3}{5}$

Solve.

25. Kim worked on the model airplane $3\frac{3}{4}$ hours on Saturday and $2\frac{1}{2}$ hours on Sunday. How many hours did she work in all?

★ 26. From the scale drawing, compute the total length of the model airplane.

★ 27. Compute the total wingspan.

★ 28. The finish color is a mixture of $1\frac{1}{4}$ ounces of white, $1\frac{1}{2}$ ounces of blue, and $\frac{3}{4}$ ounce of yellow paint. How many ounces of finish color did the plans call for?

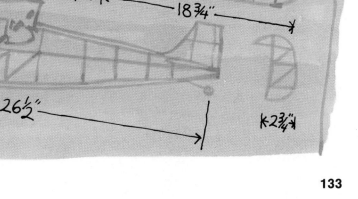

Subtracting mixed numbers

Here is how to subtract mixed numbers.

EXAMPLE 1. **Step 1.** Change to fractions with a common denominator.

Step 2. Subtract fractions.

Step 3. Subtract whole numbers.

$$5\frac{5}{8} = 5\frac{5}{8}$$
$$-2\frac{1}{4} = -2\frac{2}{8}$$
$$\overline{\phantom{-2\frac{1}{4}}}$$
$$3\frac{3}{8}$$

EXAMPLE 2. **Step 1.** Change to fractions with a common denominator.

Step 2. Regroup 1 for $\frac{20}{20}$.

Step 3. Subtract.

$$6\frac{3}{5} = 6\frac{12}{20} = 5\frac{32}{20}$$
$$-2\frac{3}{4} = -2\frac{15}{20} = -2\frac{15}{20}$$
$$\overline{}$$
$$3\frac{17}{20}$$

You can show regrouping as you did with whole numbers.

$$\overset{5\ \ 10}{\cancel{6}\frac{\cancel{2}}{7}}$$
$$-1\frac{4}{7}$$
$$\overline{}$$
$$4\frac{6}{7}$$

EXERCISES

Subtract. Write each difference in simplest form.

1. $8\frac{1}{2}$
$-3\frac{1}{4}$

2. $9\frac{3}{5}$
$-2\frac{1}{2}$

3. $12\frac{3}{4}$
$-4\frac{2}{3}$

4. $16\frac{7}{8}$
$-9\frac{2}{3}$

5. $18\frac{1}{2}$
$-9\frac{3}{4}$

6. $15\frac{3}{8}$
$-7\frac{2}{3}$

7. $23\frac{1}{4}$
$-14\frac{1}{2}$

8. 18
$-12\frac{3}{4}$

9. $21\frac{1}{3}$
$-19\frac{2}{3}$

10. $26\frac{1}{3}$
$-14\frac{5}{6}$

11. $32\frac{9}{10}$
$-23\frac{2}{5}$

12. 35
$-26\frac{5}{8}$

134

13. $5\frac{1}{6}$
    $-1\frac{1}{4}$

14. $10\frac{1}{3}$
    $-6\frac{3}{4}$

15. 9
    $-2\frac{2}{5}$

16. $6\frac{3}{8}$
    $-5\frac{5}{6}$

17. 7
    $-\frac{3}{4}$

18. $50\frac{1}{3}$
    $-16\frac{3}{8}$

19. $18\frac{5}{7}$
    $-12\frac{1}{3}$

20. $34\frac{2}{9}$
    $-18\frac{2}{3}$

21. $21\frac{1}{5}$
    $-20\frac{3}{4}$

22. 27
    $-16\frac{5}{8}$

23. $23\frac{1}{8}$
    $-15\frac{3}{4}$

24. 22
    $-8\frac{3}{5}$

High-Jump Results	
Name	Height in inches
Bowers	$56\frac{7}{8}$
Davis	58
Faulin	$61\frac{5}{8}$
Jones	61
Morris	$62\frac{1}{4}$
Porter	$57\frac{3}{8}$
Richardson	$58\frac{1}{4}$
Wilson	$60\frac{1}{8}$

Solve.

25. How many jumped higher than $58\frac{1}{2}$ in.?

26. Who came in first? second? last?

27. How much higher did Faulin jump than Porter?

28. How much higher did Wilson jump than Bowers?

29. How much higher would Richardson have had to jump to tie Jones?

30. ★ MAKE IT MAGIC!

Copy and complete this magic square.

1	?	$\frac{1}{2}$
?	$1\frac{1}{4}$	?
2	?	?

Estimate to find the two incorrect answers.

1. a. $8.5 \times 2.04 = 1.734$

   b. $12.4 \times 0.95 = 11.78$

   c. $1.8 \times 10.2 = 18.36$

   d. $0.11 \times 8.73 = 0.09603$

Multiply.

2. 5.8
   $\times 2.9$

3. 0.26
   $\times 1.4$

4. 7.4
   $\times 0.35$

5. 9.3
   $\times 6.4$

6. 0.52
   $\times 18$

7. 45
   $\times 0.25$

8. 3.81
   $\times 16$

9. 28.4
   $\times 0.38$

Problem solving—not enough information

BADLANDS RAILROAD — RIDE LEAVES EVERY 20 MINUTES — 1 TICKET

HAUNTED MINE — RIDE LEAVES EVERY 10 MINUTES — 2 TICKETS

FRONTIERLAND — ADMISSION: ADULTS $3.50 — CHILDREN UNDER 12 $1.75 — RIDE TICKETS: $5 PER BOOK

STUNT SHOW — SHOW AT 2:00, 4:00, & 6:00 — 1 TICKET

RAFT TO FORT PIKE — RIDE LEAVES EVERY 15 MINUTES — 2 TICKETS

FORT PIKE

HAUNTED MINE

Sometimes not enough facts are given in a problem. You need to find a fact so you can solve the problem.

How much did Juan and his 9-year-old sister Maria pay to get into Frontierland?

Missing fact: Juan's age.

What is the missing fact not found in the picture or problem?
If you know the missing fact, solve the problem.

1. How many books of tickets would Juan and Maria have to buy so they could go on the 3 rides?

2. How many tickets did they have left after their first ride, which was the Raft to Fort Pike?

3. How long did they have to wait to see the Stunt Show?

4. How many hours was the intermission between Stunt Shows?

5. How many Badlands Railroad rides leave every hour?

6. How many people can ride on an 8-car Haunted Mine train?

SKILL GAME

This game is for two players.

1. Copy the game board shown below.

2. Player X picks two mixed numbers from the mixed-number board, adds them, and marks the sum on the game board with an X.

3. Player O picks two mixed numbers, adds them, and marks the sum with an O.

4. The first player to get 5 marks in any row, column, or diagonal wins.

5. If a player's sum is already marked, then the player loses that turn.

CHAPTER CHECKUP

Complete this table. Give each fraction in lowest terms. [pages 118–121]

	1.	2.	3.	4.	5.	6.
Fraction	$\frac{3}{10}$	$\frac{1}{8}$	$\frac{1}{15}$	?	?	?
Decimal	?	?	?	0.4	0.75	0.025

< or >? [pages 122–123]

7. $\frac{3}{7}$ ● $\frac{3}{5}$ 8. $\frac{2}{3}$ ● $\frac{3}{5}$ 9. $\frac{4}{7}$ ● $\frac{1}{2}$ 10. $\frac{5}{4}$ ● $\frac{3}{2}$

Give each sum in lowest terms. [pages 124–125]

11. $\frac{3}{8} + \frac{1}{2}$ 12. $\frac{2}{9} + \frac{1}{3}$ 13. $\frac{1}{3} + \frac{2}{5}$ 14. $\frac{3}{10} + \frac{1}{4}$ 15. $\frac{1}{2} + \frac{1}{3}$

Give each difference in lowest terms. [pages 126–127]

16. $\frac{7}{8} - \frac{1}{4}$ 17. $\frac{4}{5} - \frac{1}{2}$ 18. $\frac{3}{4} - \frac{2}{5}$ 19. $\frac{4}{9} - \frac{1}{6}$ 20. $\frac{3}{4} - \frac{5}{12}$

Complete this table. [pages 128–131]

	21.	22.	23.	24.	25.	26.
Fraction	$\frac{8}{3}$	$\frac{12}{5}$	$\frac{34}{7}$	?	?	?
Mixed number	?	?	?	$3\frac{1}{2}$	$5\frac{3}{4}$	$9\frac{5}{8}$

Add or subtract. Give answers in simplest form. [pages 132–135]

27. $3\frac{1}{2}$ 28. $4\frac{3}{5}$ 29. $1\frac{2}{3}$ 30. $4\frac{7}{8}$ 31. $3\frac{2}{7}$ 32. $6\frac{1}{2}$
$+2\frac{1}{4}$ $+2\frac{4}{5}$ $+\frac{5}{6}$ $-1\frac{1}{4}$ $-1\frac{5}{7}$ $-3\frac{5}{8}$

Solve. [page 136]

33. The school long-jump record was $15\frac{1}{2}$ feet. Andrew jumped $13\frac{3}{4}$ feet. By how much did he miss the record?

34. At birth a baby weighed $8\frac{1}{4}$ pounds. During the next week it lost $\frac{3}{8}$ pound, but during the next month it gained $2\frac{1}{2}$ pounds. How much did the baby weigh then?

SLIDE RULERS AND ADDITION

You will need two rulers marked in inches and fractions of inches. Follow these steps to see how to use your rulers to add $1\frac{3}{4}$ and $2\frac{1}{8}$.

Step 1. Slide ruler A so that its 0 mark is directly under the mark for $1\frac{3}{4}$ inches on ruler B.

Step 2. Locate the mark for $2\frac{1}{8}$ inches on ruler A. Read the answer on ruler B directly above the mark for $2\frac{1}{8}$ inches on ruler A.

$$1\frac{3}{4} + 2\frac{1}{8} = 3\frac{7}{8}$$

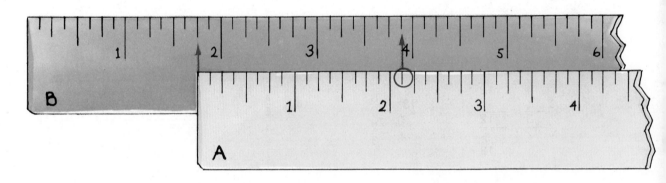

Use your slide rulers to find each sum.

1. $2\frac{1}{2} + 1\frac{3}{4}$ 2. $4\frac{1}{4} + 2\frac{1}{2}$ 3. $1\frac{1}{8} + 2\frac{3}{4}$

4. $1\frac{3}{8} + 2\frac{1}{4}$ 5. $2\frac{5}{8} + 3\frac{1}{2}$ 6. $2\frac{7}{8} + 3\frac{1}{4}$

7. $2\frac{5}{8} + 3\frac{5}{8}$ 8. $3\frac{3}{8} + 1\frac{7}{8}$ 9. $4\frac{1}{2} + 3\frac{7}{8}$

Find a way to use your slide rulers to give each difference.

10. $3\frac{1}{2} - 1\frac{1}{2}$ 11. $5\frac{3}{4} - 2\frac{1}{2}$ 12. $6\frac{3}{8} - 4\frac{3}{4}$

CHAPTER REVIEW

Divide both terms by their greatest common factor.

$$\frac{6}{15} \overset{\div 3}{=} \frac{2}{5}$$
$\div 3$

Write in lowest terms.

1. $\frac{8}{12}$ 2. $\frac{15}{10}$ 3. $\frac{8}{18}$ 4. $\frac{12}{30}$

$\frac{3}{4} = ?$ $4\overline{)3.00}$ 0.75
$\frac{3}{4} = 0.75$

Write as a decimal.

5. $\frac{3}{5}$ 6. $\frac{5}{4}$ 7. $\frac{7}{9}$ 8. $\frac{3}{8}$

$$\begin{array}{r} \frac{1}{5} = \frac{3}{15} \\ +\frac{2}{3} = +\frac{10}{15} \\ \hline \frac{13}{15} \end{array}$$

Add. Give each sum in lowest terms.

9. $\frac{1}{4}$ 10. $\frac{3}{8}$ 11. $\frac{1}{10}$ 12. $\frac{2}{5}$

$+\frac{2}{3}$ $+\frac{1}{6}$ $+\frac{2}{5}$ $+\frac{1}{4}$

$$\begin{array}{r} \frac{3}{4} = \frac{9}{12} \\ -\frac{1}{3} = -\frac{4}{12} \\ \hline \frac{5}{12} \end{array}$$

Subtract. Give each difference in lowest terms.

13. $\frac{8}{9}$ 14. $\frac{4}{5}$ 15. $\frac{1}{2}$ 16. $\frac{9}{10}$

$-\frac{2}{3}$ $-\frac{1}{2}$ $-\frac{1}{6}$ $-\frac{3}{4}$

$$\begin{array}{r} 2\frac{3}{5} = 2\frac{9}{15} \\ +1\frac{2}{3} = +1\frac{10}{15} \\ \hline 4\frac{4}{15} \end{array}$$

Add. Give each sum in simplest form.

17. $2\frac{3}{7}$ 18. $2\frac{5}{8}$ 19. $4\frac{1}{4}$ 20. $2\frac{3}{4}$

$+3\frac{1}{7}$ $+4\frac{3}{8}$ $+3\frac{5}{6}$ $+\frac{7}{8}$

$$\begin{array}{r} 3\frac{1}{5} = 2\frac{6}{5} \\ -1\frac{4}{5} = -1\frac{4}{5} \\ \hline 1\frac{2}{5} \end{array}$$

Subtract. Give each difference in simplest form.

21. $4\frac{3}{8}$ 22. $4\frac{3}{10}$ 23. $5\frac{1}{3}$ 24. 8

$-3\frac{1}{8}$ $-1\frac{4}{5}$ $-3\frac{1}{2}$ $-1\frac{5}{6}$

The examples below show how to change a repeating decimal to an equivalent fraction.

EXAMPLE 1. Change $0.\overline{3}$ to a fraction.

Let n be the fraction.

$$n = 0.\overline{3}$$

$$10n = 3.\overline{3}$$

When one digit repeats, multiply each side of the equation by 10.

$$10n - n = 3.\overline{3} - 0.\overline{3}$$

Subtract n from each side. Since $n = 0.\overline{3}$, we subtract $0.\overline{3}$ from the right side of the equation.

$$9n = 3$$

$$n = \frac{3}{9}$$

$$n = \frac{1}{3}$$

EXAMPLE 2. Change $0.\overline{36}$ to a fraction.

$$n = 0.\overline{36}$$

$$100n = 36.\overline{36}$$

When two digits repeat, multiply each side of the equation by 100.

$$100n - n = 36.\overline{36} - 0.\overline{36}$$

Subtract n from each side. Since $n = 0.\overline{36}$, we subtract $0.\overline{36}$ from the right side of the equation.

$$99n = 36$$

$$n = \frac{36}{99}$$

$$n = \frac{4}{11}$$

Change each repeating decimal to its equivalent fraction in lowest terms.

1. $0.\overline{6}$ 2. $0.\overline{4}$ 3. $0.\overline{7}$ 4. $0.\overline{8}$ 5. $0.\overline{16}$ 6. $0.\overline{45}$

7. $0.\overline{72}$ 8. $0.\overline{09}$ 9. $0.\overline{39}$ 10. $0.\overline{132}$ 11. $0.\overline{037}$ 12. $0.\overline{123}$

MAJOR CHECKUP
STANDARDIZED FORMAT

Choose the correct letter.

1. The standard numeral for two and three hundredths is

    a. 2.3
    b. 0.23
    c. 2.03
    d. none of these

2. Subtract.

$4.3 - 0.29$

    a. 4.01
    b. 3.01
    c. 0.14
    d. none of these

3. Multiply.

$$\begin{array}{r} 3.2 \\ \times 0.06 \\ \hline \end{array}$$

    a. 19.2
    b. 1.92
    c. 0.192
    d. none of these

4. Divide.

$0.32\overline{)1.984}$

    a. 0.62
    b. 6.2
    c. 62
    d. none of these

5. The prime factorization of 48 is

    a. $2^4 \times 3$
    b. $4^2 \times 3$
    c. $2^8 \times 3$
    d. none of these

6. Solve.

$4y - 6 = 34$

    a. 7
    b. 10
    c. 40
    d. none of these

7. 4.7 cm = __?__ m

    a. 0.047
    b. 470
    c. 4700
    d. none of these

8. What is the circumference? Use 3.14 for π.

1 m

    a. 6.28 m
    b. 3.14 m
    c. 2 m
    d. none of these

9. Add.

$$\begin{array}{r} 3\frac{2}{3} \\ +\ 2\frac{3}{4} \\ \hline \end{array}$$

    a. $6\frac{5}{12}$
    b. $5\frac{1}{12}$
    c. $5\frac{5}{12}$
    d. none of these

10. Subtract.

$$\begin{array}{r} 4\frac{1}{3} \\ -\ 1\frac{1}{2} \\ \hline \end{array}$$

    a. $3\frac{1}{6}$
    b. $3\frac{5}{6}$
    c. $2\frac{1}{6}$
    d. none of these

11. The TV program was $\frac{1}{2}$ hour long. 6 minutes were used for ads. How many minutes were not used for ads?

    a. 24   **b.** 44
    c. 54   **d.** none of these

12. Sandra bought 5 12¢ stamps and 15 18¢ stamps. What was the total cost of the stamps?

    a. $6   **b.** $3.30
    c. $2.10   **d.** none of these

Multiplying and Dividing Fractions

5

Multiplying fractions

We can multiply to find the fraction of the cake that is left in the pan.

The width that remains is $\frac{2}{3}$ of the pan's width.

The length that remains is $\frac{4}{5}$ of the pan's length.

The area that remains is $\frac{8}{15}$ of the pan's area.

$$\frac{2}{3} \times \frac{4}{5} = \frac{8}{15}$$

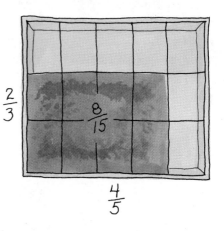

To multiply two fractions, multiply the numerators to get the numerator of the product, and multiply the denominators to get the denominator of the product.

$$\frac{2}{3} \times \frac{4}{5} = \frac{8}{15}$$

Here is a shortcut often used when multiplying fractions. The shortcut, called **canceling,** is to divide both a numerator and a denominator by a common factor *before* multiplying.

Long method

Multiply, and then divide by the common factor 3.

$$\frac{3}{8} \times \frac{5}{24} = \frac{15}{192}$$
$$= \frac{5}{64}$$

Canceling shortcut

Divide by the common factor 3 and then multiply.

$$\frac{\overset{1}{\cancel{3}}}{8} \times \frac{5}{\underset{8}{\cancel{24}}} = \frac{5}{64}$$

I worked with smaller numbers and the product is in lowest terms.

Here is another example:

Long method

Multiply, and then divide by the common factor 15.

$$\frac{5}{9} \times \frac{21}{20} = \frac{105}{180}$$
$$= \frac{7}{12}$$

Canceling shortcut

Divide by the common factors 3 and 5 and then multiply.

$$\frac{\overset{1}{\cancel{5}}}{\underset{3}{\cancel{9}}} \times \frac{\overset{7}{\cancel{21}}}{\underset{4}{\cancel{20}}} = \frac{7}{12}$$

EXERCISES

Give each product in simplest form.

1. $\frac{1}{2} \times \frac{1}{3}$ 　　 2. $\frac{2}{3} \times \frac{4}{5}$ 　　 3. $\frac{3}{8} \times \frac{4}{5}$ 　　 4. $\frac{1}{6} \times \frac{2}{9}$ 　　 5. $\frac{3}{7} \times \frac{5}{3}$

6. $\frac{6}{5} \times \frac{51}{9}$ 　　 7. $\frac{12}{4} \times \frac{4}{3}$ 　　 8. $8 \times \frac{1}{2}$ 　　 9. $\frac{3}{5} \times \frac{0}{2}$ 　　 10. $6 \times \frac{2}{3}$

11. $\frac{2}{3} \times \frac{0}{5}$ 　　 12. $\frac{4}{3} \times 5$ 　　 13. $\frac{2}{3} \times \frac{3}{2}$ 　　 14. $\frac{5}{4} \times \frac{4}{5}$ 　　 15. $\frac{6}{7} \times \frac{7}{6}$

16. $\frac{8}{3} \times \frac{3}{8}$ 　　 17. $\frac{3}{8} \times \frac{3}{3}$ 　　 18. $\frac{5}{4} \times \frac{5}{5}$ 　　 19. $\frac{2}{3} \times \frac{4}{4}$ 　　 20. $\frac{6}{7} \times \frac{2}{2}$

Use canceling to give each product in simplest form.

21. $\frac{3}{4} \times \frac{2}{9}$ 　　 22. $\frac{5}{8} \times \frac{3}{20}$ 　　 23. $\frac{1}{2} \times \frac{8}{5}$ 　　 24. $6 \times \frac{3}{4}$ 　　 25. $\frac{2}{9} \times 3$

26. $\frac{2}{5} \times \frac{5}{4}$ 　　 27. $\frac{9}{2} \times \frac{8}{21}$ 　　 28. $\frac{7}{2} \times \frac{8}{12}$ 　　 29. $\frac{4}{14} \times \frac{21}{6}$ 　　 30. $\frac{18}{3} \times \frac{15}{27}$

31. $\frac{2}{5} \times \frac{5}{2}$ 　　 32. $\frac{12}{16} \times \frac{16}{12}$ 　　 33. $\frac{7}{12} \times \frac{12}{7}$ 　　 34. $\frac{15}{36} \times \frac{36}{15}$ 　　 35. $\frac{38}{45} \times \frac{45}{38}$

Solve.

36. A muffin recipe calls for $\frac{3}{4}$ of a cup of flour. How much flour is needed to make $\frac{2}{3}$ of a recipe?

37. A roll recipe calls for $\frac{2}{3}$ of a cup of whole-wheat flour. How much flour is needed to make $\frac{3}{2}$ of a recipe?

38. A muffin recipe makes 2 dozen muffins. How many muffins will $\frac{2}{3}$ of a recipe make?

★ 39. A cheese-square recipe calls for 1 cup of grated cheese for sixteen 2-inch by 2-inch squares. Jill had $\frac{3}{4}$ of a cup of grated cheese and borrowed another $\frac{1}{2}$ cup from a neighbor. How many cheese squares can she make?

Reciprocals

Two numbers are **reciprocals** if their product is 1:

$$\frac{3}{4} \times \frac{4}{3} = 1 \qquad\qquad 5 \times \frac{1}{5} = 1$$

$\frac{4}{3}$ is the reciprocal of $\frac{3}{4}$. $\qquad$ $\frac{1}{5}$ is the reciprocal of 5.

$\frac{3}{4}$ is the reciprocal of $\frac{4}{3}$. $\qquad$ 5 is the reciprocal of $\frac{1}{5}$.

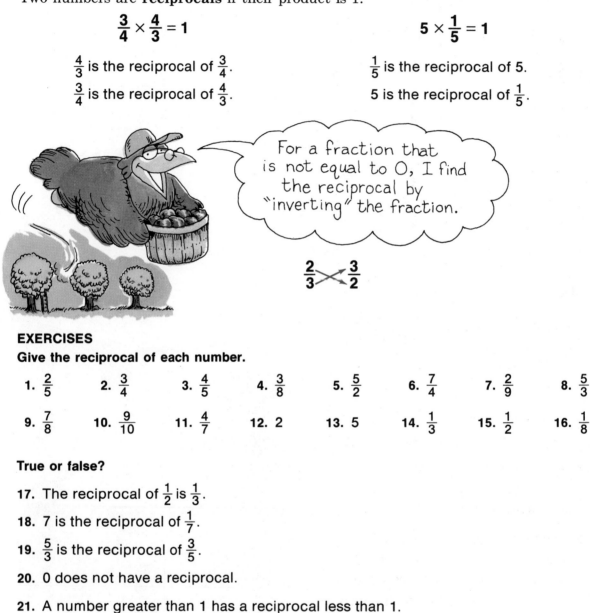

For a fraction that is not equal to 0, I find the reciprocal by "inverting" the fraction.

$$\frac{2}{3} \diagup\!\!\!\!\diagdown \frac{3}{2}$$

EXERCISES

Give the reciprocal of each number.

1. $\frac{2}{5}$ $\qquad$ 2. $\frac{3}{4}$ $\qquad$ 3. $\frac{4}{5}$ $\qquad$ 4. $\frac{3}{8}$ $\qquad$ 5. $\frac{5}{2}$ $\qquad$ 6. $\frac{7}{4}$ $\qquad$ 7. $\frac{2}{9}$ $\qquad$ 8. $\frac{5}{3}$

9. $\frac{7}{8}$ $\qquad$ 10. $\frac{9}{10}$ $\qquad$ 11. $\frac{4}{7}$ $\qquad$ 12. 2 $\qquad$ 13. 5 $\qquad$ 14. $\frac{1}{3}$ $\qquad$ 15. $\frac{1}{2}$ $\qquad$ 16. $\frac{1}{8}$

True or false?

17. The reciprocal of $\frac{1}{2}$ is $\frac{1}{3}$.

18. 7 is the reciprocal of $\frac{1}{7}$.

19. $\frac{5}{3}$ is the reciprocal of $\frac{3}{5}$.

20. 0 does not have a reciprocal.

21. A number greater than 1 has a reciprocal less than 1.

22. A number less than 1 has a reciprocal greater than 1.

23. No number is its own reciprocal.

Give each product in simplest form.

24. $\frac{3}{4} \times 2$

25. $\frac{5}{9} \times \frac{3}{5}$

26. $\frac{6}{5} \times \frac{4}{3}$

27. $\frac{7}{8} \times \frac{8}{7}$

28. $\frac{6}{5} \times \frac{5}{12}$

29. $8 \times \frac{3}{5}$

30. $\frac{4}{3} \times \frac{6}{10}$

31. $\frac{3}{4} \times \frac{3}{4}$

32. $\frac{5}{2} \times \frac{2}{5}$

33. $\frac{5}{6} \times \frac{2}{3}$

34. $6 \times \frac{3}{2}$

35. $\frac{2}{5} \times \frac{7}{8}$

36. $\frac{3}{8} \times \frac{8}{3}$

37. $\frac{5}{9} \times \frac{1}{5}$

38. $6 \times \frac{5}{9}$

39. $\frac{5}{8} \times \frac{3}{5}$

40. $\frac{2}{9} \times \frac{3}{2}$

41. $6 \times \frac{1}{6}$

True or false?

42. Dividing 6 by 2 gives the same result as multiplying 6 by $\frac{1}{2}$.

43. Dividing 12 by 3 gives the same result as multiplying 12 by $\frac{1}{3}$.

44. Dividing 8 by 4 gives the same result as multiplying 8 by 4.

45. Dividing 10 by 5 gives the same result as multiplying 10 by the reciprocal of 5.

 46.

Your first customer bought half of the apples. Your second customer bought $\frac{1}{4}$ of the remaining apples. Your third customer bought the 12 apples that were left. How many apples did you have to begin with?

Add or subtract. Give the answer in simplest form.

1. $\begin{aligned} 2 \\ +3\frac{3}{4} \end{aligned}$

2. $\begin{aligned} 1\frac{3}{5} \\ +5\frac{1}{10} \end{aligned}$

3. $\begin{aligned} 7\frac{1}{3} \\ +8\frac{5}{6} \end{aligned}$

4. $\begin{aligned} 9\frac{7}{8} \\ +6\frac{3}{4} \end{aligned}$

5. $\begin{aligned} 9\frac{3}{4} \\ +11\frac{5}{6} \end{aligned}$

6. $\begin{aligned} 8\frac{1}{2} \\ -6 \end{aligned}$

7. $\begin{aligned} 11 \\ -4\frac{5}{6} \end{aligned}$

8. $\begin{aligned} 13\frac{1}{2} \\ -8\frac{7}{8} \end{aligned}$

9. $\begin{aligned} 16\frac{5}{12} \\ -7\frac{2}{3} \end{aligned}$

Dividing fractions

Kurt wants to give each of his friends $\frac{3}{4}$ of an apple. Altogether he has $4\frac{1}{2}$ apples. How many people can share the apples?

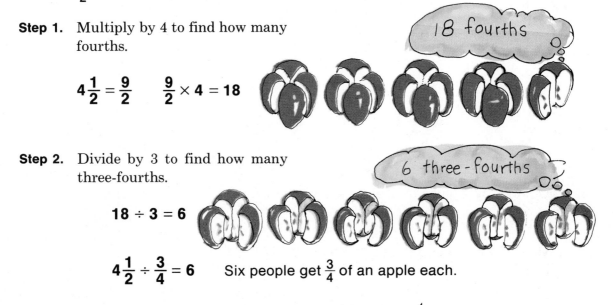

Step 1. Multiply by 4 to find how many fourths.

$$4\frac{1}{2} = \frac{9}{2} \qquad \frac{9}{2} \times 4 = 18$$

18 fourths

Step 2. Divide by 3 to find how many three-fourths.

$$18 \div 3 = 6$$

6 three-fourths

$$4\frac{1}{2} \div \frac{3}{4} = 6 \qquad \text{Six people get } \frac{3}{4} \text{ of an apple each.}$$

Multiplying by 4 and dividing by 3 is like multiplying by $\frac{4}{3}$.

> To divide by a fraction, multiply by its reciprocal.

$$4\frac{1}{2} \; \div \; \overset{\displaystyle \overbrace{\qquad\qquad\qquad}^{\text{reciprocal}}}{\underset{\underbrace{\qquad\qquad\qquad}_{\text{multiplication}}}{\frac{3}{4} \; = \; \frac{9}{2} \; \times \; \frac{4}{3}}}$$

EXAMPLE 1. $\dfrac{4}{5} \div 2 = ?$

$$\frac{4}{5} \div 2 = \frac{\overset{2}{\cancel{4}}}{5} \times \frac{1}{\underset{1}{\cancel{2}}}$$

$$= \frac{2}{5}$$

EXAMPLE 2. $\dfrac{9}{5} \div \dfrac{3}{10} = ?$

$$\frac{9}{5} \div \frac{3}{10} = \frac{\overset{3}{\cancel{9}}}{\underset{1}{\cancel{5}}} \times \frac{\overset{2}{\cancel{10}}}{\underset{1}{\cancel{3}}}$$

$$= 6$$

EXERCISES

Complete.

1. To divide by 2, you can multiply by ?.

2. To divide by $\frac{4}{5}$, you can multiply by ?.

3. Dividing by $\frac{2}{3}$ is the same as multiplying by ?.

4. Multiplying by $\frac{3}{8}$ is the same as dividing by ?.

Give each quotient in simplest form.

5. $\frac{3}{8} \div \frac{1}{8}$

6. $2 \div \frac{1}{4}$

7. $3 \div \frac{1}{3}$

8. $\frac{4}{5} \div 4$

9. $\frac{5}{9} \div \frac{1}{9}$

10. $\frac{8}{9} \div \frac{2}{9}$

11. $\frac{3}{5} \div \frac{1}{2}$

12. $\frac{3}{8} \div \frac{1}{4}$

13. $\frac{3}{5} \div 6$

14. $\frac{3}{8} \div \frac{5}{6}$

15. $\frac{3}{5} \div \frac{3}{2}$

16. $\frac{5}{6} \div \frac{2}{3}$

17. $5 \div \frac{2}{3}$

18. $\frac{0}{6} \div \frac{2}{9}$

19. $3 \div \frac{1}{4}$

20. $\frac{5}{8} \div 2$

A **complex fraction** can be used to express the quotient of two fractions.

$$\frac{\frac{2}{3}}{\frac{3}{4}} = \frac{2}{3} \div \frac{3}{4}$$

$$= \frac{2}{3} \times \frac{4}{3}$$

$$= \frac{8}{9}$$

Change to simplest form.

21. $\frac{\frac{5}{6}}{\frac{2}{3}}$

22. $\frac{\frac{9}{2}}{\frac{3}{8}}$

23. $\frac{\frac{3}{10}}{\frac{4}{5}}$

24. $\frac{\frac{1}{9}}{\frac{7}{8}}$

25. $\frac{\frac{4}{3}}{\frac{2}{5}}$

26. $\frac{\frac{9}{16}}{\frac{3}{8}}$

27. $\frac{2}{\frac{4}{9}}$

28. $\frac{\frac{5}{8}}{\frac{8}{6}}$

Change to simplest form.

29. $\left(\frac{1}{2} + \frac{1}{4}\right) \div \frac{1}{8}$

30. $\left(\frac{3}{8} \times \frac{8}{3}\right) \div \frac{1}{2}$

31. $\left(\frac{2}{5} - \frac{1}{4}\right) + \frac{1}{4}$

32. $\left(\frac{3}{5} \div \frac{3}{4}\right) \times \frac{2}{3}$

33. $\left(\frac{5}{4} + \frac{3}{5}\right) - \frac{5}{8}$

34. $\frac{7}{12} \times \left(\frac{3}{5} - \frac{3}{5}\right)$

35. **FRACTION ACTION**

Copy, and draw the path that will take you from the starting number to the ending number.

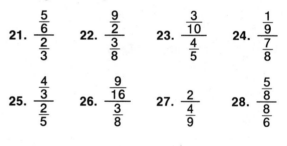

Practice

Give each sum in simplest form.

1. $\frac{1}{2} + \frac{1}{4}$

2. $\frac{1}{3} + \frac{1}{2}$

3. $\frac{1}{3} + \frac{1}{4}$

4. $\frac{2}{3} + \frac{1}{4}$

5. $\frac{3}{8} + \frac{1}{4}$

6. $\frac{5}{8} + \frac{1}{6}$

7. $\frac{3}{5} + \frac{1}{4}$

8. $\frac{3}{4} + \frac{1}{6}$

9. $\frac{5}{8} + \frac{1}{7}$

10. $\frac{2}{3} + \frac{1}{6}$

11. $2 + \frac{4}{5}$

12. $\frac{3}{10} + \frac{1}{6}$

13. $\frac{5}{9} + \frac{3}{8}$

14. $\frac{4}{7} + \frac{2}{5}$

15. $\frac{5}{7} + \frac{3}{8}$

16. $1 + \frac{1}{10}$

Give each difference in simplest form.

17. $\frac{3}{4} - \frac{1}{2}$

18. $\frac{1}{2} - \frac{1}{3}$

19. $\frac{2}{3} - \frac{1}{2}$

20. $\frac{1}{3} - \frac{1}{4}$

21. $\frac{3}{4} - \frac{1}{6}$

22. $\frac{3}{8} - \frac{1}{6}$

23. $\frac{8}{7} - 1$

24. $\frac{2}{5} - \frac{1}{10}$

25. $\frac{4}{5} - \frac{1}{4}$

26. $3 - \frac{4}{5}$

27. $\frac{4}{3} - \frac{3}{8}$

28. $\frac{3}{7} - \frac{1}{5}$

29. $\frac{7}{10} - \frac{2}{3}$

30. $\frac{5}{6} - \frac{1}{9}$

31. $\frac{9}{10} - \frac{3}{8}$

32. $\frac{4}{9} - \frac{1}{10}$

Give each product in simplest form.

33. $\frac{2}{3} \times \frac{1}{2}$

34. $\frac{3}{4} \times \frac{2}{3}$

35. $\frac{4}{5} \times \frac{3}{7}$

36. $\frac{2}{5} \times \frac{3}{2}$

37. $\frac{5}{6} \times \frac{2}{3}$

38. $\frac{2}{3} \times 7$

39. $\frac{7}{5} \times \frac{3}{8}$

40. $\frac{4}{5} \times \frac{2}{3}$

41. $\frac{7}{8} \times \frac{4}{5}$

42. $\frac{2}{9} \times \frac{3}{4}$

43. $4 \times \frac{3}{8}$

44. $\frac{4}{5} \times \frac{3}{8}$

45. $\frac{5}{12} \times \frac{4}{3}$

46. $\frac{3}{2} \times 6$

47. $\frac{3}{4} \times \frac{4}{3}$

48. $\frac{2}{5} \times \frac{5}{2}$

Give each quotient in simplest form.

49. $\frac{2}{3} \div 2$

50. $\frac{2}{3} \div \frac{1}{2}$

51. $8 \div \frac{1}{2}$

52. $5 \div 2$

53. $\frac{3}{4} \div \frac{2}{3}$

54. $\frac{3}{4} \div \frac{3}{2}$

55. $\frac{5}{6} \div 3$

56. $\frac{4}{5} \div \frac{1}{5}$

57. $\frac{3}{8} \div 3$

58. $\frac{7}{8} \div \frac{1}{4}$

59. $\frac{3}{7} \div \frac{2}{5}$

60. $\frac{6}{7} \div \frac{2}{3}$

61. $4 \div \frac{1}{2}$

62. $\frac{7}{8} \div \frac{3}{4}$

63. $\frac{5}{12} \div \frac{1}{3}$

64. $\frac{9}{10} \div 3$

Mathematics in United States history

The Land Ordinance of 1785 provided a method of surveying the Northwest Territory as it was being settled by pioneers. The method is still used in today's land surveys.

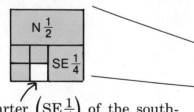

Northwest Ordinance
of 1785
Land Survey

——— Present State Boundaries
------- Ordinance Boundary

A **township** is a square that is 6 miles on a side. The sections (square miles) in a township are numbered in the order shown. Each section contains 640 acres and can be further subdivided as shown:

6	5	4	3	2	1
7	8	9	10	11	12
18	17	16	15	14	13
19	20	21	22	23	24
30	29	28	27	26	25
31	32	33	34	35	36

southeast quarter $\left(\text{SE}\frac{1}{4}\right)$ of the southwest quarter $\left(\text{SW}\frac{1}{4}\right)$ of Section 30

1. How many acres in a half section? In a quarter section?

Draw a section and shade in the region described by

2. $S\frac{1}{2}$ **3.** $SW\frac{1}{4}$ **4.** $NW\frac{1}{4}$ of the $SE\frac{1}{4}$ **5.** $SE\frac{1}{4}$ of the $NW\frac{1}{4}$

Solving fraction equations

The regular price of a Star Wars poster is $2.40. It is on sale for $\frac{2}{3}$ of its regular price. What is its sale price?

To find a fraction of a number, we can multiply the number by the fraction. To find the sale price, we can solve this equation:

Fraction of regular price   Regular price   Sale price

$$\frac{2}{3} \times \$2.40 = s$$

$$\frac{\$4.80}{3} = s$$

$$\$1.60 = s$$

The sale price is $1.60.

The Superman poster is on sale for $\frac{3}{4}$ of its regular price. The sale price is $1.80. What is its regular price?

To find the regular price, we can solve this equation:

Fraction of regular price   Regular price   Sale price

$$\frac{3}{4}r = \$1.80$$

Multiply both sides by the reciprocal of $\frac{3}{4}$:

$$\frac{4}{3} \times \frac{3}{4}r = \frac{4}{3} \times \$1.80$$

$$r = \frac{\$7.20}{3}$$

$$r = \$2.40$$

The regular price is $2.40.

EXERCISES

Solve.

1. $\frac{1}{3} \times 18 = n$ 2. $\frac{1}{4} \times 21 = n$

3. $\frac{3}{2} \times 32 = n$ 4. $\frac{3}{4} \times 48 = n$

5. $\frac{3}{5} \times 22 = n$ 6. $\frac{5}{2} \times 47 = n$

7. $\frac{3}{8} \times \$16 = n$ 8. $\frac{5}{9} \times \$36 = n$

9. $\frac{1}{4} \times \$8.60 = n$ 10. $\frac{2}{3} \times \$9.30 = n$

Solve.

11. $\frac{1}{4}n = 6$ 12. $\frac{1}{5}n = 8$

13. $\frac{2}{3}n = 16$ 14. $\frac{3}{8}n = 27$

15. $\frac{3}{2}n = 36$ 16. $\frac{4}{3}n = 48$

17. $\frac{1}{3}n = \$9$ 18. $\frac{2}{3}n = \$18$

19. $\frac{3}{8}n = \$6.30$ 20. $\frac{4}{5}n = \$9.12$

Write and solve an equation.

21. There are 20 large science-fiction posters on sale for $\frac{4}{5}$ of the regular price. What is the sale price of a poster that usually sells for $2.20?

22. All 11″ by 17″ posters of rock groups are on sale for $\frac{3}{4}$ of the regular price. What is the sale price of a poster that usually sells for $1.90?

23. The Wolf Man poster is on sale for $\frac{2}{3}$ of its regular price. The sale price is $1.72. What is the regular price?

24. There are 15 old posters of movie stars on sale for $\frac{3}{5}$ of the regular price. What is the regular price of a poster that costs $1.44?

KEEPING SKILLS SHARP

Divide. Round each quotient to the nearest hundredth.

1. $0.3\overline{)1.4}$

2. $0.08\overline{)3.57}$

3. $0.6\overline{)0.25}$

4. $0.12\overline{)2.13}$

5. $3.4\overline{)2.87}$

6. $5.1\overline{)5.94}$

7. $7.4\overline{)0.382}$

8. $12.5\overline{)6.468}$

9. $3.94\overline{)87.5}$

10. $0.514\overline{)0.6381}$

11. $0.821\overline{)52.60}$

12. $6.35\overline{)9.758}$

13. $92.4\overline{)41.092}$

14. $83.7\overline{)26.751}$

15. $1.55\overline{)9.368}$

Multiplying mixed numbers

Here are three ways to multiply mixed numbers.

Step 1.
Change to fractions.

$$3\frac{1}{4} \times 1\frac{2}{3} = \frac{13}{4} \times \frac{5}{3}$$

Step 2.
Multiply.

$$3\frac{1}{4} \times 1\frac{2}{3} = \frac{13}{4} \times \frac{5}{3}$$
$$= \frac{65}{12}$$

Step 3.
Change the product to a mixed number.

$$3\frac{1}{4} \times 1\frac{2}{3} = \frac{13}{4} \times \frac{5}{3}$$
$$= \frac{65}{12}$$
$$= 5\frac{5}{12}$$

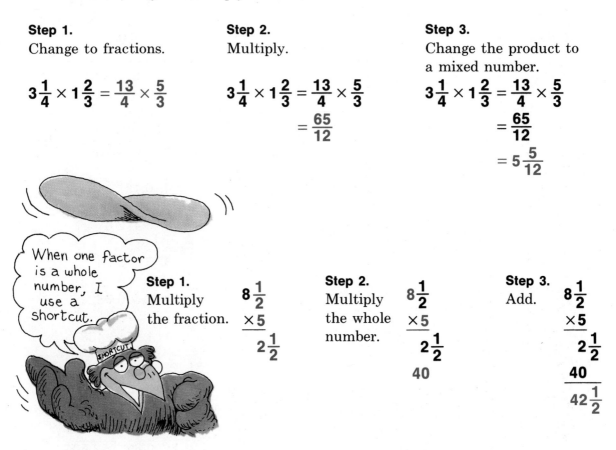

When one factor is a whole number, I use a shortcut.

Step 1.
Multiply the fraction.

$$8\frac{1}{2}$$
$$\times 5$$
$$\overline{2\frac{1}{2}}$$

Step 2.
Multiply the whole number.

$$8\frac{1}{2}$$
$$\times 5$$
$$\overline{2\frac{1}{2}}$$
$$40$$

Step 3.
Add.

$$8\frac{1}{2}$$
$$\times 5$$
$$\overline{2\frac{1}{2}}$$
$$\underline{40}$$
$$42\frac{1}{2}$$

A third way to multiply mixed numbers is to change each number to a decimal.

$$2\frac{4}{5} \times 3\frac{1}{2} = ?$$

$$\begin{array}{r} 2.8 \\ \times 3.5 \\ \hline 140 \\ 84 \\ \hline 9.80 \end{array}$$

So, $2\frac{4}{5} \times 3\frac{1}{2} = 9\frac{4}{5}$

Before multiplying, you should think about the numbers involved and pick the method you think is easiest.

EXERCISES

Give each product in simplest form. (*Hint:* Use the easiest method.)

1. $1\frac{1}{2} \times 4$ 2. $2\frac{1}{2} \times 3$ 3. $3\frac{1}{3} \times 4$ 4. $2\frac{3}{4} \times 3$ 5. $4\frac{1}{3} \times 2$

6. $6 \times 2\frac{2}{3}$ 7. $4 \times 3\frac{3}{8}$ 8. $6 \times 12\frac{3}{5}$ 9. $8 \times 15\frac{1}{4}$ 10. $10 \times 16\frac{1}{3}$

11. $1\frac{1}{2} \times 1\frac{1}{2}$ 12. $2\frac{1}{4} \times 1\frac{1}{2}$ 13. $3\frac{1}{8} \times 4\frac{1}{3}$ 14. $5\frac{3}{5} \times 2\frac{1}{2}$ 15. $6\frac{3}{5} \times 5\frac{1}{4}$

16. $4\frac{2}{3} \times 2\frac{3}{8}$ 17. $2\frac{1}{2} \times 5\frac{1}{4}$ 18. $8 \times 7\frac{1}{2}$ 19. $1\frac{3}{8} \times 2\frac{3}{8}$ 20. $3\frac{1}{4} \times 3$

21. $9\frac{1}{2} \times 6\frac{1}{4}$ 22. $7\frac{1}{3} \times 8\frac{1}{5}$ 23. $2\frac{1}{4} \times 2\frac{3}{8}$ 24. $3\frac{1}{3} \times 2\frac{5}{8}$ 25. $1\frac{2}{3} \times 5\frac{3}{4}$

This time sheet shows the number of hours that the part-time help worked at The Pizza House during one week.

Hours Worked						
Employee	Mon	Tues	Wed	Thur	Fri	Sat
Allan	$1\frac{3}{4}$	$2\frac{1}{2}$	$3\frac{1}{4}$	$1\frac{3}{4}$	$2\frac{3}{4}$	✕
Becker	$2\frac{3}{4}$	$3\frac{1}{2}$	✕	$2\frac{3}{4}$	✕	$6\frac{1}{2}$
Davis	$2\frac{3}{4}$	✕	3	$2\frac{1}{4}$	$1\frac{3}{4}$	5
Folder	✕	$3\frac{1}{4}$	$2\frac{1}{4}$	✕	$2\frac{1}{2}$	$7\frac{1}{2}$
Logan	$2\frac{1}{4}$	2	3	$2\frac{3}{4}$	$3\frac{1}{4}$	✕
Monroe	$1\frac{3}{4}$	$3\frac{1}{4}$	✕	$2\frac{3}{4}$	✕	8
Sanchez	$2\frac{1}{2}$	✕	$3\frac{1}{2}$	4	$5\frac{1}{2}$	$6\frac{1}{4}$

26. Who worked the most hours on Saturday?

27. On which day did Allan work the most hours?

28. How many hours did Sanchez work during the week?

29. Who worked more hours, Folder or Monroe? How many more?

30. How many hours of part-time help were used on Thursday?

31. Were more hours of part-time help used on Wednesday or Thursday? How many more?

32. Allan is paid $3.55 an hour. How much did Allan earn for the week?

33. During the week, Sanchez earned $78.30. How much is this an hour?

34. Davis earns $3.60 an hour and Logan $3.80. Who earned more during this particular week? How much more?

35. Becker is paid $3.50 an hour. What were Becker's earnings for the week?

Dividing mixed numbers

To divide mixed numbers, change each mixed number to an equivalent fraction and divide.

$$9\frac{3}{4} \div 1\frac{1}{2} = \frac{39}{4} \div \frac{3}{2} = \frac{\overset{13}{\cancel{39}}}{\underset{2}{\cancel{4}}} \times \frac{\overset{1}{\cancel{2}}}{\underset{1}{\cancel{3}}}$$

$$= \frac{13}{2}$$

$$= 6\frac{1}{2}$$

Estimate the quotient by rounding each mixed number to the nearest whole number. Is the answer $6\frac{1}{2}$ reasonable?

We could have found the quotient by changing each number to a decimal and dividing:

$$9\frac{3}{4} \div 1\frac{1}{2} = ?$$

⟨9.75⟩   ⟨1.5⟩

$$\begin{array}{r} 6.5 \\ 1.5\overline{)9.75} \\ -9\,0 \\ \hline 75 \\ -75 \\ \hline 0 \end{array}$$

So, $9\frac{3}{4} \div 1\frac{1}{2} = 6\frac{1}{2}$

Use whichever method is easier.

EXERCISES
Give each quotient in simplest form.

1. $6 \div 2\frac{1}{2}$

2. $4 \div 1\frac{1}{4}$

3. $4\frac{3}{4} \div 2$

4. $4 \div 1\frac{1}{2}$

5. $4\frac{1}{2} \div 1\frac{1}{2}$

6. $8\frac{3}{4} \div 2\frac{1}{3}$

7. $6\frac{3}{8} \div 3$

8. $9\frac{2}{3} \div 3\frac{3}{4}$

9. $8\frac{1}{2} \div 3\frac{2}{5}$

10. $9\frac{1}{4} \div 1\frac{1}{3}$

11. $8\frac{1}{2} \div 2\frac{1}{4}$

12. $4\frac{2}{3} \div 1\frac{3}{4}$

CAR WASH 1.75

50

Solve.

19. To advertise the car wash, the students ordered 1200 handouts from a local printer. The printer charged $1\frac{1}{4}$ ¢ each for the first 1000 and $\frac{3}{4}$ ¢ each for the remaining handouts. What was the total cost?

20. Nine students signed up to work $3\frac{1}{2}$ hours in the morning and 12 students signed up to work $4\frac{1}{2}$ hours in the afternoon. How many hours were volunteered?

21. A merchant sold them 4 boxes of detergent for $\frac{2}{3}$ of the regular price. The regular price was $1.80 a box. What was the total price of the detergent?

22. One team washed 6 cars in $1\frac{1}{4}$ hours. What was their average time in hours for washing a car? What was the average time in minutes?

★ 23. During the $3\frac{1}{2}$-hour morning session, 9 students washed an average of one car every $5\frac{1}{4}$ minutes. How many cars did they wash during the morning?

★ 24. During the day they washed 76 cars for $1.75 each and vacuumed 37 cars for $.50 each. Their total expenses were $28.42. How much profit did they make?

13. $16 \div 2\frac{1}{2}$

14. $12\frac{1}{2} \div 8\frac{3}{4}$

15. $6\frac{7}{8} \div 1\frac{3}{4}$

16. $8\frac{2}{3} \div 8\frac{2}{3}$

17. $5\frac{2}{3} \div 2\frac{1}{4}$

18. $3\frac{3}{4} \div 4\frac{2}{3}$

157

Problem solving

How big is a million dollars?

A million $1 bills laid end to end would be about $96\frac{9}{10}$ miles long. A million dollars in $10 bills would be $\frac{1}{10}$ as long, or about $9\frac{7}{10}$ miles long.

Solve these million-dollar problems. Remember to follow these steps:

1. Study and understand.
2. Plan and do.
3. Answer and check.

EXERCISES
Solve.

1. A million pennies laid end to end would be about $11\frac{5}{6}$ miles long.

   a. The diameter of a quarter is about $1\frac{1}{4}$ times the diameter of a penny. About how many miles long would a million quarters laid end to end be?

   b. About how many miles long would a million dollars' worth of quarters be?

2. The Sears Tower in Chicago is 1454 feet high.

   a. A million pennies placed one on top of another would make a stack about $3\frac{4}{9}$ times as high as the Sears Tower. About how many feet high would the stack be?

   b. About how many feet high would a stack of pennies worth a million dollars be?

3. A million dollars in new $5 bills weighs about 408.16 pounds and has a volume of about 7.96 cubic feet.

   a. A $5 bill and a $1 bill weigh the same. About how many pounds would a million dollars in $1 bills weigh?

   b. A $5 bill and a $1 bill have the same dimensions. About how many cubic feet would a million dollars in $1 bills be?

4. A million nickels weigh about 10,047 pounds.

   a. A penny weighs about $\frac{5}{8}$ as much as a nickel. About how many pounds would a million pennies weigh?

   b. About how many pounds would a million dollars in pennies weigh?

5. You can earn a million dollars if you get a job that pays $3 an hour and work 8 hours a day, 250 days a year, for $166\frac{2}{3}$ years.

   a. Suppose you earned $15 an hour and worked the same number of hours a year. How many years would it take you to earn a million dollars?

   b. Suppose you earned $24 an hour and worked the same number of hours a year. How many years would it take you to earn a million dollars?

159

CHAPTER CHECKUP

Multiply. Give each product in simplest form. [pages 144–145, 150]

1. $\frac{3}{8} \times \frac{1}{2}$

2. $\frac{4}{5} \times 6$

3. $\frac{3}{4} \times \frac{4}{3}$

4. $\frac{7}{8} \times \frac{3}{4}$

5. $\frac{8}{15} \times \frac{3}{4}$

6. $\frac{1}{3} \times 2$

7. $\frac{4}{5} \times \frac{3}{8}$

8. $\frac{5}{7} \times \frac{2}{3}$

Divide. Give each quotient in simplest form. [pages 146–150]

9. $\frac{3}{5} \div \frac{2}{3}$

10. $\frac{5}{8} \div \frac{1}{2}$

11. $6 \div \frac{2}{3}$

12. $\frac{3}{4} \div 2$

13. $\frac{4}{5} \div 2$

14. $\frac{3}{8} \div \frac{3}{8}$

15. $\frac{3}{5} \div \frac{5}{6}$

16. $\frac{4}{5} \div \frac{2}{3}$

Multiply. Give each product in simplest form. [pages 154–155]

17. $2\frac{1}{2} \times 6$

18. $3\frac{1}{2} \times 1\frac{1}{4}$

19. $3\frac{3}{4} \times 2\frac{1}{2}$

20. $4\frac{2}{3} \times 3\frac{1}{4}$

21. $5\frac{1}{3} \times 2\frac{1}{4}$

22. $8 \times 1\frac{3}{10}$

23. $2\frac{2}{3} \times \frac{3}{8}$

24. $1\frac{3}{5} \times 2\frac{5}{8}$

Divide. Give each quotient in simplest form. [pages 156–157]

25. $5 \div 2\frac{1}{2}$

26. $3\frac{3}{4} \div 3$

27. $3\frac{1}{2} \div 2\frac{2}{3}$

28. $1\frac{3}{4} \div 4\frac{1}{2}$

29. $2\frac{2}{5} \div 1\frac{7}{8}$

30. $6 \div 1\frac{4}{5}$

31. $5\frac{1}{3} \div 4$

32. $3\frac{3}{5} \div 7\frac{1}{2}$

Solve. [pages 152–153, 158–159]

33. John had $6.48. He spent $\frac{2}{3}$ of this amount to buy a book. How much did the book cost?

34. When Mia works on Saturday, she is paid $5.70 an hour. This amount is $\frac{3}{2}$ times as much as she is paid when she works on a weekday. How much is she paid an hour on a weekday?

The facts below are about the common stock of the Raytheon Co.

Today's high was $45\frac{3}{8}$.

Today's low was $44\frac{1}{4}$.

When the market closed, the stock was selling at $44\frac{1}{2}$ a share.

		Sales (hds)	High	Low	Close	Net Chg.
		P-E				
Ralston	.72	7	234	$11\frac{5}{8}$	$11\frac{1}{2}$	p$11\frac{5}{8}$	$-\frac{1}{8}$
Ramada	.12	8	8718	7	r$6\frac{1}{4}$	p$6\frac{5}{8}$	$-1\frac{1}{8}$
Rampc	.90b	16	99	$23\frac{5}{8}$	$22\frac{7}{8}$	$23\frac{1}{2}$	$+\frac{1}{8}$
Ranco	.84	45	20	$12\frac{3}{8}$	12	$12\frac{1}{4}$	$+\frac{3}{8}$
Raybsto	.60	12	16	$17\frac{1}{2}$	$17\frac{1}{4}$	$17\frac{1}{4}$	$-\frac{1}{4}$
Raymintl	1	10	55	25	$24\frac{3}{4}$	$24\frac{3}{4}$	$-\frac{1}{2}$
Raythn	1.20	12	1005	$45\frac{3}{8}$	$44\frac{1}{4}$	$44\frac{1}{2}$	$-\frac{1}{2}$
RB Inds	.28	18	55	$7\frac{1}{2}$	$7\frac{1}{4}$	$7\frac{1}{4}$	$-\frac{1}{4}$
RCA Cp	1.80	8	3785	$21\frac{1}{8}$	$20\frac{3}{4}$	$20\frac{7}{8}$	$-\frac{1}{8}$
RCA cv pf	4	...	2	48	$47\frac{1}{2}$	$47\frac{1}{2}$	$-\frac{7}{8}$
RCA pf	2.12	...	40	$19\frac{1}{8}$	$18\frac{7}{8}$	19	...
RCA pf	3.65	...	106	$24\frac{5}{8}$	$24\frac{1}{8}$	$24\frac{1}{8}$	$-\frac{1}{2}$
ReadBts	.80	10	762	$42\frac{1}{8}$	$40\frac{1}{2}$	$40\frac{7}{8}$	-1

1. Find the stock quotations in a newspaper. Choose one of the stock listings. How many shares could you buy for $1000?

EXAMPLE. Suppose you choose Raytheon at the closing price.

$$\$1000 \div 44\frac{1}{2} = 1000 \div \frac{89}{2}$$
$$= 1000 \times \frac{2}{89}$$
$$= \frac{2000}{89}$$
$$= 22\frac{42}{89}$$

So, you could buy **22** shares with $1000.

2. Every day for a week, record the closing price of the stock you chose. For each day, compute the value of the stock you "bought." Graph the daily value of your shares of stock.

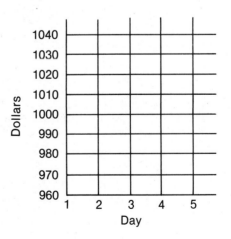

Multiply numerators.
Multiply denominators.

$$\frac{3}{\overset{8}{\underset{4}{8}}} \times \frac{\overset{3}{6}}{5} = \frac{9}{20}$$

Multiply. Give each product in simplest form.

1. $\frac{4}{5} \times \frac{1}{3}$ 2. $\frac{5}{6} \times \frac{3}{4}$ 3. $\frac{2}{3} \times \frac{1}{6}$

4. $\frac{5}{8} \times \frac{3}{4}$ 5. $\frac{2}{5} \times 10$ 6. $8 \times \frac{5}{4}$

7. $\frac{2}{3} \times \frac{3}{4}$ 8. $\frac{5}{6} \times \frac{2}{5}$ 9. $\frac{3}{8} \times \frac{9}{10}$

To divide by a fraction, multiply by its reciprocal.

$$\frac{3}{8} \div \frac{6}{5} = \frac{3}{8} \times \frac{5}{\overset{\overset{1}{6}}{2}}$$

$$= \frac{5}{16}$$

Divide. Give each quotient in simplest form.

10. $\frac{3}{4} \div \frac{1}{4}$ 11. $\frac{5}{8} \div \frac{3}{8}$ 12. $9 \div \frac{2}{3}$

13. $\frac{3}{5} \div \frac{2}{3}$ 14. $\frac{3}{5} \div \frac{3}{2}$ 15. $\frac{5}{6} \div \frac{10}{3}$

16. $\frac{2}{3} \div \frac{2}{3}$ 17. $\frac{1}{4} \div \frac{2}{5}$ 18. $\frac{3}{8} \div \frac{9}{10}$

$$2\frac{3}{4} \times 3\frac{1}{2} = \frac{11}{4} \times \frac{7}{2}$$

$$= \frac{77}{8}$$

$$= 9\frac{5}{8}$$

Multiply. Give each product in simplest form.

19. $1\frac{3}{4} \times 1\frac{1}{3}$ 20. $3\frac{1}{2} \times 2$ 21. $6 \times 1\frac{3}{4}$

22. $2\frac{1}{4} \times \frac{1}{2}$ 23. $3\frac{3}{8} \times 1\frac{3}{5}$ 24. $4\frac{2}{3} \times 3\frac{5}{6}$

$$2\frac{3}{4} \div 3\frac{1}{2} = \frac{11}{4} \div \frac{7}{2}$$

$$= \frac{11}{\underset{2}{4}} \times \frac{\overset{1}{2}}{7}$$

$$= \frac{11}{14}$$

Divide. Give each quotient in simplest form.

25. $2\frac{1}{4} \div 1\frac{3}{4}$ 26. $3\frac{1}{2} \div 2$ 27. $6 \div 1\frac{1}{2}$

28. $2\frac{3}{4} \div \frac{1}{2}$ 29. $2\frac{5}{8} \div 1\frac{4}{5}$ 30. $1\frac{4}{5} \div 2\frac{5}{8}$

a b c d   a b c d   a b c d   a b c d   a b c d   a b c
2.   5.   6.
a b c d   a b c d   a b c d   a b c d   a b c d   a b c
8.   9.   10.   11.   12.

MAJOR CHECKUP
STANDARDIZED FORMAT

Choose the correct letter.

1. 39.624 rounded to the nearest whole number is

a. 40
b. 39
c. 39.6
d. none of these

2. Add.

35.7 + 6.84

a. 10.41
b. 104.1
c. 41.54
d. none of these

3. Multiply.

4.16
× 20.3

a. 84.448
b. 9.568
c. 80.448
d. none of these

4. Divide.

14.496 ÷ 4.8

a. 3.2
b. 3.02
c. 30.2
d. none of these

5. Which of these numbers is composite?

a. 51
b. 61
c. 71
d. none of these

6. 76.1 mm = $\underline{?}$ m

a. 76,100
b. 0.761
c. 0.0761
d. none of these

7. Subtract.

$\frac{7}{10} - \frac{1}{2}$

a. $\frac{1}{5}$
b. $1\frac{2}{5}$
c. $\frac{3}{4}$
d. none of these

8. Add.

$3\frac{5}{8} + 2\frac{3}{4}$

a. $5\frac{3}{8}$
b. $6\frac{3}{8}$
c. $5\frac{2}{3}$
d. none of these

9. Multiply.

$\frac{5}{8} \times \frac{4}{5}$

a. $\frac{1}{2}$
b. $\frac{25}{32}$
c. 2
d. none of these

10. Divide.

$1\frac{1}{3} \div \frac{3}{4}$

a. $1\frac{7}{9}$
b. $\frac{9}{16}$
c. 1
d. none of these

11. José watched TV for $\frac{2}{5}$ of an hour. How many minutes was that?

a. 40   b. 24
c. 12   d. none of these

12. Betty had $1. She bought 4 pears for 17¢ each. How much money did she have left?

a. 32¢   b. 83¢
c. 68¢   d. none of these

164

Measurement— Area and Volume

6

Area—rectangles and squares

The **area** of a region is the number of square units needed to cover the region.

RECTANGLE

The area of a rectangle is its length times its width.

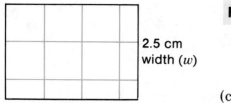

2.5 cm
width (w)

3.5 cm
length (l)

Formula $A = lw$

$A = 3.5 \text{ cm} \times 2.5 \text{ cm}$

$A = 8.75 \text{ cm}^2$

(cm^2 stands for square centimeters)

SQUARE

The area of a square is the square of the length of a side.

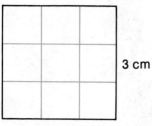

3 cm

side (s)

Formula $A = s^2$

$A = 3 \text{ cm} \times 3 \text{ cm}$

$A = 9 \text{ cm}^2$

You can count the squares to check each answer.

EXERCISES

Tell whether the question involves perimeter or area.
(Remember that the perimeter of a figure is the distance
around it.)

1. How much fence is needed to fence in a yard?

2. How much tile is needed for your classroom floor?

3. How much grass seed is needed to seed a lawn?

4. How much ceiling molding is needed to go around a room?

Find the area of each region.

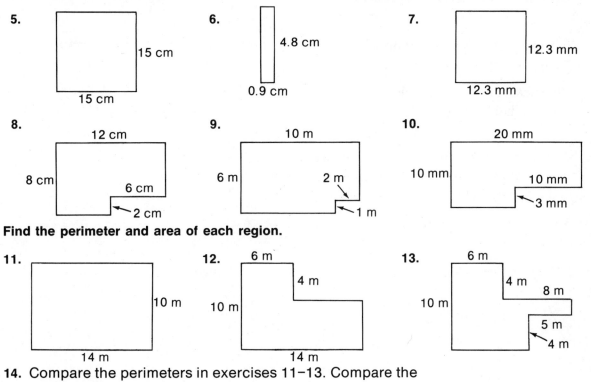

5. 15 cm, 15 cm

6. 4.8 cm, 0.9 cm

7. 12.3 mm, 12.3 mm

8. 12 cm, 8 cm, 6 cm, 2 cm

9. 10 m, 6 m, 2 m, 1 m

10. 20 mm, 10 mm, 10 mm, 3 mm

Find the perimeter and area of each region.

11. 10 m, 14 m

12. 6 m, 4 m, 10 m, 14 m

13. 6 m, 4 m, 8 m, 10 m, 5 m, 4 m

14. Compare the perimeters in exercises 11–13. Compare the areas in exercises 11–13.

Solve. (*Hint:* You may want to draw a picture.)

15. A rectangular floor 6.2 m by 4.5 m is to be covered with carpet costing $14.75 a square meter. How much will the carpet cost? Round your answer to the nearest dollar.

16. A solid wooden fence is 1.2 m high and 84 m long. How many cans of paint are needed to paint both sides if 1 can will cover 30.2 m²? Round your answer up to the nearest whole number.

★ **17.** A hotel ballroom is being changed into a discotheque. The ballroom measures 30 m by 40 m. Its floor, except for a rectangular region 15 m by 19 m, will be tiled. Each square tile is 30 cm on a side. How many tiles will be needed?

18. a. How many square centimeters are in a square meter?

  b. What is the area of the floor in exercise 15 in square centimeters?

167

Area–parallelogram

A **parallelogram** is a four-sided figure whose opposite sides are parallel.

The base of this parallelogram is 3 cm and the height is 2 cm.

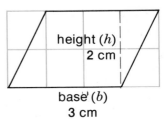

To find a formula for the area of the parallelogram, we can cut the parallelogram into two pieces and arrange the pieces to make a rectangle:

Step 1.   **Step 2.**

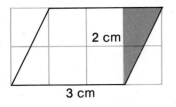

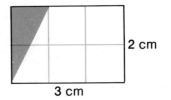

The parallelogram and the rectangle have the same base and the same height. They have the same area of 6 cm².

We can find the area of a parallelogram by multiplying base and height.

Formula $A = bh$

$A = 3 \text{ cm} \times 2 \text{ cm}$

$A = 6 \text{ cm}^2$

EXAMPLE.

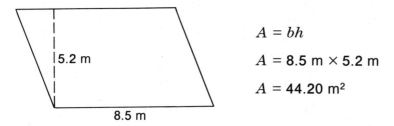

$A = bh$

$A = 8.5 \text{ m} \times 5.2 \text{ m}$

$A = 44.20 \text{ m}^2$

EXERCISES
Find the area of each shaded region.

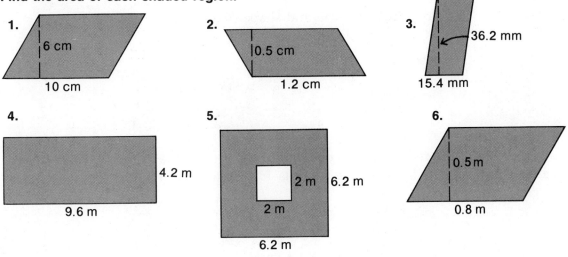

1.
6 cm
10 cm

2.
0.5 cm
1.2 cm

3.
36.2 mm
15.4 mm

4.
4.2 m
9.6 m

5.
2 m 6.2 m
2 m
6.2 m

6.
0.5 m
0.8 m

Find the perimeter and area of each region.

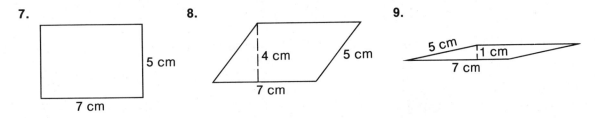

7.
5 cm
7 cm

8.
4 cm 5 cm
7 cm

9.
5 cm 1 cm
7 cm

10. Compare the perimeters in exercises 7–9. Compare the areas in exercises 7–9.

★ 11. A rectangular piece of stained glass was 10 cm long and 5 cm wide. It was cut to get a rectangular piece 9 cm long and 4 cm wide. What fraction of the original piece was used?

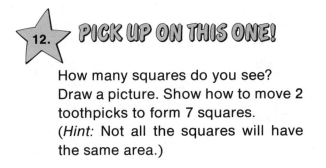

12. **PICK UP ON THIS ONE!**

How many squares do you see?
Draw a picture. Show how to move 2 toothpicks to form 7 squares.
(*Hint:* Not all the squares will have the same area.)

Area—triangles and trapezoids

The two triangles have the same size and shape. We can put them together to make a parallelogram.

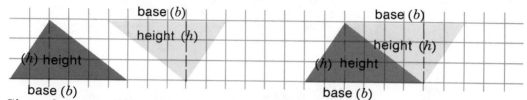

Since the area of the red triangle is one half of the area of the parallelogram, we get the following formula for the area of a triangle:

Formula ▶ $A = \frac{1}{2}bh$

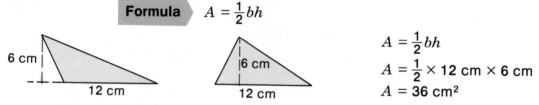

$A = \frac{1}{2}bh$

$A = \frac{1}{2} \times 12 \text{ cm} \times 6 \text{ cm}$

$A = 36 \text{ cm}^2$

A **trapezoid** is a four-sided figure with two opposite sides parallel.

The two trapezoids are the same size and shape. If we put them together, we get a parallelogram.

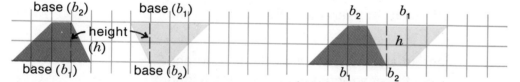

Since the area of the red trapezoid is one half of the area of the parallelogram, we get the following formula for the area of a trapezoid:

Formula ▶ $A = \frac{1}{2}(b_1 + b_2)h$

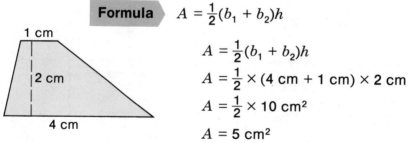

$A = \frac{1}{2}(b_1 + b_2)h$

$A = \frac{1}{2} \times (4 \text{ cm} + 1 \text{ cm}) \times 2 \text{ cm}$

$A = \frac{1}{2} \times 10 \text{ cm}^2$

$A = 5 \text{ cm}^2$

EXERCISES
Compute each area.

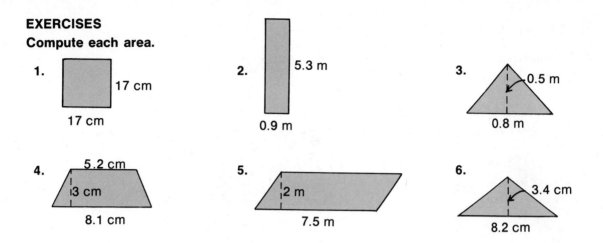

1. 17 cm, 17 cm

2. 5.3 m, 0.9 m

3. 0.5 m, 0.8 m

4. 5.2 cm, 3 cm, 8.1 cm

5. 2 m, 7.5 m

6. 3.4 cm, 8.2 cm

First make the necessary measurements to the nearest millimeter. Then compute the area.

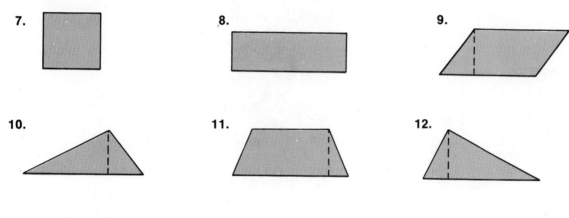

7.

8.

9.

10.

11.

12.

Find the area of the shaded region.

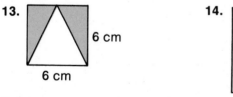

13. 6 cm, 6 cm

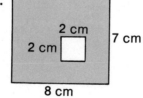

14. 2 cm, 2 cm, 7 cm, 8 cm

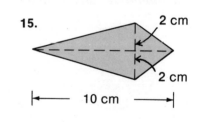

15. 2 cm, 2 cm, 10 cm

Solve.

16. A bumper sticker is shaped like a trapezoid. Its bases are 40 cm and 35 cm, and its height is 7 cm. What is the area of the bumper sticker?

17. A baseball pennant is shaped like a triangle. Its base is 30 cm and its area is 1440 cm². What is its height?

Area—circle

These pictures will help you to see that the formula for the area
of a circle is reasonable.

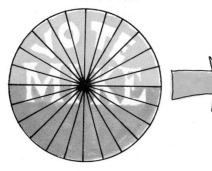 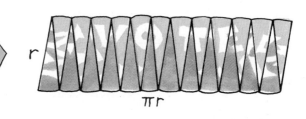

The figure made from the circle is like a
parallelogram with height r (radius of the
circle) and base πr (half the circumference of the circle).

Formula $A = \pi r^2$

$A \approx 3.14(1.2 \text{ cm})^2$

$A \approx 3.14(1.44 \text{ cm}^2)$

$A \approx 4.52 \text{ cm}^2$

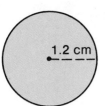

Remember:
$\pi r^2 = \pi \times r \times r$

[Read $\approx$ as "is approximately equal to."]

EXERCISES
Compute the area to the nearest hundredth.

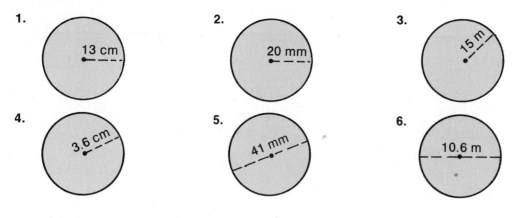

1. 13 cm

2. 20 mm

3. 15 m

4. 3.6 cm

5. 41 mm

6. 10.6 m

First measure the diameter to the nearest millimeter. Then compute the area.

7.   8.   9.

10.   11.   12.

Compute the area to the nearest 0.01 m².

13.

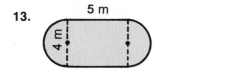

5 m

4 m

14.

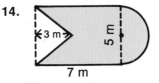

←3 m→   5 m

7 m

Solve. (*Hint:* First draw a picture.)

15. What is the area of the largest circle that can be cut from a square measuring 6.8 cm on a side?

16. A horse is tied to a stake in the middle of a large pasture. The farthest the horse can move from the stake is 15 meters. Over how much area can the horse graze?

17. A goat is tied to the corner of a barn that is 12 m wide and 18 m long. The farthest the goat can move from the place where it is tied is 10 meters. Over how much area can the goat graze?

Give the product in simplest form.

1. $2 \times 3\frac{1}{3}$

2. $3 \times 2\frac{1}{4}$

3. $4\frac{1}{5} \times 4$

4. $2\frac{2}{3} \times 5$

5. $7\frac{3}{4} \times 3$

6. $9 \times 3\frac{2}{5}$

7. $3\frac{3}{4} \times 4\frac{1}{4}$

8. $1\frac{1}{5} \times 4\frac{3}{8}$

9. $5\frac{1}{6} \times 1\frac{3}{4}$

10. $4\frac{1}{3} \times 6\frac{1}{5}$

11. $2\frac{1}{9} \times 8\frac{3}{4}$

12. $7\frac{2}{5} \times 9\frac{2}{5}$

13. $2\frac{1}{2} \times 1\frac{1}{4}$

14. $3\frac{2}{3} \times 2\frac{1}{3}$

15. $2\frac{1}{2} \times 3\frac{2}{5}$

16. $4 \times 2\frac{5}{6}$

Surface area—prism and cylinder

A **prism** has two **bases** that are the same size and shape and are in parallel planes. The other faces are all rectangles.

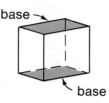

base

base

2 bases
4 other faces

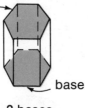

base

base

2 bases
6 other faces

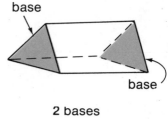

base

base

2 bases
3 other faces

The **surface area** of a prism is the sum of the areas of the faces.

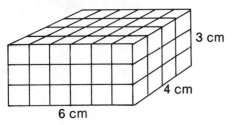

3 cm

4 cm

6 cm

The areas of the faces are:

top	24 cm²
bottom	24 cm²
right	12 cm²
left	12 cm²
front	18 cm²
back	18 cm²

The surface area is 108 cm²

A **cylinder** has two circular bases that are the same size and are in parallel planes. It has one curved face.

To find the surface area of a cylinder, you can think about cutting the cylinder apart like this:

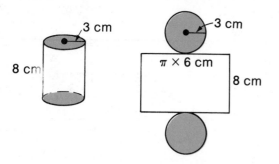

3 cm

8 cm

3 cm

$\pi \times 6$ cm

8 cm

Using 3.14 as an approximation of π, the areas of the faces are:

base $3.14 \times 3^2 = 28.26$ cm²

base $3.14 \times 3^2 = 28.26$ cm²

curved face $8 \times 6 \times 3.14 = 150.72$ cm²

The surface area is about **207.24 cm²**

Notice that the length of the rectangle is the circumference of each base.

EXERCISES

Find the surface area of each prism and cylinder. Use 3.14 as an approximation for π.

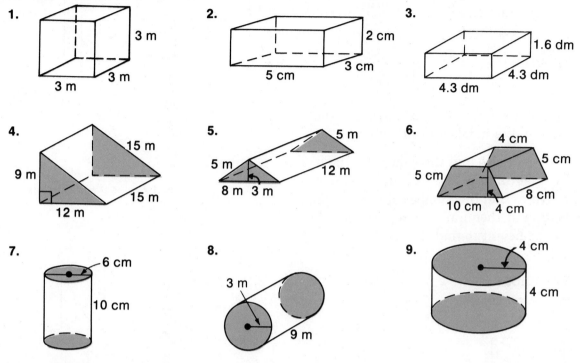

1.

3 m
3 m
3 m

2.

2 cm
5 cm
3 cm

3.

1.6 dm
4.3 dm
4.3 dm

4.

15 m
9 m
15 m
12 m

5.

5 m
5 m
12 m
8 m 3 m

6.

4 cm
5 cm
5 cm
8 cm
10 cm 4 cm

7.

6 cm
10 cm

8.

3 m
9 m

9.

4 cm
4 cm

Solve. (*Hint:* Draw a picture.)

10. A hatbox has the shape of a cylinder. The diameter is 38 cm and the height is 26 cm. How much paper is needed to cover the hatbox?

11. What is the surface area of a box that has a square base 32.5 cm on a side and is 40 cm high?

12. A cylindrical silo has a height of 15.5 meters and a diameter of 4.2 meters. If 1 can of paint covers 10 square meters, how many cans will be needed to paint the curved face with 1 coat? Round your answer up to the next whole number.

13. An open cylinder is made from a square piece of sheet metal measuring 5.25 m on a side. What will be the radius of the cylinder? Round your answer to the nearest 0.01 m.

★ 14. Determine how 64 blocks can be stacked to get a rectangular prism having the least surface area.

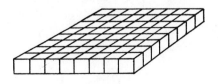

Volume

To find the volume of this box, we can pick a unit cube, for example, a cubic centimeter (cm³),

and then count the number of these cubic units it takes to fill the box.

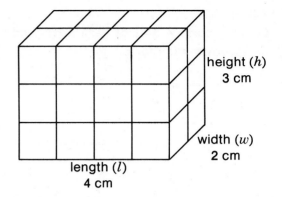

height (h)
3 cm

width (w)
2 cm

length (l)
4 cm

We could also find the volume of the box by first multiplying the length by the width to find the number of cubes in one layer and then multiplying that number by the height to find the total number of cubes.

Formula $V = lwh$

$V = 4 \text{ cm} \times 2 \text{ cm} \times 3 \text{ cm}$

$V = 24 \text{ cm}^3$

EXERCISES

Find each volume.

1.
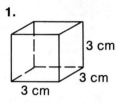
3 cm
3 cm
3 cm

2.
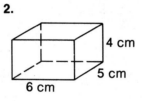
4 cm
5 cm
6 cm

3.
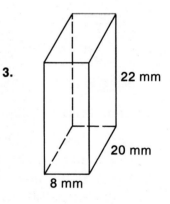
22 mm
20 mm
8 mm

4.
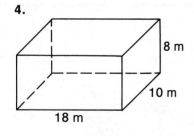
8 m
10 m
18 m

5.
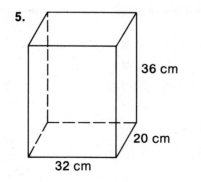
36 cm
20 cm
32 cm

6.
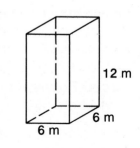
12 m
6 m
6 m

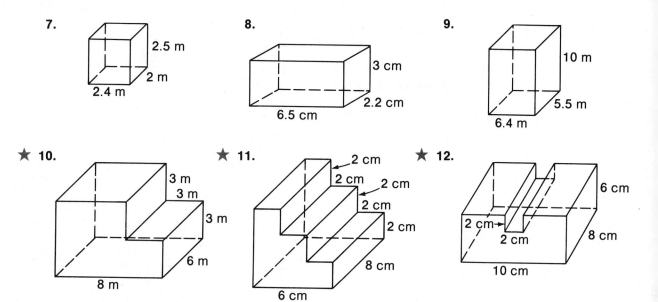

7. 2.5 m, 2 m, 2.4 m

8. 3 cm, 2.2 cm, 6.5 cm

9. 10 m, 5.5 m, 6.4 m

★ **10.** 3 m, 3 m, 3 m, 6 m, 8 m

★ **11.** 2 cm, 2 cm, 2 cm, 2 cm, 8 cm, 6 cm

★ **12.** 6 cm, 8 cm, 2 cm, 2 cm, 10 cm

Tell whether the question involves perimeter, area, or volume.

13. How much sand is needed to fill a trench?

14. How many shrubs are needed to border a yard?

15. How much sod is needed to cover a lawn?

16. How much concrete is needed for a wall?

17. How much fence is needed to fence in a patio?

Solve.
A rectangular swimming pool is 12 m long, 6 m wide, and 2 m deep.

18. How many cans of waterproof paint are needed to paint the inside of the pool if 1 can covers 20 m^2?

19. How many m^3 of water does it take to fill the pool to 1 dm from the top?

20. What are the dimensions of a plastic cover that covers the top of the pool and extends 3 dm past each edge?

21. How many cubic decimeters are in a cubic meter?

22. What is the volume of the water in the pool in cubic decimeters? (See exercise 19.)

Volume—prisms and cylinders

To find the volume of a prism or cylinder, you can find the area of a base (B), which is the number of unit cubes in one layer, and multiply that number by the height (h), which is the number of layers.

Recall that a prism has two parallel bases that are the same size and shape. The remaining faces are rectangles.

Formula ▶ $V = Bh$

$V = (3 \text{ cm} \times 2 \text{ cm}) \times 8 \text{ cm}$

$V = 6 \text{ cm}^2 \times 8 \text{ cm}$

$V = 48 \text{ cm}^3$

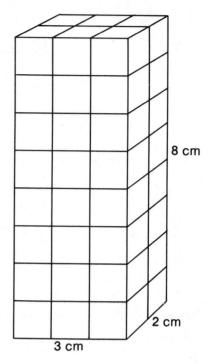

8 cm

2 cm

3 cm

EXAMPLE 1.

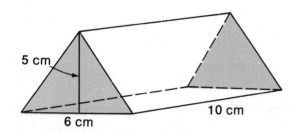

5 cm

6 cm

10 cm

$V = Bh$

$V = \left(\frac{1}{2} \times 6 \text{ cm} \times 5 \text{ cm}\right) \times 10 \text{ cm}$

$V = 15 \text{ cm}^2 \times 10 \text{ cm}$

$V = 150 \text{ cm}^3$

EXAMPLE 2.

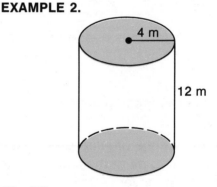

4 m

12 m

$V = Bh$

$V = (\pi \times (4 \text{ m})^2) \times 12 \text{ m}$

$V \approx (3.14 \times 16 \text{ m}^2) \times 12 \text{ m}$

$V \approx 50.24 \text{ m}^2 \times 12 \text{ m}$

$V \approx 602.88 \text{ m}^3$

EXERCISES

Compute each volume to the nearest hundredth. Use 3.14 as an approximation for π.

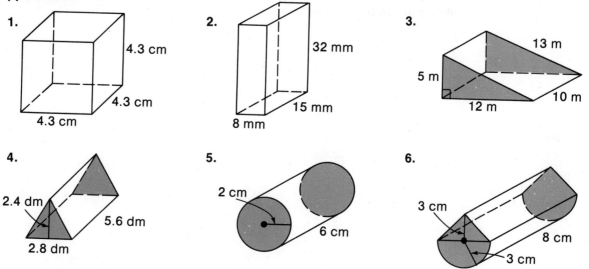

1. 4.3 cm, 4.3 cm, 4.3 cm

2. 32 mm, 15 mm, 8 mm

3. 13 m, 5 m, 10 m, 12 m

4. 2.4 dm, 2.8 dm, 5.6 dm

5. 2 cm, 6 cm

6. 3 cm, 3 cm, 8 cm

Solve.

7. What is the volume of a cube whose sides are 3 cm long?

8. What is the volume of a cube with a side 2 times as long as the one in exercise 7?

9. Look at your answers to exercises 7 and 8. What happens to the volume of a cube when the length of its edge is doubled?

10. A metal cylinder is 30 cm in height and has a radius of 6 cm. A 2-cm hole is drilled from the center of one base to the center of the other base. What is the volume of the metal that remains?

11. **TRUTH OR BALONEY?**

Who's right?

There are more cubic centimeters in a cubic meter than there are minutes in a year.

I don't believe it! You're wrong.

Volume—pyramid, cone, and sphere

PYRAMID

The volume of a pyramid is $\frac{1}{3}$ the volume of a prism having the same base and height.

Formula $\quad V = \frac{1}{3}Bh$

EXAMPLE 1.

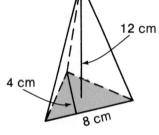

12 cm

4 cm

8 cm

$V = \frac{1}{3}Bh$

$V = \frac{1}{3}\left(\frac{1}{2} \times 8 \text{ cm} \times 4 \text{ cm}\right) \times 12 \text{ cm}$

$V = \frac{1}{3} \, 192 \text{ cm}^3$

$V = 64 \text{ cm}^3$

CONE

The volume of a cone is $\frac{1}{3}$ the volume of a cylinder having the same base and height.

Formula $\quad V = \frac{1}{3}Bh$

EXAMPLE 2.

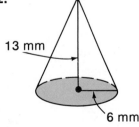

13 mm

6 mm

$V = \frac{1}{3}Bh$

$V = \frac{1}{3}(\pi \times 6 \text{ mm} \times 6 \text{ mm}) \times 13 \text{ mm}$

$V \approx \frac{1}{3}(3.14 \times 6 \text{ mm} \times 6 \text{ mm}) \times 13 \text{ mm}$

$V \approx \frac{1}{3} \times 1469.52 \text{ mm}^3$

$V \approx 489.84 \text{ mm}^3$

SPHERE

The volume of a sphere is $\frac{4}{3}\pi$ times the cube of the radius.

Formula $V = \frac{4}{3}\pi r^3$

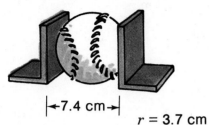

$$V \approx \frac{4}{3}(3.14)(3.7 \text{ cm})^3$$
$$V \approx \frac{4}{3}(3.14)(50.653 \text{ cm}^3)$$
$$V \approx 212.067 \text{ cm}^3$$

|←7.4 cm→|
$r = 3.7$ cm

EXERCISES

Give each volume to the nearest hundredth. Use 3.14 as an approximation for π.

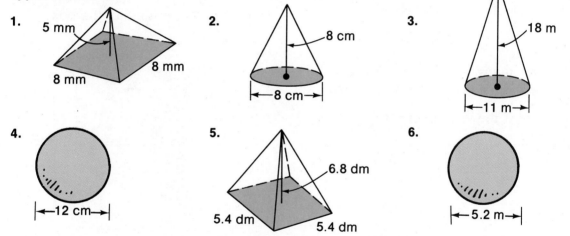

1. 5 mm, 8 mm, 8 mm

2. 8 cm, 8 cm

3. 18 m, 11 m

4. 12 cm

5. 6.8 dm, 5.4 dm, 5.4 dm

6. 5.2 m

Solve. Use 3.14 as an approximation for π. Give each answer to the nearest hundredth.

7. What is the volume of a spherical water tank that has a diameter of 16 m?

8. A drinking cup shaped like a cone has a radius of 8.4 cm and a height of 11.6 cm. What is its volume?

9. A certain railroad tank car in the shape of a cylinder has a length of 19.8 m and a diameter of 2.4 m. What is its volume?

10. When the Great Pyramid of Egypt was built, its square base was about 234.1 m on a side and its height was about 146.9 m. What was its approximate volume?

Practice

Give each volume.

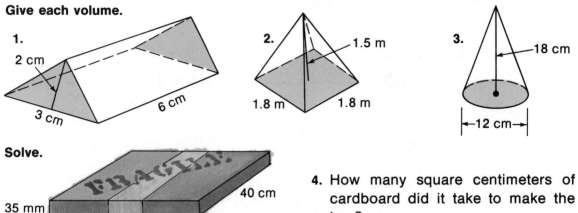

1.
2 cm
3 cm
6 cm

2.
1.5 m
1.8 m   1.8 m

3.
18 cm
|←12 cm→|

Solve.

35 mm
40 cm
65 cm
FRAGILE

4. How many square centimeters of cardboard did it take to make the box?

5. What is the volume of the box?

6. How many square centimeters of metal did it take to make the can?

7. What is the volume of the can?

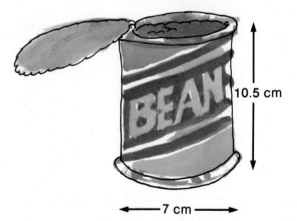

10.5 cm
←—— 7 cm ——→
BEANS

8. If the radius of a sphere is doubled, how many times is its volume increased?

9. If the radius of a cone is doubled, how many times is its volume increased?

10. A cylindrical oatmeal box is 30 cm tall. If it has a radius of 7.5 cm, what is its volume?

11. A Styrofoam cone used to protect roses from cold winter temperatures is 60 cm tall and has a radius of 30 cm. What is its volume?

12. If a beach ball is 50 cm in diameter, what volume of air can it hold?

Problem solving—drawing a picture

How many liters of water are in a swimming pool that is 5 m wide and 12 m long? The bottom is rectangular and slanted so the water is 1 m deep at one end and 3 m deep at the other.

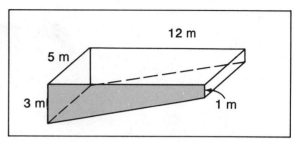

The water forms a prism. The base (in blue) is a trapezoid. Compute the volume by finding the area of the base (the trapezoid) and multiplying that by the height of the prism (the width of the pool, 5 m).

$$V = \tfrac{1}{2} \times (3 \text{ m} + 1 \text{ m}) \times 12 \text{ m} \times 5 \text{ m}$$

$$V = 120 \text{ m}^3$$

Since 1 cubic meter equals 1000 liters, the volume of water is 120,000 L.

Solve.

1. Mrs. Perez wants to put a fence around her yard, which is a rectangle 20 m wide and 40 m long. The fence is to have posts 2.5 m apart. How many fence posts are needed?

2. A large tree is in the center of a circular flower bed. The tree has a diameter of 0.8 m. Mrs. Perez can just reach from the edge of the flower bed to the tree, a distance of 1 m. What is the area of the flower bed?

3. Mrs. Perez is going to make a patio paved with tiles. The patio is to be as close to 6 m by 10 m as she can make it using tiles that are 8.2 dm by 1.5 dm. How many tiles does she need?

★ 4. Mrs. Perez has a sprinkler that sprinkles a 10-m by 20-m rectangle at the rate of 30 L per minute. She uses the sprinkler to water her 20-m by 40-m lawn. How long will she have to use the sprinkler in order to give the lawn as much water as in a 1-cm rainfall?

Conversion fractions

Here are some **conversion fractions.** The numerator and denominator of each fraction are the same length.

$$\frac{1 \text{ ft}}{12 \text{ in.}} \qquad \frac{12 \text{ in.}}{1 \text{ ft}} \qquad \frac{1 \text{ yd}}{3 \text{ ft}} \qquad \frac{3 \text{ ft}}{1 \text{ yd}}$$

I change from one unit to another by using a conversion fraction.

EXAMPLE 1. Change 4 feet to inches.

$$4 \text{ ft} = 4 \text{ ft} \times \frac{12 \text{ in.}}{1 \text{ ft}}$$

$$= 4 \cancel{\text{ ft}} \times \frac{12 \text{ in.}}{1 \cancel{\text{ ft}}}$$

$$= 48 \text{ in.}$$

Cancel units as you would cancel numbers.

EXAMPLE 2. Change 28 inches to feet.

$$28 \text{ in.} = 28 \text{ in.} \times \frac{1 \text{ ft}}{12 \text{ in.}}$$

$$= 28 \cancel{\text{ in.}} \times \frac{1 \text{ ft}}{12 \cancel{\text{ in.}}}$$

$$= \frac{28}{12} \text{ ft}$$

$$= 2\frac{1}{3} \text{ ft}$$

Notice that the numerator of the conversion fraction contains the unit you are changing to and the denominator contains the unit you are changing from.

EXERCISES
Use a conversion fraction to change the following.

1. 28 yd to ft

2. 28 ft to yd

3. 208 in. to ft

4. 108 in. to yd

5. 16 ft to in.

6. 10 yd to in.

7. 2640 yd to mi

8. 2640 ft to mi

Solve by using a conversion fraction.

9. A height record for walking stilts was 21 feet. How many inches is that?

10. A distance record for tightrope walking was 3790 yards. How many miles is that?

We can also use conversion fractions for area and volume.

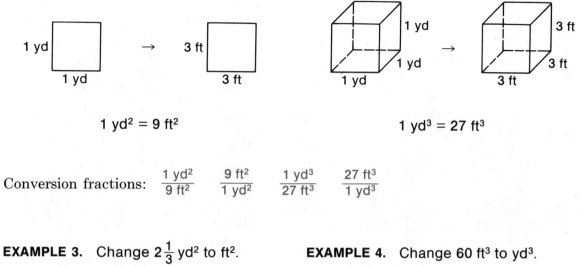

$$1 \text{ yd}^2 = 9 \text{ ft}^2 \qquad\qquad 1 \text{ yd}^3 = 27 \text{ ft}^3$$

Conversion fractions: $\dfrac{1 \text{ yd}^2}{9 \text{ ft}^2}$ $\dfrac{9 \text{ ft}^2}{1 \text{ yd}^2}$ $\dfrac{1 \text{ yd}^3}{27 \text{ ft}^3}$ $\dfrac{27 \text{ ft}^3}{1 \text{ yd}^3}$

EXAMPLE 3. Change $2\frac{1}{3}$ yd² to ft².

$$2\frac{1}{3} \text{ yd}^2 = 2\frac{1}{3} \text{ yd}^2 \times \frac{9 \text{ ft}^2}{1 \text{ yd}^2}$$
$$= 2\frac{1}{3} \cancel{\text{yd}^2} \times \frac{9 \text{ ft}^2}{1 \cancel{\text{yd}^2}}$$
$$= 21 \text{ ft}^2$$

EXAMPLE 4. Change 60 ft³ to yd³.

$$60 \text{ ft}^3 = 60 \text{ ft}^3 \times \frac{1 \text{ yd}^3}{27 \text{ ft}^3}$$
$$= 60 \cancel{\text{ft}^3} \times \frac{1 \text{ yd}^3}{27 \cancel{\text{ft}^3}}$$
$$= \frac{60}{27} \text{ yd}^3$$
$$= 2\frac{2}{9} \text{ yd}^3$$

Copy and complete each conversion fraction.

11. $\dfrac{1 \text{ ft}^2}{? \text{ in.}^2}$

12. $\dfrac{? \text{ in.}^2}{1 \text{ ft}^2}$

13. $\dfrac{1 \text{ ft}^3}{? \text{ in.}^3}$

14. $\dfrac{? \text{ in.}^3}{1 \text{ ft}^3}$

Use a conversion fraction to change the following.

15. 5 ft² to in.²

16. 6 ft³ to in.³

17. $1\frac{2}{3}$ yd² to ft²

18. 50 ft³ to yd³

19. 300 in.² to ft²

20. 72 in.² to ft²

Solve.

21. What is the area in ft² of a rectangle 2 yd long and $1\frac{1}{3}$ yd wide?

22. What is the volume in yd³ of a box 6 ft long, 5 ft wide, and 4 ft high?

Area—customary units

When measurements are given in more than one unit, change to a single unit before multiplying. Below, you are shown two ways to change units.

1 ft 4 in.

3 ft 9 in.

Change to inches.

$A = lw$

$A = (3 \text{ ft } 9 \text{ in.}) \times (1 \text{ ft } 4 \text{ in.})$

$A = 45 \text{ in.} \times 16 \text{ in.}$

$A = 720 \text{ in.}^2$

Change to feet.

$A = lw$

$A = (3 \text{ ft } 9 \text{ in.}) \times (1 \text{ ft } 4 \text{ in.})$

$A = 3\frac{3}{4} \text{ ft} \times 1\frac{1}{3} \text{ ft}$

$A = \frac{\overset{5}{\cancel{15}}}{\underset{1}{\cancel{4}}} \text{ ft} \times \frac{\overset{1}{\cancel{4}}}{\underset{1}{\cancel{3}}} \text{ ft}$

$A = 5 \text{ ft}^2$

We can compare these answers by changing 5 ft² to square inches. Using a conversion fraction, we have

$$5 \text{ ft}^2 \times \frac{144 \text{ in.}^2}{1 \text{ ft}^2} = 720 \text{ in.}^2$$

EXERCISES
Give the number of

1. square feet in a square yard.

2. square inches in a square foot.

3. square inches in a square yard.

4. square inches in $2\frac{1}{2}$ square feet.

5. square yards in 36 square feet.

6. square feet in 436 square inches.

Give each area.

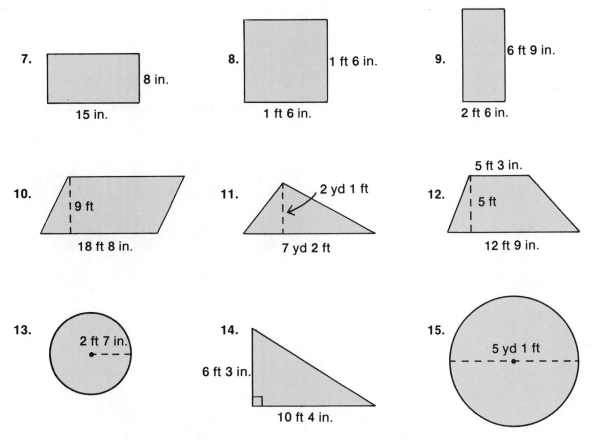

7. 8 in. 15 in.

8. 1 ft 6 in. 1 ft 6 in.

9. 6 ft 9 in. 2 ft 6 in.

10. 9 ft 18 ft 8 in.

11. 2 yd 1 ft 7 yd 2 ft

12. 5 ft 3 in. 5 ft 12 ft 9 in.

13. 2 ft 7 in.

14. 6 ft 3 in. 10 ft 4 in.

15. 5 yd 1 ft

Solve.

16. A square flower bed measures 10 ft 6 in. on a side. The width of a rectangular garden having the same area is 5 ft 3 in. What is its length?

17. A circular garden with a radius of 10 yd has a brick walk around it that is 1 yard wide. What is the area of the walk?

18. The acre is a customary unit for measuring land area. There are **640** acres in a square mile. How many square feet are in an acre?

19. A football field, including the end zones, is 360 feet long by 160 feet wide. What is the area of a football field in acres?

Volume—customary units

When measurements are given in more than one unit, change to a single unit before multiplying.

Study these examples.

10 in.

1 ft 3 in.

1 ft 9 in.

EXAMPLE 1.

$V = Bh$

$V = (1 \text{ ft } 9 \text{ in.} \times 10 \text{ in.}) \times 1 \text{ ft } 3 \text{ in.}$

$V = (21 \text{ in.} \times 10 \text{ in.}) \times 15 \text{ in.}$

$V = 210 \text{ in.}^2 \times 15 \text{ in.}$

$V = 3150 \text{ in.}^3$

EXAMPLE 2.

$V = Bh$

$V = \pi(5.5 \text{ in.} \times 5.5 \text{ in.}) \times 15 \text{ in.}$

$V = \pi(30.25 \text{ in.}^2) \times 15 \text{ in.}$

$V = \pi(453.75 \text{ in.}^3)$

$V \approx 1424.8 \text{ in.}^3$

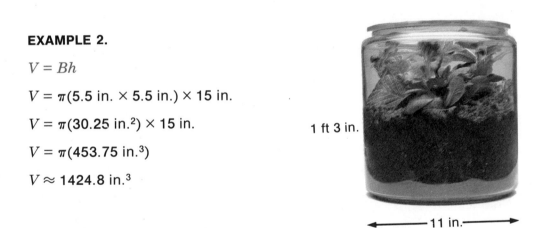

1 ft 3 in.

11 in.

EXERCISES

Give the number of

1. cubic feet in a cubic yard.

2. cubic inches in a cubic foot.

3. cubic inches in a cubic yard.

4. cubic feet in 5 cubic yards.

5. cubic feet in $3\frac{1}{3}$ cubic yards.

6. cubic yards in 84 cubic feet.

Give each volume.

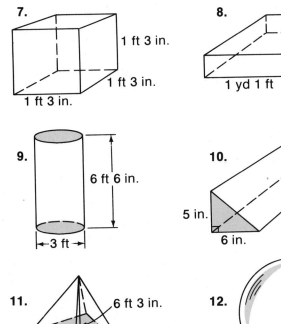

7. 1 ft 3 in. / 1 ft 3 in. / 1 ft 3 in.

8. 1 ft / 1 yd 1 ft / 1 yd 1 ft

9. 6 ft 6 in. / 3 ft

10. 1 ft 9 in. / 5 in. / 6 in.

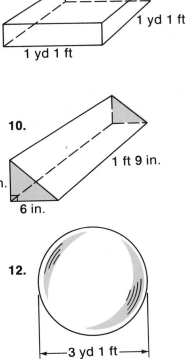

11. 6 ft 3 in. / 4 ft / 4 ft

12. 3 yd 1 ft

Solve.

13. A rectangular box is 2 ft by 3 ft by 6 ft. What is its volume in cubic feet? In cubic yards?

14. A cylindrical tank has a diameter of 1 yard and a height of 2 yd 1 ft. What is its volume?

15. How many cubic yards of concrete are needed to pour a garage floor that is 25 ft by 25 ft and 4 inches thick?

16. A swimming pool is 16 ft wide and 36 ft long. When it is full, the average water depth is 4 ft 6 in. If the water was pumped into the pool at a rate of 2.5 ft³ per minute, how many hours did it take to fill the pool?

Divide. Give the quotient in simplest form.

1. $5 \div 1\frac{1}{2}$

2. $7\frac{2}{3} \div 4$

3. $4\frac{5}{9} \div 1$

4. $3\frac{3}{4} \div 3$

5. $4 \div 1\frac{1}{9}$

6. $5\frac{1}{2} \div 1\frac{1}{3}$

7. $3\frac{1}{4} \div 2$

8. $5 \div 2\frac{1}{3}$

9. $4\frac{1}{2} \div 2$

10. $4\frac{2}{3} \div 1\frac{1}{4}$

11. $6\frac{1}{2} \div 2\frac{2}{3}$

12. $8\frac{3}{4} \div 3$

13. $5 \div 3\frac{1}{4}$

14. $6\frac{1}{2} \div 3$

15. $5\frac{2}{3} \div 1\frac{1}{4}$

16. $4\frac{3}{8} \div 2\frac{1}{4}$

CHAPTER CHECKUP

Find each area. [pages 166–173]

1.
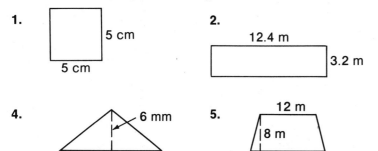
5 cm
5 cm

2.
12.4 m
3.2 m

3.
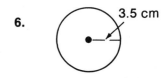
7 cm
9 cm
12 cm

4.
6 mm
15 mm

5.
12 m
8 m
16 m

6.
3.5 cm

Find the surface area. [pages 174–175]

7.
4 cm
5 cm
7 cm

8.
5 cm
10 cm

Find the volume. [pages 176–179]

9.
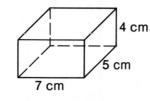
3 m
3 m
3 m

10.
24 cm
5 cm
9 cm

11.
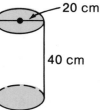
20 cm
40 cm

Find the area. [pages 186–187]

12.

1 ft 6 in.
2 ft 4 in.

Find the volume. [pages 188–189]

13.
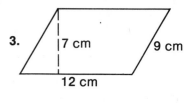
1 yd 1 ft
1 yd 1 ft
1 yd 1 ft

Solve. [page 183]

14. A sheep is in a 23-m by 32-m pen. How much area does the sheep have for grazing?

15. How many cubic meters of concrete are needed to fill a form that is 6 m wide, 10 m long, and 0.1 m thick?

CHAPTER PROJECT

You can find the volume of an irregular-shaped solid by following these steps:

Step 1. Set a container inside a rectangular pan. Fill the container right to the top with water.

Step 2. Completely submerge the solid object.

Step 3. Determine the volume of the displaced water in the pan.

The volume of the displaced water is equal to the volume of the solid object. *Remember:* $1 \text{ mL} = 1 \text{ cm}^3$.

1. Get several irregular solids and find the volume of each.
2. The **density** of a substance is the ratio of its mass to its volume. In the metric system, density can be expressed in grams per cubic centimeter. Find the mass of each of the objects and compute the density by dividing its mass in grams by its volume in cm^3. Round each density to the nearest tenth.

Area of a parallelogram
$$A = bh$$

Area of a triangle
$$A = \frac{1}{2}bh$$

Area of a trapezoid
$$A = \frac{1}{2}(b_1 + b_2)h$$

Area of a circle
$$A = \pi r^2$$

The surface area of a prism or cylinder is the sum of the areas of the faces.

Volume of a prism or cylinder
$$V = Bh$$

(B is the area of the base.)

Volume of a cone or pyramid
$$V = \frac{1}{3}Bh$$

Give each area. Use 3.14 as an approximation for π.

1.
5.3 m
2.6 m

2.
7 cm
9 cm
12 cm

3.
4.2 m
5.1 m

4.
7.2 cm
4.1 cm
10.6 cm

5.
6 mm

Give the surface area.

6.
6 cm
8 cm
15 cm

7.
6 cm
10 cm

Give each volume.

8.
8 cm
8 cm
8 cm

9.
8 m
2.4 m
10 m
10 m

10.
10 mm
28.2 mm

11.
10 cm
9 cm
9 cm

CHAPTER CHALLENGE

1. Suppose that a circular pizza with a 9-inch diameter is just enough for 1 person. How many circular pizzas with a 15-inch diameter would you have to buy to feed 20 people?

2. What would your answer be if the pizzas were square instead of round?

3. A cheese ball with a 3-inch diameter is just enough for 3 people. How many cheese balls with a 6-inch diameter are needed to feed 30 people?

a b c d   a b c d   a b c d   a b
1. ▯▯▯▯ 2. ▯▯▯▯   **MAJOR CHECKUP**   5. ▯▯▯▯ 6. ▯▯
a b c d   a b c d   STANDARDIZED FORMAT   a b c d   a b
7. ▯▯▯▯ 8. ▯▯▯▯ 9. ▯▯▯▯ 10. ▯▯▯▯ 11. ▯▯▯▯ 12. ▯▯

Choose the correct letter.

1. Which number is less than 382.529?

    a. 382.6
    b. 382.592
    c. 382.06
    d. none of these

2. Give the quotient.

$0.13\overline{)7.8}$

    a. 0.6
    b. 6
    c. 60
    d. none of these

3. $8.25 \times 10^4 = \underline{?}$

    a. 82,500
    b. 825,000
    c. 8,250,000
    d. none of these

4. The prime factorization of 54 is

    a. 2×3^3
    b. $3^3 \times 6$
    c. $2 \times 3 \times 9$
    d. none of these

5. 12.5 cm = $\underline{?}$

    a. 0.125 km
    b. 12,500 mm
    c. 125 m
    d. none of these

6. <, =, or >?

$\frac{7}{10}$ ⑦ $\frac{3}{4}$

    a. <
    b. =
    c. >
    d. none of these

7. Subtract.

$8\frac{1}{4} - 3\frac{1}{2}$

    a. $4\frac{3}{4}$
    b. $5\frac{3}{4}$
    c. $5\frac{1}{4}$
    d. none of these

8. Multiply.

$\frac{3}{4} \times \frac{6}{7}$

    a. $\frac{7}{8}$
    b. $\frac{9}{14}$
    c. $\frac{3}{14}$
    d. none of these

9. Find the area.

3 m   4 m
5 m

    a. 20 m²
    b. 15 m²
    c. 40 m²
    d. none of these

10. Find the surface area.

4 mm
4 mm
4 mm

    a. 24 mm²
    b. 64 mm²
    c. 96 mm²
    d. none of these

11. A 6-m by 4-m floor was covered with 0.1-m square tiles. How many tiles were there?

    a. 24   **b.** 240
    c. 2400   **d.** none of these

12. Roger had $\frac{1}{4}$ the number of tapes that David had. Roger had 8 tapes. How many tapes did David have?

    a. 32   **b.** 12
    c. 2   **d.** none of these

194

Ratio and
Proportion

7

Ratios

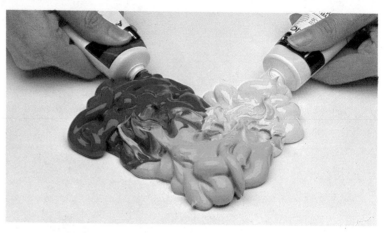

Are the two fractions equivalent?

1. $\frac{1}{2}$ $\frac{2}{4}$

2. $\frac{2}{3}$ $\frac{6}{9}$

3. $\frac{4}{1}$ $\frac{8}{2}$

4. $\frac{5}{10}$ $\frac{1}{2}$

5. $\frac{3}{4}$ $\frac{8}{12}$

6. $\frac{5}{6}$ $\frac{15}{18}$

7. $\frac{3}{5}$ $\frac{12}{15}$

8. $\frac{16}{20}$ $\frac{8}{10}$

9. $\frac{8}{5}$ $\frac{7}{4}$

10. $\frac{5}{6}$ $\frac{6}{7}$

An artist made a special shade of green by mixing 2 parts of canary yellow with 4 parts of sky blue. If the artist wished to tell someone how to mix the same color, which of these ways would be correct?

a. "Use 2 parts of yellow for each 4 parts of blue."
b. "Use 4 parts of yellow for each 2 parts of blue."
c. "Use 4 parts of yellow for each 8 parts of blue."
d. "Use 2 parts more of blue than yellow."

Statements **b** and **d** are incorrect. Think of a way to follow the directions in **d** and get the wrong color.

A **ratio** compares two numbers. The ratio of parts of yellow to parts of blue is 2 to 4. Here are three ways to write the ratio:

$$2 \text{ to } 4 \qquad\qquad 2:4 \qquad\qquad \frac{2}{4}$$

[You can read each ratio as "2 to 4."]

Remember that order is important when working with ratios. The ratio of yellow to blue is $\frac{2}{4}$ and the ratio of blue to yellow is $\frac{4}{2}$.

These ratios are equal:

$$\frac{1}{2} = \frac{2}{4} = \frac{3}{6}$$

You can find equal ratios by thinking about equivalent fractions.

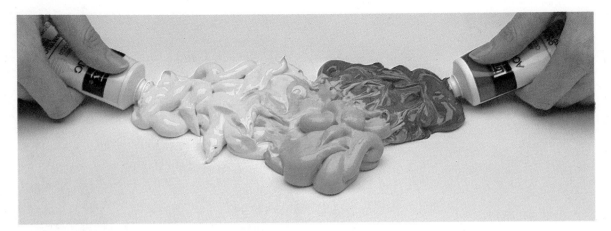

EXERCISES

The artist made some orange paint by mixing 6 parts of yellow with 2 parts of red.

1. Did the artist use more yellow paint than red paint?

2. What is the ratio of parts of yellow to parts of red?

3. What is the ratio of parts of red to parts of yellow?

4. Suppose that you wanted to mix 16 grams of the orange paint. How many grams of each color would you use?

5. Suppose that you had only 3 g of yellow paint and 3 g of red. How many grams of orange could you make?

Write each ratio as a fraction in lowest terms.

6. 9 : 6
7. $\frac{8}{6}$
8. 21 to 14
9. $\frac{14}{21}$
10. 36 to 24

11. 18 meters to 12 meters
12. 12 grams to 20 grams
13. 12 hours to 16 hours

14. 32 kg to 18 kg
15. 24 min to 18 min
16. 14 liters to 8 liters

Complete the equal ratios.

17. $\frac{2}{3} = \frac{?}{6}$
18. $\frac{1}{4} = \frac{?}{12}$
19. $\frac{10}{4} = \frac{5}{?}$
20. $\frac{18}{12} = \frac{9}{?}$
21. $\frac{3}{4} = \frac{?}{24}$

22. $\frac{3}{?} = \frac{15}{20}$
23. $\frac{8}{3} = \frac{?}{21}$
24. $\frac{?}{16} = \frac{5}{4}$
25. $\frac{?}{3} = \frac{10}{30}$
26. $\frac{1}{3} = \frac{?}{12}$

27. $\frac{4}{16} = \frac{?}{4}$
28. $\frac{12}{?} = \frac{24}{22}$
29. $\frac{10}{15} = \frac{?}{3}$
30. $\frac{15}{30} = \frac{?}{2}$
31. $\frac{7}{9} = \frac{?}{36}$

32. 27 : ? = 9 : 5
33. 24 : 36 = ? : 6
34. 20 : 32 = 5 : ?

197

Proportions

An equation stating that two ratios are equal is called a **proportion.** Every proportion has a related multiplication equation.

Proportion	$\frac{3}{5} = \frac{6}{10}$
Related multiplication equation	$3 \times 10 = 5 \times 6$

The two products 3×10 and 5×6 are called **cross products.**

If the ratios are equal, then the cross products are equal. Also, if the cross products are equal, then the ratios are equal. This gives us an easy way to decide whether the two ratios are equal.

I made 6 out of 10. I'm the best shot!

I made 3 out of 5. I'm just as good as she is!

EXAMPLE 1.

The cross products are equal, so the ratios are equal:

$$\frac{4}{6} = \frac{6}{9}$$

EXAMPLE 2.

The cross products are not equal, so the ratios are not equal:

$$\frac{3}{5} \neq \frac{6}{11}$$

[Read $\neq$ as "is not equal to."]

EXAMPLE 3.

Jan made 3 of 5 free throws. At that ratio, how many free throws would she make if she shot 35 times?

We can solve the problem by solving a proportion.

$\frac{3}{5} = \frac{n}{35}$ ← free throws made
← free throws attempted

$5n = 3 \times 35$

$5n = 105$

$n = 21$

> To solve a proportion, solve its multiplication equation.

She would make **21** free throws.

EXERCISES

Compare the cross products to tell whether the ratios are equal (=) or not equal (≠).

1. $\frac{3}{4}$ ⬤ $\frac{7}{9}$

2. $\frac{7}{2}$ ⬤ $\frac{11}{3}$

3. $\frac{2}{3}$ ⬤ $\frac{3}{4\frac{1}{2}}$

4. $\frac{2\frac{1}{4}}{8}$ ⬤ $\frac{5}{16}$

5. $\frac{3.5}{2}$ ⬤ $\frac{10.5}{6}$

6. $\frac{4}{5}$ ⬤ $\frac{12.8}{16}$

Solve each proportion.

7. $\frac{3}{8} = \frac{n}{32}$

8. $\frac{3}{4} = \frac{n}{20}$

9. $\frac{5}{7} = \frac{35}{n}$

10. $\frac{2}{3} = \frac{n}{18}$

11. $\frac{2}{9} = \frac{12}{n}$

12. $\frac{5}{n} = \frac{20}{40}$

13. $\frac{2.7}{8.1} = \frac{n}{18}$

14. $\frac{4.2}{1.4} = \frac{15}{n}$

15. $\frac{0.13}{0.52} = \frac{3.2}{n}$

16. $\frac{2}{3} = \frac{n}{7}$

17. $\frac{3}{4} = \frac{11}{n}$

18. $\frac{5}{8} = \frac{8}{n}$

Solve.

GAME RECORD		
Player	Free Throws Made	Free Throws Attempted
Sarah D.	5	12
Jill G.	6	9
Maria M.	5	10
Ingrid P.	4	6
Paige R.	9	14
Sue V.	10	17

19. What was Jill's ratio of free throws made to free throws attempted?

20. What was Paige's ratio of free throws missed to free throws made?

21. By the ratio shown in the table, how many free throws would Sue make if she shot 50 times? Round your answer to the nearest whole number.

Write as decimals.

1. $\frac{1}{2}$

2. $\frac{1}{3}$

3. $\frac{2}{3}$

4. $\frac{5}{8}$

5. $\frac{7}{4}$

6. $\frac{9}{2}$

7. $\frac{16}{5}$

8. $\frac{16}{10}$

9. $\frac{24}{5}$

10. $\frac{32}{3}$

11. $\frac{37}{2}$

12. $\frac{43}{8}$

13. $\frac{22}{5}$

14. $\frac{34}{4}$

15. $\frac{27}{5}$

16. $\frac{19}{8}$

Proportions—estimating the solution

Earlier you learned that you can find an equivalent fraction by multiplying the numerator and denominator of a fraction by the same nonzero number. You can use this fact to estimate the solution of a proportion. Study these examples.

EXAMPLE 1.

$\dfrac{5}{9} = \dfrac{n}{19}$

The solution is about 2 times 5, or 10.

about 2 times

$9n = 5 \cdot 19$

$9n = 95$

$n = 10\dfrac{5}{9}$

EXAMPLE 2.

$\dfrac{n}{17} = \dfrac{5}{4}$

The solution is about 20.

about $\dfrac{1}{4}$

$4n = 17 \cdot 5$

$4n = 85$

$n = 21\dfrac{1}{4}$

Is the solution close to the estimate?

EXERCISES
First estimate the solution. Then solve the proportion.

1. $\dfrac{n}{5} = \dfrac{8}{11}$

2. $\dfrac{6}{n} = \dfrac{23}{16}$

3. $\dfrac{5}{9} = \dfrac{n}{29}$

4. $\dfrac{22}{15} = \dfrac{7}{n}$

5. $\dfrac{n}{12} = \dfrac{9}{35}$

6. $\dfrac{9}{n} = \dfrac{14}{8}$

7. $\dfrac{16}{9} = \dfrac{2}{n}$

8. $\dfrac{n}{8} = \dfrac{18}{23}$

9. $\dfrac{5}{12} = \dfrac{1}{n}$

10. $\dfrac{14}{29} = \dfrac{n}{9}$

11. $\dfrac{8}{5} = \dfrac{n}{4}$

12. $\dfrac{15}{n} = \dfrac{7}{2}$

13. $\dfrac{11}{5} = \dfrac{2}{n}$

14. $\dfrac{25}{16} = \dfrac{n}{3}$

15. $\dfrac{n}{42} = \dfrac{15}{20}$

16. $3:8 = n:32$

17. $7:n = 15:26$

18. $9:2 = n:9$

19. $n:11 = 4:6$

20. $36:15 = 9:n$

21. $40:n = 19:32$

Mathematics in careers

Foresters must be experts in the planting and harvesting of trees. They also have to protect forests against fire, insects, and disease.

Sometimes foresters do a population study of a forest to find out how many trees are in a certain area.

Each sample listed below was taken at the location shown on the forest map.

Sample no.	1	2	3	4	5	6
Number of trees per 100 m²	42	36	44	39	41	34

1. Find the average number of trees per 100 m² in the samples.

2. Compute the area of the forest in m². (See map.)

3. Solve a proportion to estimate the population of the forest.

4. Suppose that 3 of every 5 trees have to be harvested so that the remaining trees can mature properly. About what would the population be then?

Problem solving—using proportions

A popular model-railroad scale is the HO scale. This scale is 1:87. This means that the ratio of the length of any model part to the real part is 1 to 87.

You can use proportions to solve problems about HO-scale models.

EXAMPLE. A baggage car is 18.3 meters long. How long would the HO-scale model be?

$$\text{length of model} \rightarrow \frac{1}{87} = \frac{n}{18.3} \leftarrow \text{length of model}$$
$$\text{length of real car} \rightarrow \phantom{\frac{1}{87}} \phantom{\frac{n}{18.3}} \leftarrow \text{length of real car}$$

$$87n = 18.3$$

$$n \approx 0.21$$

The model is about 0.21 meter, or 21 centimeters, long.

EXERCISES
Solve.

1. How long is an HO-scale model of a chemical tank car that is 10.7 meters in length?

2. How long is a Pullman car if an HO-scale model of it is 24.54 cm long?

3. Model railroaders build scenery to scale for their layouts. An HO-scale model bridge is 44.54 cm long. How long would the real bridge be?

4. An HO-scale model water tower is 15.8 cm tall. How tall would the real tower be?

Another popular scale in model railroading is the N scale, in which the ratio is 1:160.

5. How long would an N-scale model of an 18-meter passenger car be?

6. How many meters long is a hopper car if its N-scale model is 6.9 cm long?

7. Both an N-scale model and an HO-scale model were made of an old steam engine that was 17 meters long. Which model was longer? How much longer?

8. Standard railroad tracks are spaced 1.439 meters apart. How far apart would the tracks be in an N-scale model?

9. A model-railroad club constructed an N-scale model layout that had 105 meters of main-line track. How many kilometers of real track did their layout represent?

10. An HO-scale model of a tank car is 12.25 cm long. How long would an N-scale model of the same tank car be?

11. Another scale used in model railroading is the O scale. The O scale is 1:48. Which are longer, O-scale models or HO-scale models?

Rates

A **rate** is a ratio of two quantities. Here are some examples.

Jogged 2 km in 13 minutes.

Rate: $\dfrac{2 \text{ km}}{13 \text{ min}}$

Rate: $\dfrac{3 \text{ apples}}{35¢}$

Rate: $\dfrac{\$1.35}{1 \text{ dozen}}$

Earned $5.50 in $2\frac{1}{2}$ hours.

Rate: $\dfrac{\$5.50}{2\frac{1}{2} \text{ hours}}$

A proportion may be used to solve a rate problem.

How much paint is needed to paint 170 square meters?

$$\begin{array}{l} \text{liters} \to \\ \text{area} \to \end{array} \frac{4}{35} = \frac{n}{170} \begin{array}{l} \leftarrow \text{liters} \\ \leftarrow \text{area} \end{array}$$

$$35n = 680$$

$$n \approx 19.4$$

So, 19.4 L of paint are needed. How many cans of paint would you have to buy?

EXERCISES

Solve by using a proportion.

1. Small green peppers are on sale for 84¢ a dozen. What is the price of 20 peppers?

2. Oranges are on sale for 6 for 79¢. Find the price of 11 oranges. Round the answer to the nearest cent.

3. If 12 pencils cost 43¢, how much would 9 pencils cost? Round the answer to the nearest cent.

4. If peanuts are priced at $2.40 a kg, how many kg can be bought for $3.50? Round the answer to the nearest tenth of a kilogram.

5. George hiked 18.5 km in 4 hours. At that rate, how many kilometers could he hike in $6\frac{1}{2}$ hours? Round the answer to the nearest tenth km.

6. Mrs. Allan drove 252 km in 3 hours. At that rate, how long would it take her to drive 386 km? Round the answer to the nearest tenth of an hour.

7. John hit 5 home runs in 84 times at bat. At that rate, how many times at bat would he need to hit 7 home runs? Round the answer to the nearest whole number.

8. A certain machine can print 8000 leaflets in an hour. At that rate, how many minutes would it take to print 1750 leaflets? Round the answer to the nearest minute.

9. Donna earned $5.76 for 4 hours of baby-sitting. At that rate, what would she earn for 3 hours of baby-sitting? Round the answer to the nearest cent.

10. A certain recipe calls for 2 teaspoons of vanilla and 5 tablespoons of butter. How much vanilla is needed for 12 tablespoons of butter?

11. Mr. Jackson's automobile used 48 liters of gasoline in 280 km. At that rate, how much gasoline would be needed for a 456-km trip? Round the answer to the nearest tenth liter.

205

Practice

Solve each proportion. Round each answer to the nearest hundredth.

1. $\dfrac{7}{3} = \dfrac{8}{n}$

2. $\dfrac{5}{8} = \dfrac{a}{27}$

3. $\dfrac{11}{r} = \dfrac{8}{3}$

4. $\dfrac{7}{t} = \dfrac{9}{4}$

5. $\dfrac{1}{6} = \dfrac{11}{n}$

6. $\dfrac{2}{9} = \dfrac{12}{d}$

7. $\dfrac{3}{5} = \dfrac{x}{7}$

8. $\dfrac{n}{19} = \dfrac{9}{5}$

9. $\dfrac{2.4}{2} = \dfrac{n}{3}$

10. $\dfrac{5.6}{x} = \dfrac{3}{11.2}$

11. $\dfrac{6.2}{5} = \dfrac{m}{7}$

12. $\dfrac{5}{9.6} = \dfrac{9}{b}$

13. $\dfrac{2\frac{1}{4}}{3} = \dfrac{5}{x}$

14. $\dfrac{z}{1\frac{1}{4}} = \dfrac{5}{2\frac{1}{2}}$

15. $\dfrac{6}{y} = \dfrac{3\frac{1}{4}}{5}$

16. $\dfrac{2\frac{1}{2}}{15} = \dfrac{n}{6}$

Apples ....6 for $.89   Peas ...... 3 $\frac{16\,oz}{cans}$ $1

Oranges... 8 for $1.19   Green Beans .. 3 lb for $1.49

Bananas.. 2 lb for $.79   Onions ... 5 lb for $1.99

Solve by using a proportion. Round your answers to the nearest cent.

17. How much would 4 apples cost?

18. How much would 2 pounds of green beans cost?

19. How much would a dozen oranges cost?

20. How much would 5 pounds of bananas cost?

21. How much would 3 pounds of onions cost?

22. How much would 4 cans of peas cost?

23. How many apples could you buy for $4.45?

24. How many oranges could you buy for $5.65?

Problem solving

A 10-speed bicycle has two large gears near the pedal and five smaller gears at the rear. By using different combinations of these gears, you get 10 "speeds."

Solve by using a proportion.

1. When the bicycle is in first gear, 2 revolutions (complete turns) of the pedal make 3 revolutions of the wheel. How many pedal revolutions are needed for 78 wheel revolutions?

2. When the bicycle is in fifth gear, 6 revolutions of the pedal make 13 revolutions of the wheel. How many pedal revolutions are needed for 78 wheel revolutions?

3. In tenth gear, 7 revolutions of the pedal make 26 revolutions of the wheel. How many pedal revolutions are needed for 78 wheel revolutions?

4. The bicycle travels 21 meters for each 10 revolutions of the wheel. How many revolutions would the wheel make in a kilometer? Round your answer to the nearest whole number.

5. How many pedal revolutions are needed to travel one kilometer in tenth gear? (See exercises 3 and 4.) Round your answer to the nearest whole number.

6. During the first $2\frac{1}{4}$ hours, a bicyclist cycled 28.4 km. At that rate, how long will it take to complete a 50-km tour? Round your answer to the nearest tenth hour.

Scale drawings

A map is a scale drawing. This map shows the ski trails and chair lifts at a ski resort. Notice that 2 cm on the map stands for 0.5 km on the ski trail.

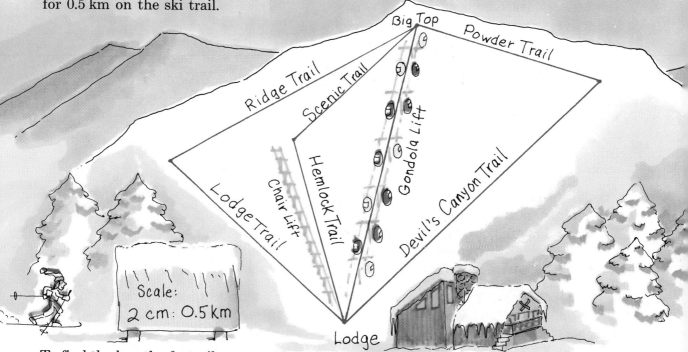

To find the length of a trail, we can measure the distance on the map and solve a proportion.

EXAMPLE.   The length of Lodge Trail on the map is 6.3 cm. How long is Lodge Trail?

$$\begin{array}{l} \text{cm on map} \rightarrow \\ \text{km on trail} \rightarrow \end{array} \frac{2}{0.5} = \frac{6.3}{n} \begin{array}{l} \leftarrow \text{cm on map} \\ \leftarrow \text{km on trail} \end{array}$$

$$2n = 3.15$$
$$n = 1.575 \quad \text{Lodge Trail is 1.575 km long.}$$

When "setting up" a proportion, be sure that the ratios are in the same order. Notice that you could also use these proportions to solve the problem:

$$\begin{array}{l} \text{km on trail} \rightarrow \\ \text{cm on map} \rightarrow \end{array} \frac{0.5}{2} = \frac{n}{6.3} \begin{array}{l} \leftarrow \text{km on trail} \\ \leftarrow \text{cm on map} \end{array} \qquad \begin{array}{l} \text{cm on map} \rightarrow \\ \text{cm on map} \rightarrow \end{array} \frac{6.3}{2} = \frac{n}{0.5} \begin{array}{l} \leftarrow \text{km on trail} \\ \leftarrow \text{km on trail} \end{array}$$

Give another proportion that could be used to solve the problem.

208

EXERCISES

1. Copy and complete this table.

Trail	Distance in km
Lodge Trail	1.575
Ridge Trail	?
Powder Trail	?
Devil's Canyon Trail	?
Scenic Trail	?
Hemlock Trail	?

2. How much shorter is the Devil's Canyon Trail than the combined Scenic–Hemlock trails?

3. What is the shortest distance that you can ski from Big Top to the Lodge? What is the longest distance?

4. The gondola lift to Big Top can pick up 24 skiers every 2 minutes. How many skiers can it pick up in 45 minutes?

5. The chair lift can pick up 32 skiers every 3 minutes. Suppose that you were 95th in line. How long would you have to wait for the lift? Round your answer to the nearest tenth of a minute.

★ 6. If the gondola lift to Big Top (see exercise 4) has a $9\frac{1}{2}$-minute waiting time, how many skiers are waiting? Round your answer to the nearest whole number.

Give each product in simplest form.

1. $\frac{3}{8} \times \frac{1}{4}$

2. $\frac{1}{2} \times \frac{2}{3}$

3. $\frac{5}{6} \times \frac{3}{8}$

4. $\frac{7}{4} \times \frac{5}{14}$

5. $\frac{7}{8} \times \frac{8}{7}$

6. $\frac{2}{3} \times \frac{9}{5}$

7. $\frac{5}{9} \times \frac{3}{10}$

8. $\frac{4}{3} \times \frac{4}{3}$

Give each quotient in simplest form.

9. $\frac{2}{3} \div \frac{1}{2}$

10. $\frac{1}{2} \div \frac{2}{3}$

11. $\frac{3}{8} \div \frac{6}{5}$

12. $\frac{5}{9} \div \frac{5}{4}$

13. $\frac{11}{2} \div \frac{3}{4}$

14. $\frac{7}{8} \div \frac{1}{2}$

15. $\frac{5}{8} \div \frac{3}{4}$

16. $\frac{3}{4} \div \frac{5}{6}$

Problem solving

A balanced diet includes food from these categories:

cereals and bread
milk
meat
citrus fruit
potatoes
leafy green and yellow vegetables
other fruit and vegetables
eggs
dried beans, peas, and nuts

The table shows the number of calories (the amount of energy) that some foods provide.

Food	Calories
apple	85
bacon, 2 slices	96
beans, green, $\frac{1}{2}$ cup	15
bread and butter, 1 slice	92
carrot, raw, 1 large	42
cereal, dry, 1 cup, with milk and sugar	205
cheese, American, 1 slice	108
cola, 8-oz glass	105
cookie, chocolate chip	50
egg, fried, 1	108
halibut, broiled, 4 oz	206
ham, 2 slices	248
ice cream, $\frac{2}{3}$ cup	186
milk, whole, 8 oz	160
orange juice, 4 oz	56
pancake, 1, 2 tablespoons of syrup	210
peas, $\frac{1}{2}$ cup	58
pie, fruit, $\frac{1}{6}$ of 9″ pie	400
pork chop, 6 oz	308
spaghetti, meat sauce	396

EXERCISES

Find the number of calories in

1. 9 oz of orange juice.

2. 7 oz of whole milk.

3. 10 oz of cola.

4. $1\frac{1}{2}$ cups of ice cream.

5. How many cups of ice cream make 480 calories? Round your answer to the nearest tenth of a cup.

6. How many calories are in this breakfast?
1 fried egg
2 slices of bacon
1 slice of bread and butter
6 oz of whole milk
6 oz of orange juice

Along with a proper diet, you need to exercise. By exercising, you can "burn off" calories that would otherwise go to a sometimes-unwanted weight gain. The table shows the approximate number of calories "burned off" each minute by different kinds of exercise. (It is based on a 100-pound person.)

Type of Exercise	Calories per Minute
Fast walking	3.5
Bicycling	5.4
Jogging-and-walking	6.3
Jogging	7.1
Swimming	8.2

Round each answer to the nearest tenth.

7. How many calories are used bicycling for 45 minutes?

8. How many calories are used in jogging-and-walking for $1\frac{1}{4}$ hours?

9. How many minutes of swimming are needed to "burn up" 500 calories?

10. Suppose that you ate 3 pancakes with syrup. How many minutes would you have to jog to "burn up" the calories?

11. Suppose that for lunch you had
    1 apple
    1 cheese sandwich
    (2 slices of bread and butter and 2 slices of American cheese)
    10 oz of whole milk
    2 chocolate chip cookies
    How many minutes would you have to walk to burn off the calories? If you averaged 3.5 miles per hour, how far would the lunch "take you"?

★ 12. Suppose that you ate $\frac{1}{4}$ of an 8″ fruit pie. How many minutes would you have to jog to burn off the calories?

CHAPTER CHECKUP

Look at the cards and give the ratio of [pages 196–197]

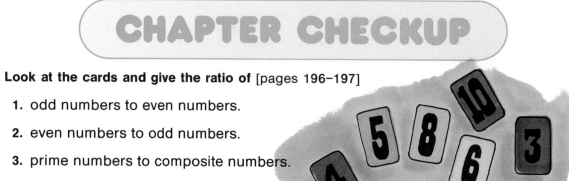

1. odd numbers to even numbers.

2. even numbers to odd numbers.

3. prime numbers to composite numbers.

4. factors of 12 to multiples of 5.

Write each ratio as a fraction in lowest terms. [pages 196–197)

5. $\frac{6}{8}$ 6. $6:9$ 7. 5 to 10   8. $15:12$ 9. 12 to 15

Solve each proportion. [pages 198–200]

10. $\frac{3}{4} = \frac{9}{n}$ 11. $\frac{5}{7} = \frac{n}{35}$ 12. $\frac{3}{8} = \frac{n}{24}$ 13. $\frac{16}{15} = \frac{32}{n}$

14. $\frac{n}{8} = \frac{7}{4}$ 15. $\frac{6}{n} = \frac{2}{9}$ 16. $\frac{n}{12} = \frac{7}{5}$ 17. $\frac{19}{n} = \frac{4}{17}$

Round each solution to the nearest hundredth. [pages 198–200, 206]

18. $\frac{n}{13} = \frac{9}{3}$ 19. $\frac{23}{n} = \frac{6}{11}$ 20. $\frac{13}{7} = \frac{n}{5}$ 21. $\frac{9}{22} = \frac{7}{n}$

Solve by using a proportion. [pages 202–205, 207, 210–211]

22. A model of a train is built to a scale of 1:80. The model engine is 20 cm long. How long is the actual engine?

23. The scale on a map is 2 cm:7.5 km. How far apart are two cities that are 16.5 cm apart on the map?

24. A junior-high class collected 2450 aluminum cans in 4 days. At that rate, how many cans would the class collect in 10 days?

25. A bicyclist rode 35 km in 2.4 hours. At that rate, how many km would he ride in 3.5 hours? Round your answer to the nearest km.

CHAPTER PROJECT

How much does a thumbtack weigh?

1. Notice that 14 thumbtacks balance 5 grams.
   To answer the question, solve this proportion:

$$\text{number of tacks} \rightarrow \frac{14}{5} = \frac{1}{n} \leftarrow \text{number of tacks}$$
$$\text{number of grams} \rightarrow \qquad\quad \leftarrow \text{number of grams}$$

Round your answer to the nearest hundredth of a gram.

2. Use the method shown above to find the weight of one

   a. small paper clip.   **b.** large paper clip.
   c. straight pin.   **d.** paper staple.

3. Use the method to determine the weight of some other small objects.

CHAPTER REVIEW

The ratio of blue cards to red cards is

$$\frac{2}{3} \leftarrow \text{blue}$$
$$\phantom{\frac{2}{3}} \leftarrow \text{red}$$

$$\frac{5}{8} = \frac{3}{n}$$
$$5n = 8 \times 3$$
$$5n = 24$$
$$n = \frac{24}{5}$$
$$n = 4\frac{4}{5}$$

A jogger ran 15 km in 2 hours. At that rate, how far could she run in 3.5 hours?

$$\begin{array}{l} \text{distance} \rightarrow \\ \text{time} \rightarrow \end{array} \frac{15}{2} = \frac{n}{3.5} \begin{array}{l} \leftarrow \text{distance} \\ \leftarrow \text{time} \end{array}$$
$$2n = 15 \times 3.5$$
$$2n = 52.5$$
$$n = 26.25$$

Answer: 26.25 km

Give each ratio.

1. yellow cards to green cards

2. green cards to yellow cards

3. vowels to consonants

4. consonants to vowels

Solve each proportion.

5. $\frac{4}{5} = \frac{12}{n}$

6. $\frac{5}{4} = \frac{n}{10}$

7. $\frac{35}{n} = \frac{5}{100}$

8. $\frac{n}{50} = \frac{3}{100}$

9. $\frac{3}{7} = \frac{n}{50}$

10. $\frac{4}{5} = \frac{25}{n}$

Solve.

11. An airplane flew 1820 km in 2.5 hours. At that rate, how far did it fly in 1 hour?

12. A racing car traveled 532 km in 2 hours. At that rate, how long would it take to travel 800 km?

13. The ratio of boys to girls in a certain school is $\frac{5}{6}$. If there are 420 girls, how many boys are there?

14. A recipe for Orange Fizz calls for 1.5 liters of ginger ale to 3 liters of orange juice. How much ginger ale is needed for 2.5 liters of orange juice?

214

Ratios can describe the shapes of rectangles. In this "thin" rectangle, the ratio of width to length is 1 : 6.

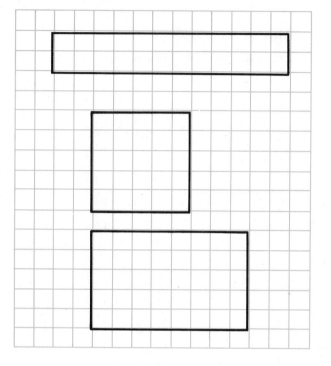

In the "fattest" rectangle (which is a square) the ratio of width to length is 1 : 1.

The ancient Greeks considered a rectangle shaped like this one as the most pleasing to the eye. It is called a *golden rectangle,* and the ratio of its width to its length is about 1 : 1.618.

1. Study this pattern of rectangles. The second rectangle was made by adding a square to the first square. The third rectangle was made by adding a square to the second rectangle. And so on.

2. Get a piece of graph paper. Copy the rectangles and continue the pattern.

3. Compute the ratio of width to length for each rectangle. Are any of your ratios close to the golden ratio of 1 : 1.618?

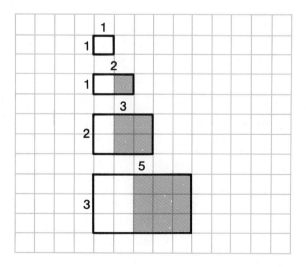

a b c d   a b c d   a b c d   a b c d   a b c d   a b c

2. ☐ ☐ ☐ ☐   ☐ ☐ ☐ ☐   5. ☐ ☐ ☐ ☐   6. ☐ ☐ ☐ ☐

a b c d   a b c d   a b c d   a b c

MAJOR CHECKUP
STANDARDIZED FORMAT

8. ☐ ☐ ☐ ☐   9. ☐ ☐ ☐ ☐   10. ☐ ☐ ☐ ☐   11. ☐ ☐ ☐ ☐   12. ☐ ☐ ☐ ☐

Choose the correct letter.

1. 9.9982 rounded to the nearest tenth is

- **a.** 9.9
- **b.** 9.10
- **c.** 10.0
- **d.** none of these

2. Multiply.

$$4.02 \\ \times 30.8$$

- **a.** 12.3816
- **b.** 1.5816
- **c.** 1.5276
- **d.** none of these

3. Solve.

$$4a + 6 = 14$$

- **a.** 5
- **b.** 20
- **c.** 2
- **d.** none of these

4. 5.2 L = _?_ mL

- **a.** 0.052
- **b.** 5200
- **c.** 520
- **d.** none of these

5. Give the difference.

$$\frac{5}{3} - \frac{1}{2}$$

- **a.** 4
- **b.** $1\frac{1}{6}$
- **c.** $\frac{2}{3}$
- **d.** none of these

6. Give the product.

$$1\frac{3}{4} \times 2\frac{4}{5}$$

- **a.** $4\frac{9}{10}$
- **b.** $4\frac{11}{20}$
- **c.** $\frac{5}{8}$
- **d.** none of these

7. Find the area. Use 3.14 for π.

10 m

- **a.** 31.4 m²
- **b.** 314 m²
- **c.** 62.8 m²
- **d.** none of these

8. Find the volume.

2 cm
4 cm
5 cm

- **a.** 76 cm³
- **b.** 40 cm³
- **c.** 11 cm³
- **d.** none of these

9. The ratio of consonants to vowels in the word NUMBER is

- **a.** 2 : 1
- **b.** 2 : 4
- **c.** 4 : 6
- **d.** none of these

10. Solve.

$$\frac{3}{8} = \frac{x}{100}$$

- **a.** 37.5
- **b.** $266\frac{2}{3}$
- **c.** 0.24
- **d.** none of these

11. There are 120 people. Of these, $\frac{2}{3}$ like baseball. How many do not like baseball?

- **a.** 80
- **b.** 90
- **c.** 40
- **d.** none of these

12. 1 cm on a map stands for 0.5 km. What length does 8 cm on the map stand for?

- **a.** 4 km
- **b.** 16 km
- **c.** 40 km
- **d.** none of these

25 % off

20% off

1. $\dfrac{3}{5} = \dfrac{x}{100}$

2. $\dfrac{x}{45} = \dfrac{40}{100}$

3. $\dfrac{40}{x} = \dfrac{125}{100}$

4. $\dfrac{18}{n} = \dfrac{37\frac{1}{2}}{100}$

5. $\dfrac{2}{3} = \dfrac{x}{100}$

6. $\dfrac{x}{36} = \dfrac{25}{100}$

7. $\dfrac{x}{24} = \dfrac{75}{100}$

8. $\dfrac{5}{6} = \dfrac{x}{100}$

9. $\dfrac{12}{x} = \dfrac{33\frac{1}{3}}{100}$

10. $\dfrac{x}{72} = \dfrac{12\frac{1}{2}}{100}$

Changing a percent to a fraction

The Emerson School Pep Club has a 100-member card section at its home basketball game. To make this E, 42% (42 percent) of the cards are red. *Percent* means "hundredths."

$$42\% = \frac{42}{100}$$

To change from a percent to a fraction, mixed number, or whole number, you can first write the percent as a fraction with a denominator of 100. Then you can write the fraction in simplest form.

$$10\% = \frac{10}{100} = \frac{1}{10}$$

$$42\% = \frac{42}{100} = \frac{21}{50}$$

$$150\% = \frac{150}{100} = 1\frac{1}{2}$$

$$100\% = \frac{100}{100} = 1$$

EXERCISES

Change to a fraction, mixed number, or whole number.

1. 20%	2. 300%	3. 10%	4. 60%	5. 96%
6. 120%	7. 65%	8. 600%	9. 25%	10. 68%
11. 800%	12. 150%	13. 500%	14. 75%	15. 160%
16. 175%	17. 900%	18. 12%	19. 50%	20. 1000%
21. 95%	22. 14%	23. 200%	24. 125%	25. 400%
26. 700%	27. 90%	28. 30%	29. 115%	30. 1200%

Change to a fraction or mixed number in simplest form.

Example. Multiply by $\frac{10}{10}$ to get whole numbers.

$$37.5\% = \frac{37.5}{100}$$

$$= \frac{375}{1000}$$

$$= \frac{3}{8}$$

31. 7.5%	32. 12.5%	33. 0.1%	34. 0.5%
35. 6.25%	36. 93.75%	37. 2.5%	38. 18.75%
39. 87.5%	40. 8.25%	41. 262.5%	42. 137.5%

Change to a fraction or mixed number in simplest form.

Example.

$$16\frac{2}{3}\% = \frac{16\frac{2}{3}}{100}$$

$$= \frac{\frac{50}{3}}{\frac{100}{1}} \leftarrow \text{Write as a complex fraction.}$$

$$= \frac{\overset{1}{\cancel{50}}}{3} \times \frac{1}{\underset{2}{\cancel{100}}}$$

$$= \frac{1}{6}$$

43. $14\frac{1}{7}\%$	44. $5\frac{1}{2}\%$	45. $2\frac{1}{2}\%$
46. $33\frac{1}{3}\%$	47. $41\frac{2}{3}\%$	48. $37\frac{1}{2}\%$
49. $62\frac{1}{2}\%$	50. $12\frac{1}{2}\%$	51. $66\frac{2}{3}\%$
52. $16\frac{2}{3}\%$	53. $81\frac{1}{4}\%$	54. $87\frac{1}{2}\%$
55. $6\frac{1}{4}\%$	56. $166\frac{2}{3}\%$	57. $137\frac{1}{2}\%$

219

Changing a fraction to a percent

Andrew got $\frac{3}{4}$ of the problems correct on a math test.

Here is how to change the fraction to a percent:

First change to an equivalent fraction with a denominator of 100. Then write as a percent.

$$\frac{3}{4} = \frac{75}{100}$$
$$= 75\%$$

Andrew got 75% of the problems correct.

To change some fractions to a percent, you may need to solve a proportion.

EXAMPLE 1.

$$\frac{7}{8} = \frac{?}{100} \qquad \frac{7}{8} = \frac{x}{100}$$

$$8x = 700$$

$$x = 87\frac{1}{2}$$

So, $\frac{7}{8} = \frac{87\frac{1}{2}}{100}$

$$= 87\frac{1}{2}\%$$

EXAMPLE 2.

$$\frac{1}{240} = \frac{?}{100} \qquad \frac{1}{240} = \frac{x}{100}$$

$$240x = 100$$

$$x = \frac{100}{240}$$

$$x = \frac{5}{12}$$

So, $\frac{1}{240} = \frac{\frac{5}{12}}{100}$

$$= \frac{5}{12}\%$$

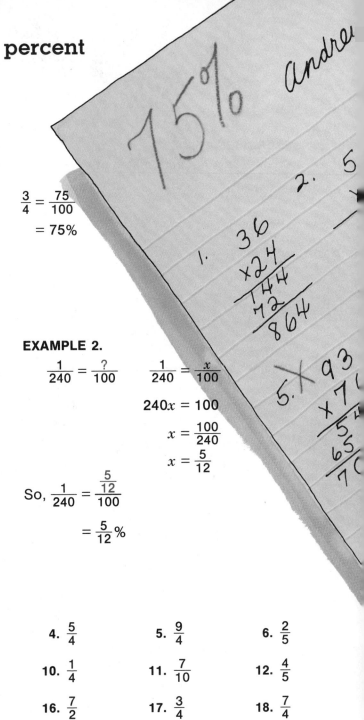

EXERCISES

Change to a percent.

1. $\frac{1}{2}$ 2. $\frac{9}{10}$ 3. $\frac{3}{5}$ 4. $\frac{5}{4}$ 5. $\frac{9}{4}$ 6. $\frac{2}{5}$

7. 1   8. $\frac{1}{5}$ 9. $\frac{1}{10}$ 10. $\frac{1}{4}$ 11. $\frac{7}{10}$ 12. $\frac{4}{5}$

13. 2   14. $\frac{3}{2}$ 15. $\frac{6}{5}$ 16. $\frac{7}{2}$ 17. $\frac{3}{4}$ 18. $\frac{7}{4}$

19. $\frac{9}{50}$ 20. $\frac{13}{20}$ 21. $\frac{3}{25}$ 22. $\frac{9}{20}$ 23. $\frac{7}{25}$ 24. $\frac{13}{50}$

Change to a percent by solving a proportion.

25. $\frac{1}{3}$ 26. $\frac{1}{6}$ 27. $\frac{1}{8}$ 28. $\frac{9}{16}$ 29. $\frac{4}{3}$

30. $\frac{5}{9}$ 31. $\frac{5}{12}$ 32. $\frac{3}{8}$ 33. $\frac{2}{3}$ 34. $\frac{1}{9}$

35. $\frac{5}{3}$ 36. $\frac{5}{6}$ 37. $\frac{11}{8}$ 38. $\frac{17}{12}$ 39. $\frac{2}{7}$

Complete.

40. If $\frac{1}{8} = 12\frac{1}{2}\%$, then $\frac{2}{8} = \underline{\ ?\ }\%$.

41. If $\frac{1}{9} = 11\frac{1}{9}\%$, then $\frac{5}{9} = \underline{\ ?\ }\%$.

42. If $\frac{1}{11} = 9\frac{1}{11}\%$, then $\frac{3}{11} = \underline{\ ?\ }\%$.

43. If $\frac{1}{6} = 16\frac{2}{3}\%$, then $\frac{2}{6} = \underline{\ ?\ }\%$.

44. If $\frac{1}{100} = 1\%$, then $\frac{1}{200} = \underline{\ ?\ }\%$.

The class results of the mathematics test are shown on the bar graph.

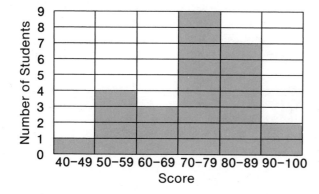

45. How many students took the test?

46. What percent of the students got a test score in the 80's?

47. What percent scored below 70?

48. What percent scored 80 or above?

49. What fraction of the students scored below 60?

50. What fraction scored in the 60's?

Give each sum in simplest form.

1. $\frac{1}{8} + \frac{3}{8}$

2. $\frac{1}{9} + \frac{1}{3}$

3. $\frac{3}{4} + \frac{1}{8}$

4. $\frac{3}{4} + \frac{3}{2}$

5. $\frac{5}{6} + \frac{2}{3}$

6. $\frac{7}{8} + \frac{5}{6}$

7. $\frac{3}{4} + \frac{4}{3}$

8. $1 + \frac{1}{3}$

9. $\frac{4}{5} + 2$

10. $\frac{5}{4} + \frac{5}{6}$

11. $\frac{2}{3} + 3$

12. $\frac{1}{2} + \frac{1}{3}$

13. $\frac{7}{8} + \frac{1}{4}$

14. $\frac{3}{5} + \frac{2}{3}$

15. $\frac{5}{6} + \frac{3}{4}$

16. $\frac{6}{5} + \frac{2}{3}$

Decimals and percents

These examples show how to change a decimal to a percent.

$0.24 = \dfrac{24}{100}$ $0.6 = \dfrac{60}{100}$ $0.66\tfrac{2}{3} = \dfrac{66\tfrac{2}{3}}{100}$

$ = 24\%$ $ = 60\%$ $\phantom{0.66\tfrac{2}{3}} = 66\tfrac{2}{3}\%$

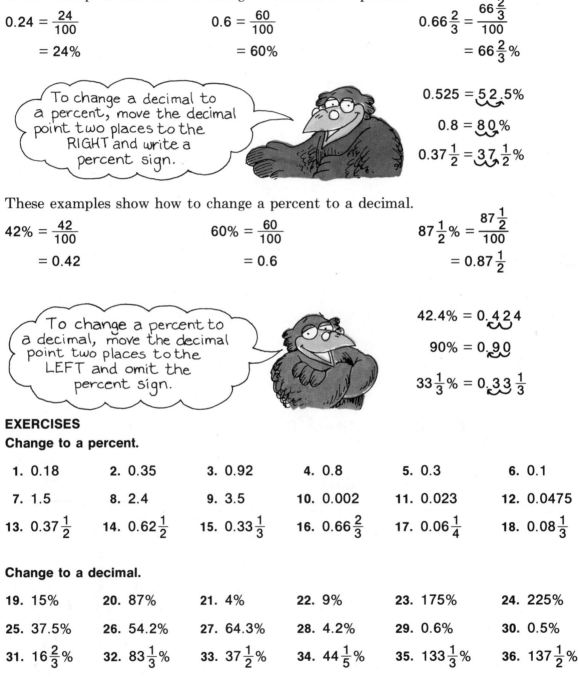

To change a decimal to a percent, move the decimal point two places to the RIGHT and write a percent sign.

$0.525 = 52.5\%$

$0.8 = 80\%$

$0.37\tfrac{1}{2} = 37\tfrac{1}{2}\%$

These examples show how to change a percent to a decimal.

$42\% = \dfrac{42}{100}$ $60\% = \dfrac{60}{100}$ $87\tfrac{1}{2}\% = \dfrac{87\tfrac{1}{2}}{100}$

$ = 0.42$ $ = 0.6$ $\phantom{87\tfrac{1}{2}\%} = 0.87\tfrac{1}{2}$

To change a percent to a decimal, move the decimal point two places to the LEFT and omit the percent sign.

$42.4\% = 0.424$

$90\% = 0.90$

$33\tfrac{1}{3}\% = 0.33\tfrac{1}{3}$

EXERCISES
Change to a percent.

1. 0.18	2. 0.35	3. 0.92	4. 0.8	5. 0.3	6. 0.1
7. 1.5	8. 2.4	9. 3.5	10. 0.002	11. 0.023	12. 0.0475
13. $0.37\tfrac{1}{2}$	14. $0.62\tfrac{1}{2}$	15. $0.33\tfrac{1}{3}$	16. $0.66\tfrac{2}{3}$	17. $0.06\tfrac{1}{4}$	18. $0.08\tfrac{1}{3}$

Change to a decimal.

19. 15%	20. 87%	21. 4%	22. 9%	23. 175%	24. 225%
25. 37.5%	26. 54.2%	27. 64.3%	28. 4.2%	29. 0.6%	30. 0.5%
31. $16\tfrac{2}{3}\%$	32. $83\tfrac{1}{3}\%$	33. $37\tfrac{1}{2}\%$	34. $44\tfrac{1}{5}\%$	35. $133\tfrac{1}{3}\%$	36. $137\tfrac{1}{2}\%$

In this game you must be able to tell whether two numbers are equal. These exercises will give you some practice.

Equal (=) or not equal (≠)?

1. $\frac{1}{6}$ ⬤ 0.2

2. $83\frac{1}{3}\%$ ⬤ 0.8

3. $\frac{5}{6}$ ⬤ $\frac{3}{4}$

4. 25% ⬤ 0.2

5. 40% ⬤ $\frac{2}{5}$

6. $\frac{1}{6}$ ⬤ $0.12\frac{1}{2}$

7. 60% ⬤ $\frac{5}{8}$

8. $37\frac{1}{2}\%$ ⬤ $\frac{3}{8}$

Here is how to play the game.

1. Make cards for these numbers.

   $\frac{1}{2}$, 0.5, 50%, $\frac{1}{3}$, $0.33\frac{1}{3}$, $33\frac{1}{3}\%$, $\frac{2}{3}$, $0.66\frac{2}{3}$, $66\frac{2}{3}\%$, $\frac{1}{4}$, 0.25, 25%

   $\frac{3}{4}$, 0.75, 75%, $\frac{1}{5}$, 0.2, 20%, $\frac{2}{5}$, 0.4, 40%, $\frac{3}{5}$, 0.6, 60%

   $\frac{4}{5}$, 0.8, 80%, $\frac{1}{6}$, $0.16\frac{2}{3}$, $16\frac{2}{3}\%$, $\frac{5}{6}$, $0.83\frac{1}{3}$, $83\frac{1}{3}\%$, $\frac{1}{8}$, $0.12\frac{1}{2}$, $12\frac{1}{2}\%$

   $\frac{3}{8}$, $0.37\frac{1}{2}$, $37\frac{1}{2}\%$, $\frac{5}{8}$, $0.62\frac{1}{2}$, $62\frac{1}{2}\%$, $\frac{7}{8}$, $0.87\frac{1}{2}$, $87\frac{1}{2}\%$

2. A game leader divides the class into two teams and picks a player from each team.

3. The game leader shuffles the deck and slowly places the cards on the chalktray, one at a time. A player who sees two numbers that are equal says "match" and identifies the cards. If the player is correct, that team earns a point. If incorrect, that team loses a point.

4. The matched cards are set aside, and play continues with two new players.

5. The team earning the greater number of points wins.

Finding a percent of a number

In a survey of a class of 36 students, it was found that 25% earned more than $10 a week. To find how many students earned more than $10, we can solve this equation:

$$25\% \text{ of } 36 = n$$

Here are 3 ways to find the solution:

1 Change the percent to a fraction and multiply.

$$25\% \text{ of } 36 = \frac{1}{\cancel{4}} \times \cancel{36}^{9}$$
$$= 9$$

2 Change the percent to a decimal and multiply.

$$25\% \text{ of } 36 = 0.25 \times 36$$
$$= 9$$

$$\begin{array}{r} 36 \\ \times 0.25 \\ \hline 180 \\ 72 \\ \hline 9.00 \end{array}$$

3 Solve a proportion.

$$25\% \text{ of } 36 = n$$
$$\frac{25}{100} = \frac{n}{36}$$
$$100n = 900$$
$$n = 9$$

Look for the easiest method to solve percent problems. The method you pick will depend on the numbers in the problem.

EXERCISES

Solve by changing the percent to a fraction and multiplying.

1. 50% of 30 = n

2. 25% of 24 = n

3. 75% of 48 = n

4. 40% of 45 = n

5. 150% of 18 = n

6. 100% of 32 = n

7. 60% of 30 = n

8. 200% of 14 = n

9. 5% of 40 = n

10. 10% of 80 = n

11. $33\frac{1}{3}$% of 21 = n

12. $66\frac{2}{3}$% of 27 = n

Solve by changing the percent to a decimal and multiplying.

13. 14% of 32 = n

14. 42% of 53 = n

15. 23% of 75 = n

16. 19% of 29 = n

17. 18% of 64 = n

18. 36% of 83 = n

19. 5.2% of 95 = n

20. 6.5% of 115 = n

21. 7.3% of 142 = n

22. 0.88% of 315 = n

23. 0.92% of 250 = n

24. 1.30% of 432 = n

Solve by solving a proportion. Round answers to the nearest hundredth.

25. $5\frac{1}{3}$% of 80 = n

26. $3\frac{3}{4}$% of 64 = n

27. $6\frac{1}{2}$% of 75 = n

28. $7\frac{2}{3}$% of 152 = n

29. $6\frac{3}{4}$% of 125 = n

30. $5\frac{1}{2}$% of 248 = n

31. $12\frac{1}{3}$% of 225 = n

32. $10\frac{3}{8}$% of 358 = n

33. $11\frac{2}{3}$% of 465 = n

Below are some more facts found in the survey of the 36 students. Write and solve an equation.

34. 50% had record collections. How many had record collections?

35. 75% had radios. How many had radios?

36. $33\frac{1}{3}$% had regular chores at home. How many had regular chores?

37. $16\frac{2}{3}$% had coin collections. How many had coin collections?

38. $11\frac{1}{9}$% saved stamps. How many saved stamps?

39. $77\frac{7}{9}$% received weekly allowances. How many received weekly allowances?

Finding the number
when a percent is known

60% of the Sonoma Junior High School band are boys. There are 30 boys in the junior high band. How many are in the band altogether?

$$60\% \text{ of } n = 30$$

Here are three ways to solve the equation.

1 Change the percent to a fraction and divide.

$$\frac{\frac{3}{5}n}{\frac{3}{5}} = \frac{30}{\frac{3}{5}}$$

$$n = 50$$

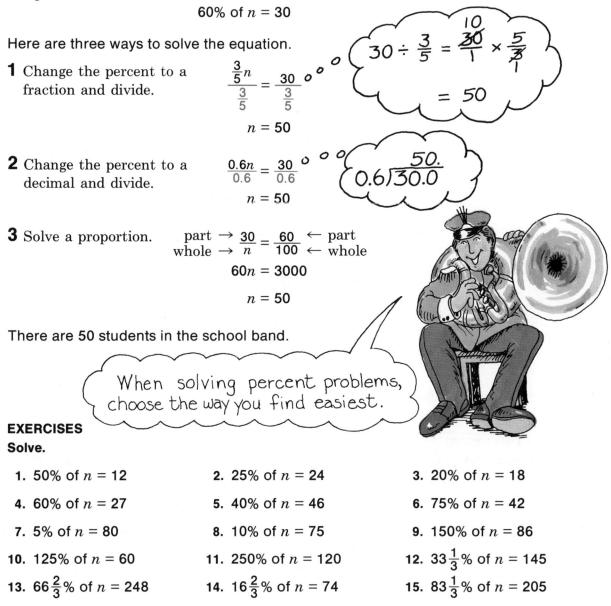

$$30 \div \frac{3}{5} = \frac{\overset{10}{\cancel{30}}}{1} \times \frac{5}{\cancel{3}} = 50$$

2 Change the percent to a decimal and divide.

$$\frac{0.6n}{0.6} = \frac{30}{0.6}$$

$$n = 50$$

$$0.6\overline{)30.0}^{50.}$$

3 Solve a proportion.

$$\begin{array}{l}\text{part} \rightarrow \\ \text{whole} \rightarrow\end{array}\frac{30}{n} = \frac{60}{100}\begin{array}{l}\leftarrow \text{part}\\ \leftarrow \text{whole}\end{array}$$

$$60n = 3000$$

$$n = 50$$

There are 50 students in the school band.

When solving percent problems, choose the way you find easiest.

EXERCISES
Solve.

1. 50% of $n = 12$

2. 25% of $n = 24$

3. 20% of $n = 18$

4. 60% of $n = 27$

5. 40% of $n = 46$

6. 75% of $n = 42$

7. 5% of $n = 80$

8. 10% of $n = 75$

9. 150% of $n = 86$

10. 125% of $n = 60$

11. 250% of $n = 120$

12. $33\frac{1}{3}\%$ of $n = 145$

13. $66\frac{2}{3}\%$ of $n = 248$

14. $16\frac{2}{3}\%$ of $n = 74$

15. $83\frac{1}{3}\%$ of $n = 205$

226

Solve.

16. 30% of $n = 15$
17. 45% of $n = 90$
18. 36% of $n = 9$

19. 72% of $n = 18$
20. 15% of $n = 45$
21. 48% of $n = 12$

22. 53% of $n = 53$
23. 56% of $n = 63$
24. 56% of $n = 56$

25. 78% of $n = 42.9$
26. 55% of $n = 40.7$
27. 79% of $n = 7.9$

28. 84% of $n = 96.6$
29. 90% of $n = 50.4$
30. 8.32% of $n = 6.24$

31. 8.5% of $n = 5.27$
32. 7.3% of $n = 4.672$
33. 6.25% of $n = 5.875$

34. $83\frac{1}{3}$% of $n = 60$
35. $62\frac{1}{2}$% of $n = 60$
36. $37\frac{1}{2}$% of $n = 60$

Solve.

37. A TV set sells for $480. A down payment of $33\frac{1}{3}$% of the cost was made. How much was the down payment?

38. Dotty was at bat 256 times during the season. She got a hit 25% of the time. How many times did she get a hit?

39. Iona read 40% of a book having 350 pages. How many pages did she have left to read?

40. Bill bought a bicycle for $126.90. This was $66\frac{2}{3}$% of the regular selling price. What was the regular selling price?

41. Henry spends 80% of his weekly allowance of $6 for lunches. How much does he spend on lunch each week?

42. A bicyclist rode $37\frac{1}{2}$% of a 56-kilometer bicycle tour and then took a break. How many kilometers did the cyclist ride before taking a break?

43. Karen made a 25% down payment of $130 on a stereo set. What was the cost of the stereo set?

44. In a school of 824 students, $62\frac{1}{2}$% ride a bus to school. How many students ride the bus to school?

45. 80% of the students in one class walk to school. 24 students in that class walk to school. How many students are in the class?

46. One type of camera sold for $18.50. This was 60% of the regular cost. What was the regular price?

47. 7.25% of $n = 35.4$
48. $9\frac{1}{2}$% of $n = \$57.60$
49. $12\frac{3}{4}$% of $n = \$160.50$

Mental computation with percents

EXAMPLE 1. You can find 10% or 1% of a number by "moving" the decimal point.

$$1\% \text{ of } 168.3 = 1.683 \qquad 10\% \text{ of } 168.3 = 16.83$$

EXAMPLE 2. You can find some percents of numbers by simple division.

$$\left(\frac{1}{4}\right) 25\% \text{ of } 84 = \frac{84}{4} \qquad \left(\frac{1}{3}\right) 33\frac{1}{3}\% \text{ of } 90 = \frac{90}{3}$$
$$= 21 \qquad\qquad\qquad = 30$$

> There are several shortcuts for computing with percents.

EXAMPLE 3. Here are some other special cases:

$$5\% \text{ of } 72 = \frac{1}{2} \text{ of } 10\% \text{ of } 72 \qquad\qquad 15\% \text{ of } 72 = 10\% \text{ of } 72 + 5\% \text{ of } 72$$
$$= \frac{1}{2} \text{ of } 7.2 \qquad\qquad\qquad\qquad = 7.2 + 3.6$$
$$= 3.6 \qquad\qquad\qquad\qquad\qquad = 10.8$$

EXERCISES
Complete. Do not use paper and pencil.

1. 10% of 58 = _?_

2. 1% of 58 = _?_

3. 10% of 6.23 = _?_

4. 1% of 6.23 = _?_

5. 20% of 85 = _?_

6. 20% of $9.20 = _?_

7. 50% of 4.6 = _?_

8. 50% of $8.30 = _?_

9. $33\frac{1}{3}\%$ of 123 = _?_

10. $33\frac{1}{3}\%$ of 66 = _?_

11. $33\frac{1}{3}\%$ of $4.50 = _?_

12. 25% of 0.44 = _?_

13. 25% of $10.80 = _?_

14. 5% of 88 = _?_

15. 5% of $2.60 = _?_

16. 15% of 60 = _?_

17. 15% of $8.20 = _?_

18. $66\frac{2}{3}\%$ of $12 = _?_

19. 75% of 40 = _?_

20. 1.5% of 80 = _?_

21. 1.5% of 600 = _?_

22. When Carol is satisfied with the service in a restaurant, she tips the waiter 15% of the cost of her meal. What would be the tip for each of these amounts?

   a. $6.00

   b. $12.40

   c. $8.45

PRACTICE EXERCISES

Change to a fraction in lowest terms.

1. 20% 2. 60% 3. 25% 4. 85% 5. 75% 6. 140%

7. $12\frac{1}{2}\%$ 8. $33\frac{1}{3}\%$ 9. $16\frac{2}{3}\%$ 10. $37\frac{1}{2}\%$ 11. $62\frac{1}{2}\%$ 12. $83\frac{1}{3}\%$

Change to a percent.

13. $\frac{3}{4}$ 14. $\frac{1}{2}$ 15. $\frac{4}{5}$ 16. $\frac{5}{4}$ 17. $\frac{8}{5}$ 18. $\frac{5}{2}$

19. $\frac{1}{8}$ 20. $\frac{5}{8}$ 21. $\frac{5}{6}$ 22. $\frac{7}{8}$ 23. $\frac{5}{12}$ 24. $\frac{9}{16}$

Change to a decimal.

25. 30% 26. 90% 27. 65% 28. 5% 29. 0.8% 30. 16.5%

31. $8\frac{1}{3}\%$ 32. $66\frac{2}{3}\%$ 33. $91\frac{2}{3}\%$ 34. $8\frac{2}{3}\%$ 35. $7\frac{3}{4}\%$ 36. $9\frac{2}{3}\%$

Solve.

37. 8% of 50 = m 38. 25% of 64 = s 39. $33\frac{1}{3}\%$ of 78 = p

40. 20% of 25 = u 41. 200% of 18 = w 42. 40% of 56 = r

43. $87\frac{1}{2}\%$ of 64 = x 44. $112\frac{1}{2}\%$ of 100 = q 45. 0.5% of 70 = v

46. $66\frac{2}{3}\%$ of 96 = t 47. $37\frac{1}{2}\%$ of 140 = y 48. 150% of 66 = n

Solve.

49. 50% of x = 17 50. 75% of x = 18 51. 20% of x = 35

52. 120% of x = 42 53. 45% of x = 18 54. $33\frac{1}{3}\%$ of x = 18

55. $37\frac{1}{2}\%$ of x = 48 56. 0.8% of x = 20 57. 0.1% of x = 60

58. $66\frac{2}{3}\%$ of x = 44 59. $44\frac{4}{9}\%$ of x = 64 60. $112\frac{1}{2}\%$ of x = 54

Finding the percent

Mary set up this aquarium. 4 of the 12 fish she bought are swordtails. To find the percent of swordtails, we can change this fraction (ratio) to a percent:

$$\text{swordtails} \longrightarrow \frac{4}{12} = \frac{1}{3}$$
$$\text{total fish bought} \rightarrow$$

$$= 0.33\frac{1}{3} \qquad 3\overline{)1.00}^{\,0.33\frac{1}{3}}$$

$$= 33\frac{1}{3}\%$$

So $33\frac{1}{3}\%$ of the fish are swordtails.

guppy

We could also find the percent by solving this proportion:

$$\frac{4}{12} = \frac{x}{100}$$
$$12x = 400$$
$$x = 33\frac{1}{3}$$

So $33\frac{1}{3}\%$ of the fish are swordtails.

angelfish

swordtail

catfish

EXERCISES
Solve by changing a fraction to a percent.

$\{$whole$\}$ $\{$part$\}$

1. $n\%$ of $18 = 12$

$$\begin{array}{l} \text{part} \longrightarrow \dfrac{12}{18} = \dfrac{2}{3} \\ \text{whole} \end{array}$$

$$= 0.66\tfrac{2}{3}$$

$$= ?\%$$

2. $n\%$ of $20 = 15$

$$\dfrac{15}{20} = \dfrac{3}{4}$$

$$= 0.75$$

$$= ?\%$$

3. $n\%$ of $16 = 10$

4. $n\%$ of $24 = 20$

5. $n\%$ of $42 = 21$

6. $n\%$ of $72 = 54$

Round answers to the nearest tenth of a percent.

7. $n\%$ of $65 = 18$

8. $n\%$ of $54 = 42$

Solve by solving a proportion. Round answers to the nearest tenth of a percent.

9. $n\%$ of $45 = 23$

10. $n\%$ of $64 = 28$

11. $n\%$ of $38 = 42$

12. $n\%$ of $75 = 92$

13. $n\%$ of $67 = 50$

14. $n\%$ of $118 = 75$

15. $n\%$ of $93 = 40$

16. $n\%$ of $236 = 156$

Solve. Give the percent of fish on page 230 that are

17. catfish.

18. guppies.

19. angelfish.

20. not swordtails.

21. Mary bought a filter and pump that regularly sold for $18.75 for 20% off. What was the sale price?

22. Mary learned that for each 5 centimeters of fish (body length), 8 liters of water are needed. Her aquarium holds 38 liters of water. How many centimeters of fish are the limit?

KEEPING SKILLS
SHARP

Give each difference in simplest form.

1. $\dfrac{7}{8} - \dfrac{3}{8}$

2. $\dfrac{5}{9} - \dfrac{1}{3}$

3. $\dfrac{5}{6} - \dfrac{2}{3}$

4. $\dfrac{7}{8} - \dfrac{3}{4}$

5. $\dfrac{7}{6} - \dfrac{5}{8}$

6. $\dfrac{6}{5} - \dfrac{5}{6}$

7. $1 - \dfrac{3}{8}$

8. $\dfrac{3}{2} - 1$

9. $\dfrac{5}{6} - \dfrac{3}{4}$

10. $\dfrac{7}{9} - \dfrac{1}{6}$

11. $\dfrac{3}{4} - \dfrac{2}{3}$

12. $\dfrac{3}{5} - \dfrac{1}{3}$

13. $\dfrac{3}{2} - \dfrac{5}{8}$

14. $\dfrac{7}{4} - 1$

15. $\dfrac{7}{6} - \dfrac{5}{9}$

16. $\dfrac{5}{3} - \dfrac{5}{4}$

Estimating with percents

Karen Daley won the election with about $\frac{2}{3}$ of the vote. The actual percentage of the vote was 65.2%.

$$65.2\% \approx \frac{2}{3}$$

We often use fraction approximations for percents.

ELECTION RESULTS FOR CLASS PRESIDENT
KAREN DALEY 65.2%
DANIEL HOLWAY 34.8%

EXERCISES
Choose the best approximation.

1. 34.8% of the voters voted no.
   a. About $\frac{1}{3}$ of the voters voted no.
   b. About $\frac{1}{4}$ of the voters voted no.
   c. About 1 out of 5 voters voted no.

2. Carol scored 47% of her team's points.
   a. Carol scored about $\frac{4}{7}$ of the points.
   b. Carol scored about $\frac{2}{5}$ of the points.
   c. Carol scored about 1 out of every 2 points.

3. 98% of all homes have a TV set.
   a. Almost every home has a TV set.
   b. About $\frac{4}{5}$ of the homes have a TV set.
   c. Some homes have 2 TV sets.

4. 12% of the students got an A.
   a. About $\frac{1}{6}$ of the students got an A.
   b. About 12 students got an A.
   c. About 1 out of every 10 students got an A.

5. Sale: 55% off
   a. Sale: prices reduced by almost half
   b. Sale: less than half price
   c. Sale: $55 off

6. 30% chance of rain
   a. There's 1 chance in 3 it will rain.
   b. Chances are 1 in 4 that it will rain.
   c. It is almost certain to rain.

Estimate.

Example.

19% of 80 = _?_

19% is near 20%

20% of 80 = 16

So, 19% of 80 is a little less than 16.

7. 26% of 60 = _?_

8. 48% of 168 = _?_

9. 31% of $1.47 = _?_

10. 12% of 286.52 = _?_

11. 34% of $6.93 = _?_

12. 53% of $268.40 = _?_

13. 73% of 80 = _?_

14. 97% of 53 = _?_

15. 29% of $700 = _?_

16. 65% of $900 = _?_

Example.

_?_ % of 26 is 12

12 is 50% of 24

So, 12 is a little less than 50% of 26.

17. _?_ % of 42 = 10

18. _?_ % of 59 = 6

19. _?_ % of 13 = 8

20. _?_ % of 31 = 3

21. _?_ % of 31 = 4

22. _?_ % of 49 = 11

23. _?_ % of $250 = $47

24. _?_ % of 61 = 19

25. _?_ % of $10.03 = $.99

26. _?_ % of 99 = 23

Estimate.

27. Altogether, 4572 voters voted in the special election and 65.2% voted yes. How many voted yes?

28. Only 28% of the eligible voters voted in the special election. How many eligible voters were there?

29. The mayor of a small city was elected with 57.2% of the votes. The total number of votes was 29,156. How many voted for the winner?

30. One of the candidates for office received only 9.6% of the 57,436 votes cast. How many votes did he receive?

31. **WATCH OUT!**

Grandpa bought a $61 watch. He paid for it with five bills. He did not use one-dollar bills. What bills did he use?

Percent of increase or decrease

A year ago Mike weighed 102 pounds. His high school sets 105 pounds as the minimum weight for joining the school wrestling team. Since then he has gained 8 pounds. To find the **percent of increase,** we express the ratio given below as a percent:

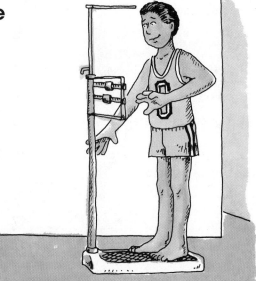

amount of increase $\longrightarrow$ $\dfrac{8}{102} = \dfrac{4}{51}$
weight before increase $\longrightarrow$

$$51\overline{)4.0000} \quad 0.0784$$

Rounded to the nearest tenth percent, his increase in weight was 7.8%.

Tom wants to maintain his weight at 127 pounds so that he can remain in his wrestling class. His doctor started him on a 2600-calorie diet, then reduced it to a 2250-calorie diet. Here is how to find the **percent of decrease:**

We first subtract to find the amount of decrease.

amount of decrease $\longrightarrow$ $\dfrac{350}{2600} = \dfrac{35}{260}$
calories before decrease $\rightarrow$

$$= \dfrac{7}{52} \quad 52\overline{)7.0000} \quad 0.1346$$

Rounded to the nearest tenth percent, his decrease in calories was 13.5%.

Solve. Round each answer to the nearest percent.

1. Roberto's height a year ago was 58 inches. This year he grew 2 inches. What was the percent of increase?

2. One type of bicycle regularly sells for $156. Now it is on sale for $132. What is the percent of decrease?

3. Jeremiah earned $18 his first week on a job. On the second week he earned $21. What was the percent of increase in weekly earnings?

4. Geraldine studied 90 minutes one night and 20 minutes less the next night. By what percent was her study time decreased?

Solve.

City	Population in Census Year		
	1960	1970	1980
New York City	7,781,984	7,894,862	7,071,030
Chicago	3,550,404	3,369,359	3,005,072
Los Angeles	2,479,015	2,809,596	2,966,763
Philadelphia	2,002,512	1,950,098	1,688,210
Houston	938,219	1,232,802	1,594,086
Detroit	1,670,144	1,513,601	1,203,339
Dallas	679,684	844,401	904,078
Baltimore	939,024	905,759	786,775
Washington, D.C.	763,956	756,510	637,651

5. **a.** Which cities had a decrease in population from 1960 to 1970? From 1970 to 1980?

   b. Which cities had an increase in population from 1960 to 1970? From 1970 to 1980?

6. **a.** How much did the population of Detroit decrease from 1970 to 1980?

   b. What was the percent of decrease? Round answer to the nearest tenth percent.

7. **a.** How much did the population of Dallas increase from 1970 to 1980?

   b. What was the percent of increase? Round to the nearest tenth percent.

8. By what percent did the population of Houston increase from 1960 to 1970?

9. A car was reduced from $7238 to $6743. What was the percent of reduction?

Give each quotient in simplest form.

1. $8 \div \frac{1}{3}$

2. $\frac{2}{3} \div 2$

3. $\frac{5}{9} \div \frac{2}{3}$

4. $\frac{7}{4} \div \frac{7}{9}$

5. $\frac{0}{4} \div \frac{5}{4}$

6. $\frac{3}{2} \div \frac{2}{3}$

7. $\frac{9}{4} \div \frac{9}{4}$

8. $\frac{15}{16} \div \frac{5}{4}$

9. $\frac{7}{6} \div \frac{2}{3}$

10. $\frac{2}{3} \div \frac{7}{6}$

11. $5 \div \frac{3}{4}$

12. $\frac{7}{8} \div \frac{3}{4}$

13. $\frac{3}{2} \div \frac{9}{8}$

14. $\frac{15}{4} \div \frac{5}{6}$

15. $\frac{5}{8} \div \frac{10}{3}$

16. $\frac{3}{4} \div 4$

Practice exercises

Copy and complete.

	1.	2.	3.	4.	5.	6.	7.	8.
Fraction	$\frac{1}{4}$	?	$\frac{5}{4}$	?	$\frac{1}{3}$	?	$\frac{5}{6}$	?
Decimal	?	?	?	0.6	?	0.875	?	?
Percent	?	50%	?	?	?	?	?	62.5%

Solve.

9. 40% of 25 = n

10. 150% of 18 = n

11. 75% of 96 = n

12. 8.5% of 50 = n

13. 22.6% of 65 = n

14. 7.35% of 84 = n

15. $33\frac{1}{3}$% of 141 = n

16. $87\frac{1}{2}$% of 128 = n

17. $66\frac{2}{3}$% of 249 = n

18. 25% of n = 16

19. 60% of n = 48

20. 125% of n = 60

21. 6.2% of n = 12.4

22. 12.5% of n = 6.25

23. 58.4% of n = 93.44

24. $37\frac{1}{2}$% of n = 36.3

25. $8\frac{1}{3}$% of n = 304

26. 22.5% of n = 36.9

27. n% of 50 = 25

28. n% of 420 = 42

29. n% of 60 = 45

30. n% of 57 = 19

31. n% of 60 = 50

32. n% of 64 = 40

33. n% of 55 = 40.7

34. n% of 185 = 11.47

35. n% of 275 = 34.1

The regular price has been marked out. The sale price is shown in red. Find the percent of decrease rounded to the nearest tenth percent.

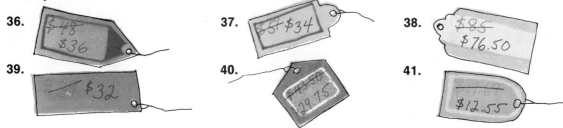

36. $48 $36

37. $51 $34

38. $85 $76.50

39. $32

40. $43.50 29.75

41. $16 $12.55

Mathematics in careers

Some salespeople are paid a salary plus a percentage of their sales above a certain number of dollars. For example, the Hearth and Home Furniture Store pays its salespeople $250 a week plus 3% of all sales from $500 to $1500 and 4% of all sales over $1500.

Below is a sales report for each salesperson of the store. Compute the weekly salary of each. Round all computations to the nearest cent.

1. Weekly Sales Report for _Krantz_ Week _5/6_ to _5/12_	**2.** Weekly Sales Report for _Adams_ Week _5/6_ to _5/12_	**3.** Weekly Sales Report for _Davis_ Week _5/6_ to _5/12_	**4.** Weekly Sales Report for _Garcia_ Week _5/6_ to _5/12_
Sales	Sales	Sales	Sales
Mon. $486.00	Mon. (day off)	Mon. $186.00	Mon. $460.00
Tues. $246.60	Tues. (no sales)	Tues. (day off)	Tues. $1463.50
Wed. (no sales)	Wed. $582.70	Wed. $314.00	Wed. (day off)
Thur. (day off)	Thur. (no sales)	Thur. (no sales)	Thur. (no sales)
Fri. $851.00	Fri. $461.25	Fri. (no sales)	Fri. $134.80
Sat. (no sales)	Sat. $1009.20	Sat. $299.00	Sat. $298.70

Problem solving

Juan Hernandez works at Heyn Sporting Goods. The store is having an end-of-the-season sale and everything in the store is marked down. Juan has to mark the sale tags.

What are the missing prices?

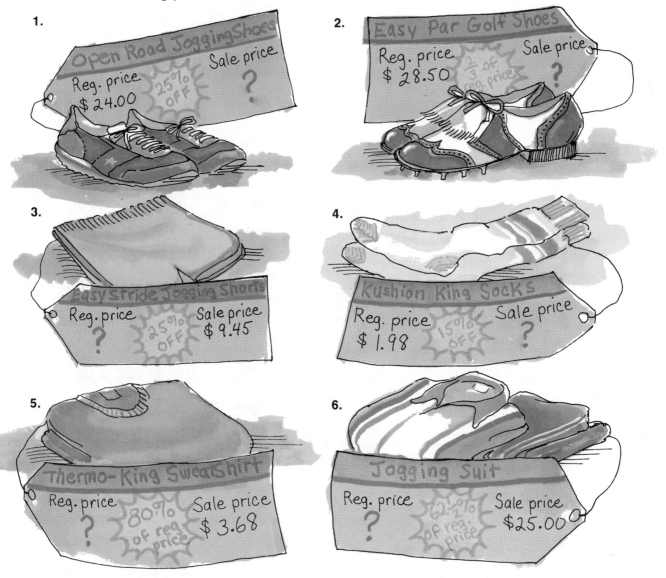

1. Open Road Jogging Shoes
Reg. price $24.00
25% OFF
Sale price ?

2. Easy Par Golf Shoes
Reg. price $28.50
⅔ of reg. price
Sale price ?

3. Easy Stride Jogging Shorts
Reg. price ?
25% OFF
Sale price $9.45

4. Kushion King Socks
Reg. price $1.98
15% OFF
Sale price ?

5. Thermo-King Sweatshirt
Reg. price ?
80% of reg. price
Sale price $3.68

6. Jogging Suit
Reg. price ?
62½% of reg. price
Sale price $25.00

Solve.

7. A $6.80 jersey is on sale at 20% off and some $21.60 shoes are on sale at 25% off. Find the total sale price of one jersey and a pair of shoes.

8. Roger works at the shop. He gets 15% off the current price on anything he buys. What would he pay for a pair of $25.00 shoes that are on sale for 40% off?

9. The most expensive running shoes that the store stocks sell for $36.50. Next year the price is to increase 8%. What will the price be then?

10. Sarah wanted to buy some running shoes that were regularly priced $28.00. They were on sale at 30% off. She had 60% of the money she needed. How much more money did she need?

11. A windbreaker that sold for $10 was put on sale at 12% off the regular price. A week later the sale price was increased by 12%. What did the windbreaker sell for then?

★ 12. The wholesale price of a jogging suit was $17.95. The retail price was 37% above the wholesale price. Later the suit was put on sale for $23.45. What was the percent of discount?

CHAPTER CHECKUP

Change to a fraction or mixed number in simplest form. [pages 218–219]

1. 50%   2. 120%   3. $33\frac{1}{3}$%   4. $55\frac{5}{9}$%   5. 1.2%   6. 0.8%

Change to a percent. [pages 220–221]

7. $\frac{3}{10}$ 8. $\frac{1}{5}$ 9. $\frac{2}{3}$ 10. $\frac{7}{4}$ 11. $\frac{5}{8}$ 12. $\frac{15}{16}$

Copy and complete. [page 222]

	13.	14.	15.	16.	17.	18.
Decimal	0.59	0.3	2.4	?	?	?
Percent	?	?	?	$37\frac{1}{2}$%	183%	0.9%

Solve. [pages 224–225]

19. 16% of 54 = n
20. $66\frac{2}{3}$% of 171 = n
21. 105% of 1240 = n

22. $6\frac{1}{4}$% of 256 = n
23. 87.5% of 584 = n
24. 0.6% of 1240 = n

Solve. [pages 226–227]

25. 30% of n = 18
26. 75% of n = 54
27. 110% of n = 22

28. $33\frac{1}{3}$% of n = 17
29. $16\frac{2}{3}$% of n = 16
30. 9.4% of n = 6.11

Solve. [pages 230–231]

31. n% of 60 = 6
32. n% of 120 = 30
33. n% of 150 = 22.5

34. n% of 57 = 19
35. n% of 40 = 6
36. n% of 48 = 54

Solve. [pages 234–235, 238–239]

37. The sales tax is 5.5%. How much is the sales tax on the reduced price?

38. The regular price is 120% of the price the dealer paid for the bike. What was the dealer's cost?

39. By what percent was the price decreased?

REGULAR PRICE $625

REDUCED PRICE $550

CHAPTER PROJECT

Number of people in each vehicle	Tally	Percent	Number of people
1	ℋℋ ℋℋ //	$\frac{12}{48} = \frac{1}{4} = 25\%$	12
2	ℋℋ ℋℋ ℋℋ ///		
3	ℋℋ ///		
4	ℋℋ /		
5 or more	////		24
Total number of vehicles: 48		Total number of people:	

Robert counted the number of people that rode in each vehicle that used the school parking lot. He used the results of his survey to construct a circle graph.

The survey shows that $\frac{1}{4}$, or 25%, of the vehicles had only 1 person. To find the angle for that part of the circle graph, you would need to find 25% of 360° (the total number of degrees in a circle).

$$25\% \times 360° = 0.25 \times 360°$$
$$= 90°$$

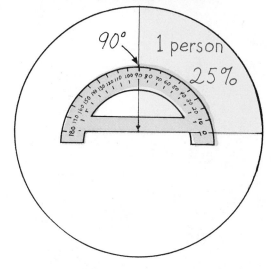

1. Copy and complete the survey.

2. Use your percent column to complete the circle graph.

3. What is the total number of people in the survey?

4. If these people had ridden 3 to a vehicle, how many vehicles would have been needed?

5. By what percent would the traffic have been reduced?

6. Repeat exercises 4 and 5 assuming that 4 people rode in a vehicle.

7. Take your own traffic survey. Repeat exercises 1–6 using the results.

$$20\% = \frac{20}{100} \quad 33\frac{1}{3}\% = \frac{33\frac{1}{3}}{100}$$

$$= \frac{1}{5} \qquad\qquad = \frac{\frac{100}{3}}{\frac{100}{1}}$$

$$= \frac{1}{3}$$

Change to a fraction in lowest terms.

1. 15%   2. 85%   3. 75%

4. 0.5%   5. 17.5%   6. $62\frac{1}{2}\%$

$$\frac{3}{5} = \frac{60}{100} \qquad\qquad \frac{5}{8} = \frac{n}{100}$$

$$= 60\% \qquad\qquad 8n = 500$$

$$n = 62\frac{1}{2}$$

$$\text{So, } \frac{5}{8} = 62\frac{1}{2}\%$$

Change to a percent.

7. $\frac{1}{2}$ 8. $\frac{3}{4}$ 9. $\frac{8}{5}$

10. $\frac{1}{3}$ 11. $\frac{2}{3}$ 12. $\frac{5}{16}$

Decimal → Percent

$$0.06\frac{1}{2} = 6\frac{1}{2}\%$$

Percent → Decimal

$$35.6\% = 0.356$$

Copy and complete.

	13.	14.	15.	16.	17.
Decimal	0.23	?	0.055	?	$0.36\frac{1}{2}$
Percent	?	6%	?	$8\frac{1}{3}\%$	?

$$40\% \text{ of } 32 = 0.40 \times 32$$

$$= 12.8$$

$$30\% \text{ of } n = 18$$

$$\frac{0.30n}{0.30} = \frac{18}{0.30}$$

$$0.3\overline{)18.0} \quad 60.$$

$$n = 60$$

Solve.

18. 25% of 48 = n 19. 42% of 67 = n

20. 9.4% of 35 = n 21. 8.5% of 24 = n

22. $33\frac{1}{3}\%$ of 112 = n 23. $8\frac{1}{2}\%$ of 72 = n

24. 50% of n = 18   25. 36% of n = 27

26. 9.6% of n = 9.6   27. 6.25% of n = 25

28. $37\frac{1}{2}\%$ of n = 27   29. $33\frac{1}{3}\%$ of n = 18.2

CHAPTER CHALLENGE

What is your percent power? Try these percent problems.

•All in the Family•
(score 1000 points)

50% of the Wilson children are on the swimming team and 75% are on the tennis team. What is the smallest possible number of children in the Wilson family?

•Ups and Downs•
(score 3000 points)

The original price of a shirt was increased by 20%. Then, at a sale, the price was decreased by 20%. What percent of the original price was the price of the shirt then? (*Warning:* The answer is not 100%.)

•Itty Bitty Cubes•
(score 5000 points)

10 cm

This wooden cube is painted on all sides. Suppose it is cut into cubic centimeters. What percent of the small cubes would have some paint on them?

•Ins and Outs•
(score 4000 points)

87% of all the books Steve read are in the school library. 3% of all the books in the school library were read by Steve. There are 13 books that Steve read which are not in the school library. How many books in the school library were not read by Steve?

•Cat Tales•
(score 2000 points)

Leon sold 50% of his cats. Then he gave away 60% of those that were left. Now he had only 8 cats. How many cats did Leon have to begin with?

•Score Yourself•

11,000–15,000 points	SUPER GREAT
8,000–10,000 points	Terrific
4,000– 7,000 points	Good

243

b c d   a b c d   a b c d   a b c d   a b c d   a b c d

2. ☐☐☐☐ ☐☐☐☐   5. ☐☐☐☐   6. ☐☐☐☐

b c d   a b c d   a b c d   a b c d

8. ☐☐☐☐ 9. ☐☐☐☐ 10. ☐☐☐☐ 11. ☐☐☐☐ 12. ☐☐☐☐

MAJOR CHECKUP

STANDARDIZED FORMAT

Choose the correct letter.

1. 58.0695 rounded to the nearest thousandth is

- **a.** 58.071
- **b.** 58.069
- **c.** 58.070
- **d.** none of these

2. Give the quotient to the nearest hundredth.

$$5.7\overline{)11.59}$$

- **a.** 2.33
- **b.** 2.03
- **c.** 23.3
- **d.** none of these

3. The prime factorization of 108 is

- **a.** $2^3 \times 3^2$
- **b.** $2^3 \times 3^3$
- **c.** $2^2 \times 3^2$
- **d.** none of these

4. Solve.

$$4y - 9 = 59$$

- **a.** $12\frac{1}{2}$
- **b.** $14\frac{3}{4}$
- **c.** 17
- **d.** none of these

5. Give the difference.

$$15\frac{1}{2} - 3\frac{5}{6}$$

- **a.** $12\frac{1}{3}$
- **b.** $12\frac{2}{3}$
- **c.** $11\frac{2}{3}$
- **d.** none of these

6. Give the quotient.

$$8\frac{1}{2} \div 3\frac{1}{4}$$

- **a.** $27\frac{5}{8}$
- **b.** $\frac{13}{34}$
- **c.** $2\frac{8}{13}$
- **d.** none of these

7. Find the surface area. Use 3.14 as an approximation for π.

3 m

8.2 m

- **a.** 231.73 m²
- **b.** 154.49 m²
- **c.** 77.25 m²
- **d.** none of these

8. Solve.

$$\frac{6}{7} = \frac{8}{y}$$

- **a.** $9\frac{1}{3}$
- **b.** $5\frac{1}{4}$
- **c.** $6\frac{6}{7}$
- **d.** none of these

9. Solve.

$$16\frac{2}{3}\% \text{ of } x = 48$$

- **a.** 288
- **b.** 80
- **c.** 8
- **d.** none of these

10. Solve.

$$x\% \text{ of } 57 = 38$$

- **a.** $33\frac{1}{3}\%$
- **b.** 150%
- **c.** $66\frac{2}{3}\%$
- **d.** none of these

11. Bagels are 80¢ a dozen. What is the cost of 9 bagels?

- **a.** 60¢
- **b.** 72¢
- **c.** $1.20
- **d.** none of these

12. Arthur was 60 in. tall. Now he is 2% taller. How tall is he now?

- **a.** 62 in.
- **b.** 72 in.
- **c.** 61.2 in.
- **d.** none of these

244

Geometry

9

Measuring angles

Look at $\angle ABC$. $\vec{BA}$ and $\vec{BC}$ are the **sides** of the angle, and point B is the **vertex**.

Match.

1. point A (A)

2. angle ABC $(\angle ABC)$

3. segment AB $(\overline{AB})$

4. ray AB $(\vec{AB})$

5. line AB $(\overleftrightarrow{AB})$

6. angle C $(\angle C)$

7. ray BA $(\vec{BA})$

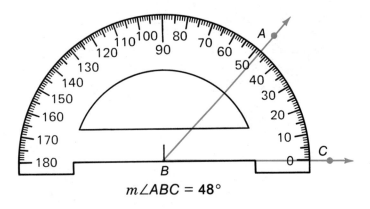

$$m\angle ABC = 48°$$

Read as "The measure of angle ABC is 48 degrees."

An **acute angle** is an angle that measures between 0° and 90°.

A **right angle** is an angle that measures 90°.

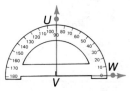

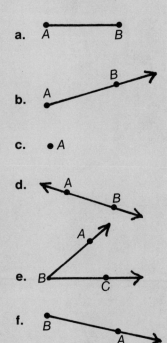

An **obtuse angle** is an angle that measures between 90° and 180°.

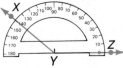

What kind of angle is $\angle ABC$?

EXERCISES

First measure the angle. Then tell whether it is acute, right, or obtuse.

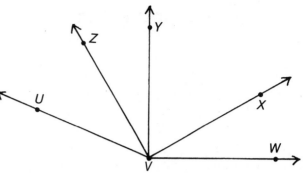

1. ∠WVX   2. ∠UVZ   3. ∠YVZ

4. ∠XVZ   5. ∠WVY   6. ∠UVY

7. ∠WVZ   8. ∠UVX   9. ∠XVY

Draw angles having these measures.

10. 25°   11. 72°   12. 132°   13. 90°   14. 168°

15. Follow these steps to **construct** a right angle.

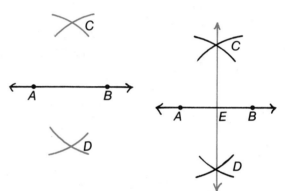

    a. Draw $\overleftrightarrow{AB}$. Using A and B as centers and using the same compass setting, draw crossing arcs above and below $\overleftrightarrow{AB}$.

    b. Using a straightedge, draw a line through the points where the arcs cross.

16. The construction in exercise 15 gives you four right angles. One angle is ∠CEB. Name the other right angles.

17. Follow these steps to **bisect** an angle.

    a. Draw ∠V. Using V as center, draw an arc that crosses the sides.

    b. Using U and W as centers and using the same compass setting, draw crossing arcs.

    c. Draw the ray from V through the point where the arcs cross.

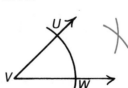

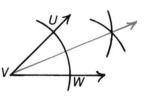

★ 18. Using only a compass and straightedge, construct a 45° angle.

★ 19. Construct a 135° angle.

Angles of polygons

The angles of the triangle were colored, torn off, and placed under the protractor.

Look at the pictures. What is the sum of the measures of the angles? The sum would have been the same regardless of the triangle we used.

For any triangle, the sum of the measures of the angles is 180°

EXERCISES

1. Draw a triangle. Use a protractor to measure each angle.

2. What is the sum of the measures of the angles?

The measures of two angles are given. Find the measure of the remaining angle.

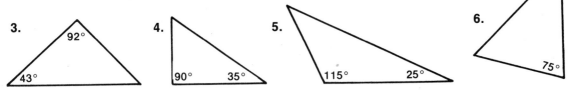

3. 92° 43°

4. 90° 35°

5. 115° 25°

6. 45° 75°

248

7. The red figure is called a **quadrilateral**.

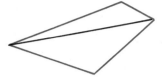

a. How many sides does a quadrilateral have?
b. How many triangles make up the quadrilateral?
c. What is the sum of the measures of the angles? (*Hint:* What is the sum of the measures of the angles of the two triangles?)

8. Copy and complete this table.

Polygon	Number of sides	Number of triangles	Sum of the measures of the angles
triangle	3	1	180°
quadrilateral	4	2	360°
pentagon	5	?	?
hexagon	6	?	?
heptagon	7	?	?
octagon	8	?	?

★ 9. Look for a pattern in your completed table. What is the relationship between the number of sides and the number of triangles?

★ 10. Give the sum of the measures of the angles for a polygon having 30 sides.

Give the sum in simplest form.

1. $8\frac{2}{5} + 3\frac{3}{4}$

2. $9\frac{1}{6} + 8\frac{1}{3}$

3. $14\frac{5}{9} + 6\frac{2}{3}$

4. $6\frac{7}{8} + 9\frac{3}{8}$

5. $3\frac{2}{5} + 6\frac{1}{2}$

6. $31\frac{1}{3} + 24\frac{2}{9}$

7. $22\frac{5}{6} + 18\frac{3}{4}$

8. $15\frac{2}{3} + 17\frac{4}{5}$

Give the difference in simplest form.

9. $9\frac{1}{2} - 4\frac{3}{4}$

10. $12 - 9\frac{3}{5}$

11. $8\frac{1}{4} - 6\frac{3}{5}$

12. $4\frac{5}{9} - 2\frac{2}{3}$

13. $15 - 12\frac{5}{8}$

14. $15\frac{1}{6} - 8\frac{1}{8}$

15. $25\frac{3}{4} - 6\frac{9}{10}$

16. $17 - 16\frac{3}{8}$

Pairs of angles

Certain pairs of angles have special names.

Adjacent angles have a common side between them and a common vertex.

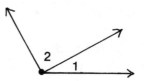

∠1 and ∠2 are adjacent angles.

Vertical angles are formed by two intersecting lines. They have a common vertex but no common side.

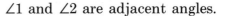

∠1 and ∠2 are vertical angles.
∠3 and ∠4 are vertical angles.

Two angles are **complementary** if the sum of their measures is 90°.

Note: Two angles need not be adjacent to be complementary.

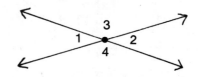

∠ADB and ∠BDC are complementary.

Two angles are **supplementary** if the sum of their measures is 180°.

Note: Two angles need not be adjacent to be supplementary.

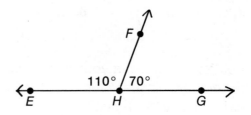

∠EHF and ∠FHG are supplementary.

EXERCISES

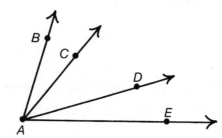

Give an angle that is adjacent to

1. ∠BAC
2. ∠DAE
3. ∠BAD
4. ∠EAC

5. Find the measures of ∠1 and ∠3.

6. Find the measures of ∠2 and ∠4.

7. Do vertical angles have the same measure?

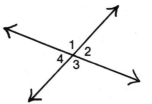

8. What angle is complementary to ∠AEB?

9. What angle is supplementary to ∠AEB?

10. What angle is complementary to ∠CED?

11. What angle is supplementary to ∠FED?

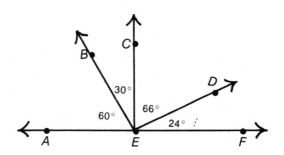

Draw a figure that satisfies the given conditions.

12. ∠ABC and ∠DBC are adjacent.

13. ∠RST and ∠VST are adjacent and complementary.

14. ∠XYZ and ∠VYZ are adjacent and supplementary.

★ 15. ∠RST and ∠OSU are vertical angles, and ∠OSR and ∠RST are supplementary.

251

Perpendicular lines and parallel lines

Two lines that intersect to form right angles are called **perpendicular lines.**

We say: "Line ℓ is perpendicular to line m."

We write: $\ell \perp m$.

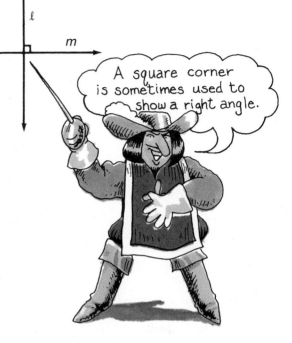

A square corner is sometimes used to show a right angle.

Two segments are perpendicular if the lines that contain them are perpendicular.

The perpendicular bisector of a segment is the line that is perpendicular to the segment at the midpoint of the segment.

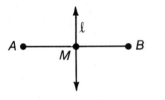

ℓ is the perpendicular bisector of $\overline{AB}$.

Two lines in a plane (a flat surface) that do not intersect are called **parallel lines.**

We say: "Line u is parallel to line v."
We write: Line $u \parallel$ line v.

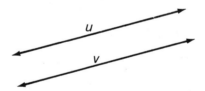

Two segments are parallel if the lines that contain them are parallel.

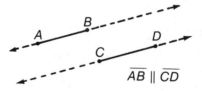

$\overline{AB} \parallel \overline{CD}$

A line that intersects two lines is called a **transversal.**

$\overleftrightarrow{CB}$ is a transversal of $\overleftrightarrow{AB}$ and $\overleftrightarrow{CD}$.

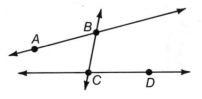

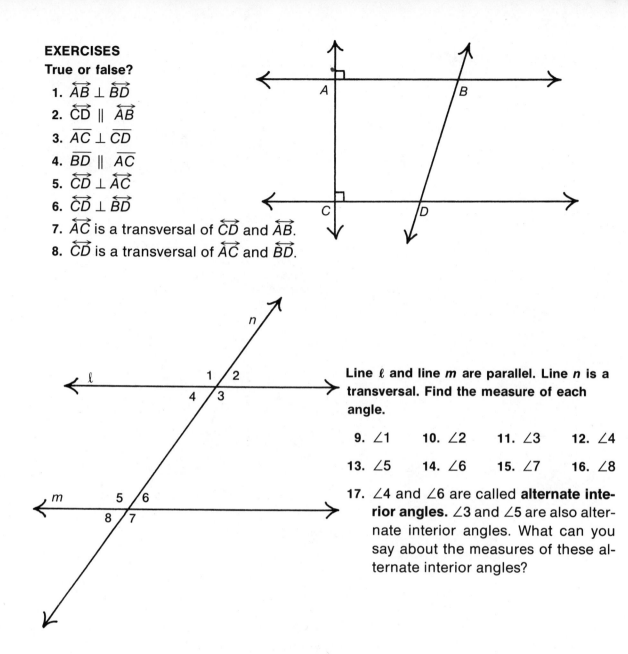

EXERCISES

True or false?

1. $\overleftrightarrow{AB} \perp \overleftrightarrow{BD}$

2. $\overleftrightarrow{CD} \parallel \overleftrightarrow{AB}$

3. $\overline{AC} \perp \overline{CD}$

4. $\overline{BD} \parallel \overline{AC}$

5. $\overleftrightarrow{CD} \perp \overleftrightarrow{AC}$

6. $\overleftrightarrow{CD} \perp \overleftrightarrow{BD}$

7. $\overleftrightarrow{AC}$ is a transversal of $\overleftrightarrow{CD}$ and $\overleftrightarrow{AB}$.

8. $\overleftrightarrow{CD}$ is a transversal of $\overleftrightarrow{AC}$ and $\overleftrightarrow{BD}$.

Line ℓ and line m are parallel. Line n is a transversal. Find the measure of each angle.

9. $\angle 1$ 10. $\angle 2$ 11. $\angle 3$ 12. $\angle 4$

13. $\angle 5$ 14. $\angle 6$ 15. $\angle 7$ 16. $\angle 8$

17. $\angle 4$ and $\angle 6$ are called **alternate interior angles.** $\angle 3$ and $\angle 5$ are also alternate interior angles. What can you say about the measures of these alternate interior angles?

Use a compass and straightedge to construct

18. a pair of perpendicular lines. (*Hint:* See exercise 15 on page 247.)

19. a pair of parallel lines.

253

Congruent figures

Figures that have the same size and shape are called **congruent figures.** Since a tracing of triangle *ABC* fits on triangle *STR*, the two triangles are congruent.

We write: $\triangle ABC \cong \triangle STR$.

We say: "Triangle *ABC* is congruent to triangle *STR*."

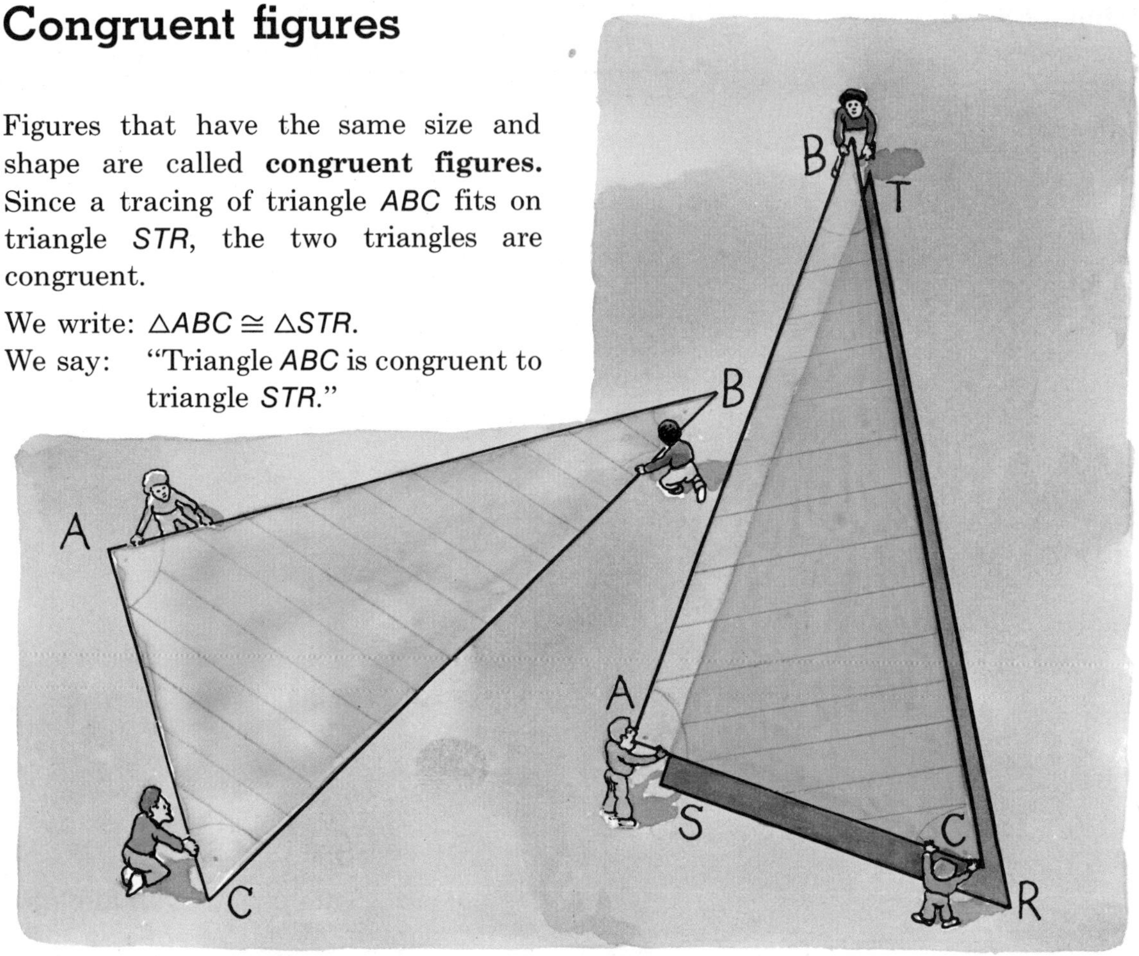

By looking at the picture above, we see that for this fitting the vertices are matched in this way:

$$A \longleftrightarrow S$$
$$B \longleftrightarrow T$$
$$C \longleftrightarrow R$$

The sides and angles that match are called **corresponding parts.** For a congruent fitting, the corresponding parts are congruent.

Congruent Angles	Congruent Sides
$\angle A \cong \angle S$	$\overline{AB} \cong \overline{ST}$
$\angle B \cong \angle T$	$\overline{BC} \cong \overline{TR}$
$\angle C \cong \angle R$	$\overline{CA} \cong \overline{RS}$

EXERCISES

Use a tracing to tell whether or not the two figures are congruent.

1.   **2.**   **3.**

The two figures are congruent. Complete.

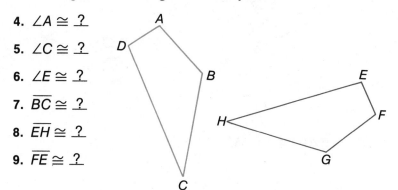

4. $\angle A \cong$?

5. $\angle C \cong$?

6. $\angle E \cong$?

7. $\overline{BC} \cong$?

8. $\overline{EH} \cong$?

9. $\overline{FE} \cong$?

Complete.

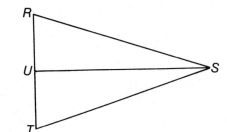

10. $\angle R \cong$?

11. $\angle RSU \cong$?

12. $\overline{RS} \cong$?

13. $\angle RUS \cong$?

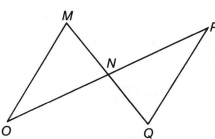

14. $\angle MNO \cong$?

15. $\overline{QN} \cong$?

16. $\angle P \cong$?

17. $\angle Q \cong$?

18. $\overline{MO} \cong$?

Constructions and triangles

Here is how to use just a compass and a straightedge to construct a segment congruent to $\overline{AB}$.

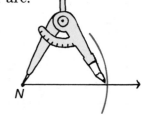

Step 1. Draw any line and pick a point on it.

Step 2. Set compass points at A and B.

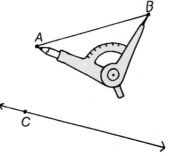

Step 3. Put the compass point at C and mark off that same distance on the line. $\overline{CD} \cong \overline{AB}$.

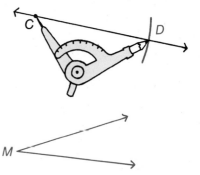

Here is how to construct an angle congruent to $\angle M$.

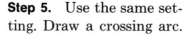

Step 1. Draw a ray.

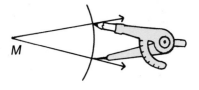

Step 2. Put the compass point at M and draw an arc.

Step 3. Keep the same compass setting. Put compass point at N and draw an arc.

Step 4. Set the compass across the angle.

Step 5. Use the same setting. Draw a crossing arc.

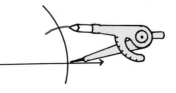

Step 6. Draw the other ray. $\angle N \cong \angle M$.

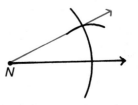

EXERCISES

1. Draw a segment and then use a straightedge and compass to construct a congruent segment.

2. Draw an acute angle and then construct a congruent angle.

3. Draw an obtuse angle and construct a congruent angle.

4. Draw a triangle *ABC* and then follow these steps to construct a triangle congruent to it.

   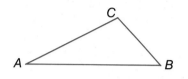

   a. Construct a segment congruent to $\overline{AB}$.

   b. Measure $\overline{AC}$ with your compass. Draw an arc as shown.

   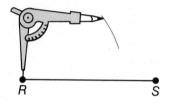

   c. Measure $\overline{BC}$ with your compass. Draw an arc as shown.

   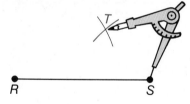

   d. Draw $\overline{RT}$ and $\overline{ST}$.

   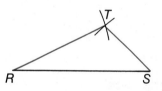

5. You did the construction in exercise 4 by ignoring the angles and just copying the three sides. Complete this statement:

   If the 3 sides of one triangle are congruent to the 3 sides of another triangle, the triangles are   ? .

6. Now construct a triangle congruent to △*ABC* by doing this:

   a. Use compass and straightedge and copy $\overline{AB}$.
   b. Copy ∠*A*.
   c. Copy $\overline{AC}$.
   d. Draw in the third side.

7. Construct a triangle congruent to △*ABC* by copying ∠*A*, $\overline{AB}$, and ∠*B*.

Line of symmetry

The dotted line divides the triangle "in half." If you fold the triangle along the dotted line, then the two halves match.

The dotted line is called a **line of symmetry.**

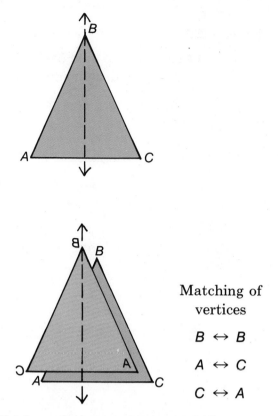

First we traced △*ABC* and the line of symmetry. Then we flipped the tracing about the line of symmetry. Notice that the flipped tracing fits exactly on △*ABC*.

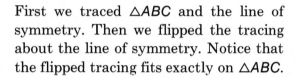

Matching of vertices

B ↔ *B*

A ↔ *C*

C ↔ *A*

Which angle is congruent to ∠*A*?
Which side is congruent to $\overline{AB}$?

EXERCISES
The dotted line is a line of symmetry. First make a tracing and flip it about the line of symmetry. Then answer each question.

1. Which side is congruent to $\overline{RS}$?

2. Which angle is congruent to ∠*R*?

3. Which angle is congruent to ∠*RUS*?

4. Are ∠*RUS* and ∠*TUS* right angles?

5. Is $\overline{SU}$ perpendicular to $\overline{RT}$?

6. Which segment is congruent to $\overline{RU}$?

7. Is *U* the midpoint of $\overline{RT}$?

8. Is $\overleftrightarrow{SU}$ the perpendicular bisector of $\overline{RT}$?

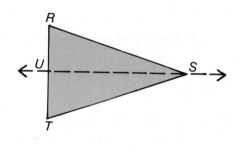

True or false?

9. If a line of symmetry of a polygon goes through a side of the polygon, it is a perpendicular bisector of that side.

10. If a line of symmetry of a polygon goes through the vertex of an angle of the polygon, it bisects the angle.

This figure has two lines of symmetry. Think about flipping a tracing about $\overleftrightarrow{EG}$.

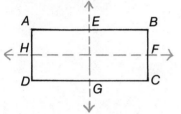

11. Is $\angle A \cong \angle B$?

12. Is $\angle D \cong \angle C$?

13. Is $\overline{AD} \cong \overline{BC}$?

Think about flipping a tracing about $\overleftrightarrow{HF}$.

14. Is $\angle A \cong \angle D$?

15. Is $\angle B \cong \angle C$?

16. Is $\overline{AB} \cong \overline{DC}$?

17. What can you say about the four angles of the figure?

18. What can you say about the opposite sides $\overline{AB}$ and $\overline{DC}$ of the figure?

This figure has four lines of symmetry.

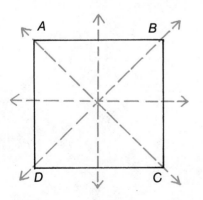

19. What can you say about the four angles?

20. What can you say about the four sides?

21. Draw a 4-sided polygon with

   a. only 1 line of symmetry, going through midpoints of sides.

   b. only 2 lines of symmetry, going through vertices.

   c. only 2 lines of symmetry, going through midpoints of sides.

Triangles

There are three basic types of triangles.

EQUILATERAL

An equilateral triangle has
3 lines of symmetry.

ISOSCELES

An isosceles triangle has
1 line of symmetry.

SCALENE

A scalene triangle has
no lines of symmetry.

EXERCISES
True or false?

An equilateral triangle has
1. 3 congruent sides.   **2.** 3 congruent angles.

An isosceles triangle has
3. 2 congruent sides.   **4.** 2 congruent angles.

A scalene triangle has
5. no congruent sides.   **6.** no congruent angles.

Complete.

7. An equilateral triangle has _?_ congruent sides.

8. An isosceles triangle has _?_ congruent sides.

9. A scalene triangle has _?_ congruent sides.

Remember that the sum of the measures of the angles of a triangle is 180°. Give the length and angle measure of each marked side and angle.

10. Equilateral

11. Equilateral

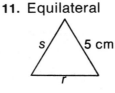

12. Isosceles

13. Isosceles

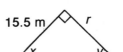

14. Can a triangle have 3 100° angles?

15. Can a triangle have 2 50° angles and 1 80° angle?

16. Can a triangle have 2 89° angles and 1 2° angle?

17. Can a triangle have 2 right angles?

18. Can a triangle have 1 right angle?

Use a compass and straightedge to construct

19. an equilateral triangle.

20. an isosceles triangle.

A **right triangle** is a triangle that has a 90° angle. Construct a right triangle that is

★ 21. isosceles.   ★ 22. scalene.

★ 23. Is it possible for a right triangle to be an equilateral triangle?

Solve. Round answers to the nearest hundredth.

1. 7% of 29 = x

2. 23% of 56 = x

3. 15% of 92 = x

4. 18% of 74 = x

5. 31% of 19 = x

6. 43% of 78 = x

7. 7.2% of 26 = x

8. 15.4% of 53 = x

9. 3.8% of 74 = x

10. 21.7% of 19 = x

11. 34.5% of 62 = x

12. 18.7% of 49 = x

13. 22.5% of 74 = x

14. 30.4% of 53 = x

15. 8.6% of 68 = x

16. 12.6% of 92 = x

Point of symmetry

If a figure fits itself after a half-turn about a point, the point is a **point of symmetry.**

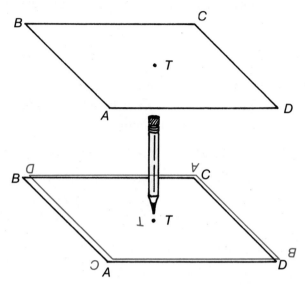

Here a tracing was given a half-turn about point *T*.
The tracing fits! So point *T* is a point of symmetry.

Which angle is congruent to ∠*A*? To ∠*B*?

Which side is congruent to $\overline{AB}$? To $\overline{AD}$?

Matching of vertices

A ⟷ C   B ⟷ D

C ⟷ A   D ⟷ B

$\overline{AD}$ and $\overline{CB}$ are called **opposite sides.** Which side is opposite $\overline{AB}$? When the figure has a point of symmetry, the opposite sides are parallel. ∠*A* and ∠*C* are called **opposite angles.** Which angle is opposite ∠*B*?

EXERCISES
Is point *T* a point of symmetry of the figure?

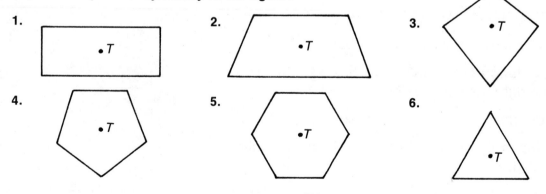

1.

2.

3.

4.

5.

6.

262

In each exercise half the figure is covered. In some of the figures there is a dashed line, which is a line of symmetry of the figure. In others there is a point *T*, which is a point of symmetry. Trace and complete each figure.

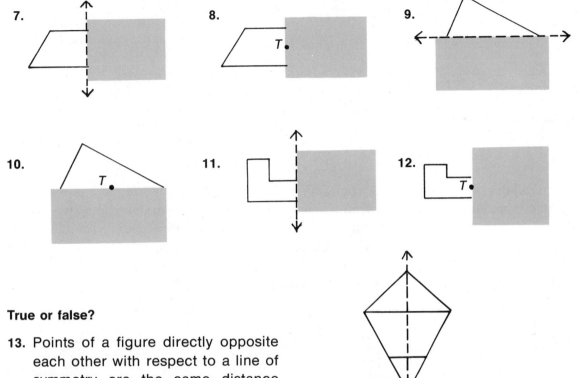

7.

8.

9.

10.

11.

12.

True or false?

13. Points of a figure directly opposite each other with respect to a line of symmetry are the same distance from the line of symmetry.

14. Points of a figure directly opposite each other with respect to the point of symmetry are the same distance from the point of symmetry.

Draw these polygons.

15. A quadrilateral (a 4-sided figure) that has a point of symmetry but no line of symmetry

16. A quadrilateral that has a line of symmetry but no point of symmetry

★ 17. A hexagon (a 6-sided figure) that has a line of symmetry but no point of symmetry

★ 18. A hexagon that has no line of symmetry but does have a point of symmetry

Special quadrilaterals

Parallelogram

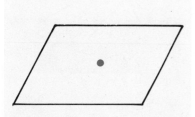

A parallelogram has a point of symmetry.

Rhombus

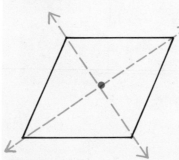

A rhombus has a point of symmetry and two lines of symmetry through opposite vertices.

Rectangle

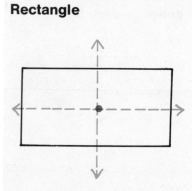

A rectangle has a point of symmetry and two lines of symmetry through opposite sides.

Square

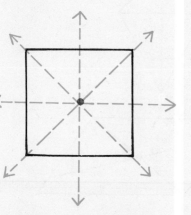

A square has a point of symmetry and four lines of symmetry.

Isosceles Trapezoid

An isosceles trapezoid has exactly one line of symmetry through opposite sides.

Kite

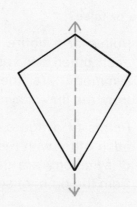

A kite has one line of symmetry through opposite vertices.

Notice that a rhombus, a rectangle, and a square are also parallelograms. Notice that a square is also a rectangle.

EXERCISES

1. What quadrilaterals have two pairs of opposite sides that are parallel?

2. What quadrilateral has exactly one pair of opposite sides that are parallel?

Two sides that have a common endpoint are called **consecutive sides.**

consecutive sides

Two angles that contain the same side of a polygon are called **consecutive angles.**

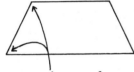

consecutive angles

3. What quadrilaterals have all pairs of consecutive sides congruent?
4. Which have all pairs of opposite sides congruent?
5. What quadrilaterals have all pairs of consecutive angles congruent?
6. Which have all pairs of opposite angles congruent?
7. What quadrilateral has exactly two pairs of consecutive angles that are congruent?

Give the measure of each side and each angle.

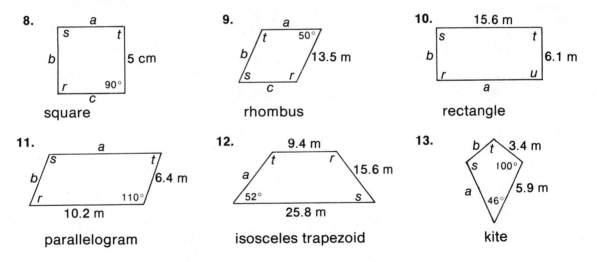

8. square

9. rhombus

10. rectangle

11. parallelogram

12. isosceles trapezoid

13. kite

★ 14. Construct each of the quadrilaterals that you studied in this lesson.

265

Regular polygons

A polygon having as many lines of symmetry as sides is called a **regular polygon.**

Regular Polygons

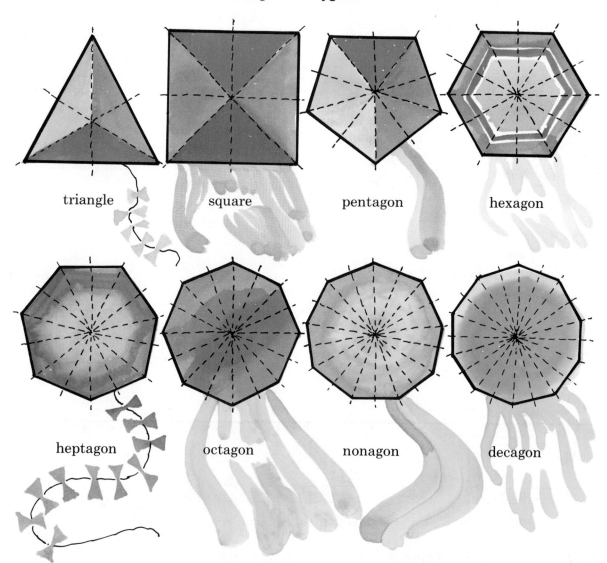

triangle   square   pentagon   hexagon

heptagon   octagon   nonagon   decagon

EXERCISES
True or false?

1. A polygon has the same number of sides as vertices.

2. A regular polygon with an odd number of sides has a point of symmetry.

3. A regular polygon with an even number of sides has a point of symmetry.

4. All sides of a regular polygon are congruent.

5. All angles of a regular polygon are congruent.

Complete this table for regular polygons. You may first need to review the table on page 249.

	Name	Sum of the measures of the angles	Number of angles	Measure of each angle
6.	Equilateral triangle	?	?	?
7.	Square	?	?	?
8.	Regular pentagon	?	?	?
9.	Regular hexagon	?	?	?
10.	Regular heptagon	?	?	?
11.	Regular octagon	?	?	?
12.	Regular nonagon	?	?	?
13.	Regular decagon	?	?	?

14. Draw a circle. With the same compass setting, draw six arcs as shown. Connect the crossing points to get a regular hexagon.

15. Use a similar method to construct an equilateral triangle.

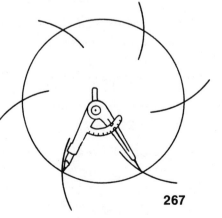

267

Acute, right, or obtuse? Complete. [pages 246–247]

1. ∠RXS is _?_.
2. ∠RXU is _?_.
3. ∠TXR is _?_.

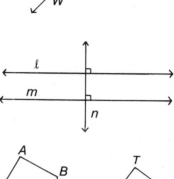

Adjacent, vertical, complementary, or supplementary? Complete. [pages 250–251]

4. ∠UXV and ∠VXW are _?_.
5. ∠SXR and ∠VXW are _?_.
6. ∠VXU and ∠UXR are adjacent and _?_.

Answer. [pages 252–253]

7. Which lines are parallel?
8. Which line is a transversal?

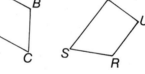

The two quadrilaterals are congruent. Complete. [pages 254–255]

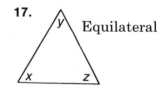

9. $\overline{AD} \cong$ _?_ 10. $\overline{BC} \cong$ _?_ 11. $\overline{DC} \cong$ _?_
12. ∠A ≅ _?_ 13. ∠C ≅ _?_ 14. ∠D ≅ _?_

Give the missing angle measures. [pages 260–261]

15.
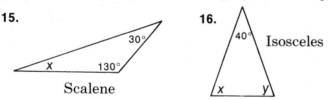
Scalene

16.
40° Isosceles
x y

17.
y Equilateral
x z

True or false? [pages 264–265]

18. The opposite sides of a parallelogram are parallel.
19. The four sides of a rhombus are congruent.
20. The four angles of a square are acute angles.
21. A rectangle is also a square.

Give the number of sides of a
[pages 266–267]

22. quadrilateral.   23. hexagon.   24. octagon.   25. pentagon.

CHAPTER PROJECT

Artwork like this is called *curve stitching*. It is generally made by connecting equally spaced points on a geometric figure with string, thread, or fine wire.

1. Draw two intersecting lines and mark off equally spaced points as shown. Use segments to connect the points on the sides of the four angles. Connect them in the order shown by the red segments.

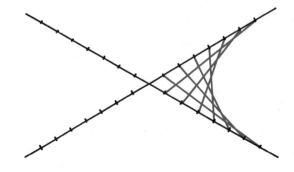

2. Make a design of your own. You may wish to work with geometric figures other than angles. Your design could consist of several geometric figures.

acute angle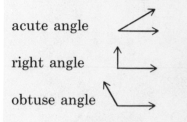

right angle

obtuse angle

Complete.

1. An angle whose measure is between 0° and 90° is called an _?_ angle.
2. An angle whose measure is 90° is called a _?_ angle.
3. An angle whose measure is between 90° and 180° is called an _?_ angle.

Vertical angles are formed by 2 intersecting lines.

Complementary angles The sum is 90°.

Supplementary angles The sum is 180°.

4. ∠AEF and _?_ are vertical angles.

5. ∠BEC and _?_ are complementary angles.

6. ∠AEC and _?_ are supplementary angles.

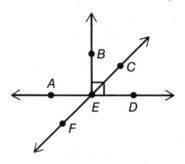

The corresponding parts of congruent figures are congruent.

The triangles are congruent.

7. ∠A ≅ _?_
8. ∠S ≅ _?_
9. $\overline{AC}$ ≅ _?_
10. $\overline{SR}$ ≅ _?_

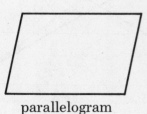

parallelogram

True or false?

11. A parallelogram has a point of symmetry.

12. A parallelogram has 2 lines of symmetry.

13. A rectangle is a parallelogram.

CHAPTER CHALLENGE

Barbara

Arthur

Carl

The grid above represents streets in a city. The points show where Arthur, Barbara, and Carl live.

1. Copy the city map shown above on graph paper.

2. If Arthur starts at his home and walks away from home for 7 blocks (along the streets), where might his walk end? On your graph paper mark in red all the points that are 7 blocks from his home.

3. Mark in blue all the points that are 7 blocks from Barbara's home.

4. Mark in green all the points that are 7 blocks from Carl's home.

5. How many points are 7 blocks from Arthur's home and also 7 blocks from Barbara's home?

6. How many points are 7 blocks from Arthur's home and also 7 blocks from Carl's home?

7. How many points are 7 blocks from Arthur's, Barbara's, and Carl's homes?

a b c d   a b c d   a b c d   a b c d   a b c d   a b c d
⬛ ⬛⬛⬛ 2.⬛ ⬛⬛⬛ **MAJOR CHECKUP** 5.⬛ ⬛⬛⬛ 6.⬛ ⬛⬛⬛
a b c d   a b c d   STANDARDIZED FORMAT   a b c d   a b c d
⬛ ⬛⬛⬛ 8.⬛ ⬛⬛⬛ 9.⬛ ⬛⬛⬛⬛ 10.⬛ ⬛⬛⬛ 11.⬛ ⬛⬛⬛ 12.⬛ ⬛⬛⬛

Choose the correct letter.

1. Give the difference.

$4.03 - 2.974$

   a. 1.056
   b. 2.056
   c. 1.156
   d. none of these

2. Give the product.

3.77×20.5

   a. 9.425
   b. 77.285
   c. 7.7285
   d. none of these

3. Give the standard numeral for $3^3 \times 5^2$.

   a. 90
   b. 270
   c. 225
   d. none of these

4. Which unit would most likely be used to measure the weight of a grain of sand?

   a. milligram
   b. kilogram
   c. liter
   d. centimeter

5. Give the difference.

$2\frac{1}{4} - 1\frac{5}{6}$

   a. $\frac{5}{12}$
   b. $\frac{7}{12}$
   c. $1\frac{7}{12}$
   d. none of these

6. Find the volume.

1 yd 2 ft
1 yd 2 ft
1 yd 2 ft

   a. 5 yd³
   b. 125 ft³
   c. 1 yd³ 8 ft³
   d. none of these

7. Solve.

$\frac{4}{x} = \frac{15}{7}$

   a. $8\frac{4}{7}$
   b. $26\frac{1}{4}$
   c. $1\frac{13}{15}$
   d. none of these

8. Change $\frac{1}{6}$ to a percent.

   a. 6%
   b. 17%
   c. $16\frac{2}{3}$%
   d. none of these

9.

110° 70°
A B

∠A and ∠B are

   a. complementary angles
   b. supplementary angles
   c. vertical angles
   d. none of these

10. A quadrilateral that has 4 lines of symmetry is

   a. rectangle
   b. parallelogram
   c. rhombus
   d. none of these

11. Slacks were on sale for 30% off the regular price of $24. What was the sale price?

   a. $16.80
   b. $7.20
   c. $23.28
   d. none of these

12. Mio bought $1\frac{1}{2}$ dozen eggs for $1.26. How much did 1 dozen of these eggs cost?

   a. $1.89
   b. $1.05
   c. $.84
   d. none of these

Consumer
Mathematics

10

Change to a percent.

1. $\frac{1}{4}$

2. $\frac{1}{3}$

3. $\frac{52.8}{66}$

4. $\frac{34.6}{51.9}$

Solve.

5. 20% of 76 = x

6. 6% of 38 = x

7. 9.5% of 50 = x

8. $33\frac{1}{3}$% of 57 = x

Solve.

9. 25% of x = 8

10. 8% of x = 36

11. 4.5% of x = 27

12. $37\frac{1}{2}$% of x = 51

Earning money

People are paid for their work in different ways.

A teacher is generally paid an annual (yearly) salary.

A hair stylist is often paid a fee for each haircut or style.

A real estate agent is usually paid a commission (a percent) of sales.

A factory worker is generally paid an hourly wage.

EXERCISES

1. A cookware company pays its sales-people a commission of 23% of all sales. How much would a person earn for selling $2340 worth of cookware?

2. A certain clothing store pays its salespeople a combination salary and commission. It pays each salesperson $105 a week plus 5% of all sales. How much would a person earn whose weekly sales were $2375?

3. A hairstyling shop pays its employees 72% of all the money they take in. One employee did 6 stylings and charged $20.75 for each. How much did the employee earn that day?

4. A paint company pays its salespeople $13,750 a year plus a bonus of $8\frac{1}{2}$% of all sales over $290,000. How much would a person whose yearly sales were $378,000 earn?

5. A factory pays its employees an hourly wage for the first 40 hours. Each hour that an employee works more than the 40 hours is called "overtime." For overtime work an employee is paid "time and a half" ($1\frac{1}{2}$ times the regular hourly wage). The factory also pays "double time" for work done on Sundays or holidays. Compute the weekly earnings for the hours shown on the time card.

6. List as many occupations as you can that are paid by fees, by an annual salary, by commission, or by an hourly rate.

Name	Roberta Davis
Employee Number	348
Hourly Wage	$5.60
	Hours Worked
Monday	8
Tuesday	9
Wednesday	8
Thursday	$9\frac{1}{2}$
Friday	11
Saturday	8
Sunday	0

Payroll and deductions

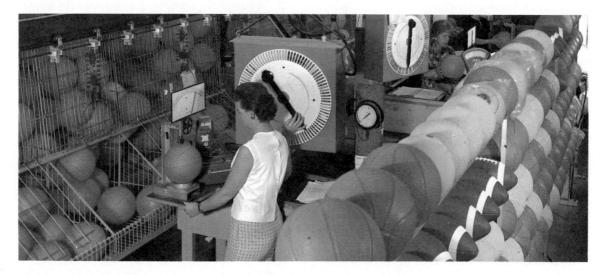

Toyland Industries pays Carol an hourly wage of $6.40 and time and a half for each hour over 40 hours per week. Each week she receives with her paycheck a *statement of withholdings* and *deductions*. This statement lists the amounts that her employer is required by law to deduct from her weekly earnings. This money is sent to the federal and state tax-collecting agencies. Toyland Industries also has optional deductions for employees who sign up for life insurance, savings bonds, and other group programs. One of Carol's weekly withholding statements is shown here:

Toyland Industries
Employee Record

Earnings

Employee Number	Hourly Wage	Total Hours Worked	Regular Earnings	Overtime Earnings	Total Earnings (Gross Pay)
3054	$6.40	44	$256.00	$38.40	$294.40

Withholdings and deductions

Social Security (F.I.C.A.)	Federal Income Tax	State Income Tax	Life Insurance	Net Pay
$17.81	$53.44	$12.80	$3.75	$206.60

EXERCISES

1. How much was Carol's net, or "take home," pay?

2. How much did she earn for her first 40 hours of work?

3. What was her overtime pay?

4. Social security withholding is for such things as retirement income and disability income if one should become disabled. How much was withheld for social security?

5. What percent of her gross pay was withheld for social security?

6. How much did the employer withhold for federal income tax? For state income tax?

7. The total income tax withheld amounted to what percent of the gross income?

8. What percent of her gross pay was her net pay?

9. A salesman for Toyland Industries is paid $360 a month and 12% of his monthly sales over $2300. What were his gross earnings for a month in which his sales totaled $11,680?

10. For the salesman in exercise 9, Toyland withholds 6.95% for social security, 18% for federal income tax, 4% for state income tax, and $6.35 for insurance. What is his net pay for the month?

KEEPING SKILLS SHARP

Solve.

1. 50% of y = 17

2. 30% of 153 = y

3. 160% of 96 = y

4. $33\frac{1}{3}$% of y = 26

5. $87\frac{1}{2}$% of y = 182

6. 39% of 68 = y

7. 15% of 450 = y

8. $66\frac{2}{3}$% of y = 54

9. $116\frac{2}{3}$% of 84 = y

10. 0.8% of y = 16

11. 67% of 72 = y

12. 9% of y = 45

13. 15% of y = 30

14. $37\frac{1}{2}$% of y = 27

15. 0.18% of 120 = y

16. 5.2% of 48 = y

17. $62\frac{1}{2}$% of y = 52

18. 110% of 150 = y

19. $133\frac{1}{3}$% of y = 76

20. 175% of 84 = y

Income tax

In the preceding lesson you learned that employers withhold federal income tax from an employee's pay. By April 15 of the following year, the employee has to file with the Internal Revenue Service an income tax form similar to the one shown below.

Use IRS label. Otherwise, please print or type.	Your first name and initial (if joint return, also give spouse's name and initial)	Last name	Your social security number
	John T. & Mary L.	Brown	516 04 1492
	Present home address (Number and street, including apartment number, or rural route)		Spouse's social security no.
	885 Scott Street		575 10 1776
	City, town or post office, State and ZIP code	Your occupation ▶ Clerk	
	Hometown, Maryland 01234	Spouse's occupation ▶ Bus Driver	

Presidential Election Campaign
Do you want $1 to go to this fund? . . . . ✓ Yes No
If joint return, does your spouse want $1 to go to this fund? . . . ✓ Yes No
Note: Checking "Yes" will not increase your tax or reduce your refund.

For Privacy Act and Paperwork Reduction Act Notice, see page 23 of Instructions

Filing Status
Check Only One Box.
1 Single
2 ✓ Married filing joint return (even if only one had income)
3 Married filing separate return. Enter spouse's social security no. above and full name here ▶
4 Head of household (with qualifying person). (See page 8 of Instructions.) If he or she is your unmarried child, enter child's name ▶

Exemptions
Always check the box labeled Yourself. Check other boxes if they apply.
5a ✓ Yourself   65 or over   Blind
 b ✓ Spouse   65 or over   Blind
| Enter number of boxes checked on 5a and b ▶ | 2 |
 c First names of your dependent children who lived with you ▶ James
| Enter number of children listed on 5c ▶ | 1 |

d Other dependents: (1) Name	(2) Relationship	(3) Number of months lived in your home.	(4) Did dependent have income of $1,000 or more?	(5) Did you provide more than one-half of dependent's support?

Enter number of other dependents ▶

6 Total number of exemptions claimed . . . .
| Add numbers entered in boxes above ▶ | 3 |

7 Wages, salaries, tips, etc. (Attach Forms W–2. See page 10 of Instructions)	7	19,558 00
8a Interest income . . (Complete page 2 if over $400 or you have any All-Savers interest.)	8a 345 00	
b Dividends . . . . . (Complete page 2 if over $400)	8b 135 00	
c Total (add lines 8a and 8b)	8c 480 00	
d Exclusion (See page 11 of Instructions)	8d 400 00	
e Subtract line 8d from line 8c (but not less than zero)	8e	80 00
9a Unemployment compensation (insurance). Total received from Form(s) 1099–UC_____		
b Taxable amount, if any, from worksheet on page 12 of Instructions	9b	
10 Adjusted gross income (add lines 7, 8e, and 9b). If under $10,000, see page 13 of Instructions on "Earned Income Credit"	10	19,638 00
11 Multiply $1,000 by the total number of exemptions claimed on line 6	11	3 000 00
12 Taxable income (subtract line 11 from line 10)	12	16,638 00
13a Credit for contributions to candidates for public office. (See page 13 of Instructions)	13a	

IF YOU WANT IRS TO FIGURE YOUR TAX, PLEASE STOP HERE AND SIGN BELOW.

| b Total Federal income tax withheld (If line 7 is more than $29,700, see page 13 of Instructions) . . . . | 13b 2306 00 | |

Please Attach Copy B of Forms W–2 Here

EXERCISES

Refer to the completed form on page 278 to answer the following questions.

1. What is the filing status?

2. An exemption is someone who is supported by the tax-payer. How many exemptions are there? Who are they?

3. What does the entry on line 7 represent?

4. What was the Browns' taxable income from interest and dividends (line 8e)?

5. What was their adjusted gross income?

6. What was their taxable income?

7. How much income tax was withheld from their pay?

This table is like the one the Browns can use to find the amount of their income tax.

If line 12 (taxable income) is —		And you are—			
At least	But less than	Single	Married filing jointly	Married filing sepa-rately	Head of a house-hold
			Your tax is—		
16,500	16,550	3,024	2,361	3,637	2,837
16,550	16,600	3,039	2,373	3,655	2,849
16,600	16,650	3,054	2,385	3,674	2,862
16,650	16,700	3,069	2,397	3,692	2,875
16,700	16,750	3,083	2,409	3,710	2,888
16,750	16,800	3,098	2,420	3,729	2,901
16,800	16,850	3,113	2,432	3,747	2,914
16,850	16,900	3,128	2,444	3,765	2,926
16,900	16,950	3,143	2,456	3,783	2,939
16,950	17,000	3,158	2,468	3,802	2,952

If line 12 (taxable income) is —		And you are—			
At least	But less than	Single	Married filing jointly	Married filing sepa-rately	Head of a house-hold
			Your tax is—		
17,000	17,050	3,172	2,480	3,820	2,965
17,050	17,100	3,187	2,491	3,838	2,978
17,100	17,150	3,202	2,503	3,856	2,991
17,150	17,200	3,217	2,515	3,875	3,003
17,200	17,250	3,232	2,527	3,893	3,016
17,250	17,300	3,246	2,539	3,911	3,029
17,300	17,350	3,261	2,551	3,930	3,042
17,350	17,400	3,276	2,563	3,948	3,055
17,400	17,450	3,291	2,574	3,966	3,068
17,450	17,500	3,306	2,586	3,984	3,081

8. Use the table to find the Browns' income tax.

9. Was the amount of tax withheld from the Browns' pay greater or less than the income tax they should pay? How much?

★ 10. Mr. and Mrs. Delano have 3 children and file a joint return. Their adjusted gross income (line 10) is $22,178. Find their taxable income (line 12) and then use the tax table to find the amount of their income tax.

Spending wisely

Mike is looking at some blue jeans. Before he decides to buy the jeans, he should ask himself such questions as

1. Is the price within my budget?
2. Do I really need or want another pair of jeans at this time?
3. Are they well made?
4. Can I buy the jeans at a better price?

Can you think of other questions that Mike should ask himself?

Mike decided to buy the jeans.
The regular price was $22.60.
They were on sale for 25% off.
Here are two ways to find the sale price:

$22.60 ← regular price
×0.25
11300
4520
$5.6500 ← discount

$22.60 ← regular price
−5.65 ← discount
$16.95 ← sale price

$22.60 ← regular price
×0.75
11300
15820
$16.9500 ← sale price

If the discount is 25%, then the sale price is 75% of the regular price.

EXERCISES

Compute the sale price.

1. Regular price
$26.40

2. Regular price
$32.80

3. Regular price
$22.40

4. Gym socks
5 pairs for $12.75

5. T-shirts
$7.98 each

6. Gym shorts
$6.96 each

The state Mike lives in has a 5% sales tax. Here is how to find the total cost of the blue jeans he bought:

$16.95 ← price
×0.05
$.8475 ← sales tax

$16.95 ← price
+.85 ← sales tax
$17.80 ← total cost

Compute the total cost, including a 5% sales tax. Round each answer to the nearest cent.

7. 1 pair of blue jeans for $17.80

8. 2 pairs of blue jeans for $21.80 each

9. 1 shirt for $8.65 and 3 pairs of socks for $1.60 a pair

10. 2 pairs of blue jeans for $21.50 each and 3 shirts for $9.28 each

Solve.

11. David bought a $24.30 pair of blue jeans that was on sale for 30% off. What was the total cost, including a 5% sales tax?

12. Jan bought a $5.60 belt that was on sale for 25% off and a $24.30 pair of jeans that was on sale for 20% off. What was the total cost, including a 5% sales tax?

★ **13.** Lou Ann returned a shirt and received a $15.73 refund. She then bought another shirt for 30% off the regular price of $22.50. She was charged 5% sales tax. How much more money did she need?

14. Find out whether the state in which you live has a sales tax. What is the rate?

Problem solving

1.

In the American colonies, the Spanish dollar was often used. To make change, the Spanish dollar was cut into *bits*. A bit was $\frac{1}{8}$ of a dollar. What was the value of 4 bits? Of 6 bits? Have you ever heard anyone call a quarter 2 bits?

2.

This was the first paper money issued by the Second Continental Congress in 1775. (Paul Revere engraved the bills.) Eighty-five years earlier, the state of Massachusetts issued paper money to pay its troops. In what year was that?

3.

The first United States coin was a one-cent piece minted in 1787. How many years ago was that?

4.

The ten-dollar gold pieces issued in 1795 contained 247.5 grains of gold. A grain is 64.799 mg. How many grams of gold were in the ten-dollar gold piece? Round your answer to the nearest tenth of a gram.

5.

The silver dollar was also issued in 1795. By law, the ratio of the weight of pure gold in the gold dollar to the weight of pure silver in the silver dollar was 1 to 15. The gold dollar contained 24.75 grains of pure gold. How many grains of pure silver were in a silver dollar?

6. In 1900, Congress enacted the Gold Standard Act, which declared the dollar the standard unit of value. It was based upon 25.8 grains of gold that was 0.9 pure. What was the value of the dollar in grains of pure gold?

Money in Circulation in U.S.
1920–1980

Each ⬚$ stands for $5 billion.

1920	1930	1940	1950	1960	1970	1980

7. About how much money was in circulation in 1940? In 1980?

8. About how much more money was in circulation in 1950 than in 1920?

9. What was the approximate increase of money in circulation from 1960 to 1970?

10. What was the approximate percent of increase from 1960 to 1980?

Borrowing money— simple interest

When you borrow money from a bank, credit union, or loan company, you pay for the use of it. The amount you pay is called **interest.** The interest paid depends upon the amount borrowed (**principal**), the length of time the money is kept (**time**), and the percent of interest charged (**rate**).

Here is how to compute the interest on an $800 loan at 18% interest. It was repaid in 6 months.

> Principal = $800
> Rate　　 = 18% per year
> Time　　 = 6 months $\frac{1}{2}$ year

Simple Interest Formula: $I = prt$

$$I = \$800 \times \frac{18}{100} \times \frac{1}{2}$$

$$I = \$72$$

Important: When you use the simple interest formula, the time and the interest period of the rate must be expressed in the same unit. In the example above, the rate was a yearly rate, so the time had to be expressed in years.

EXERCISES

Compute the interest. Round to the nearest cent.

1. Principal = $1000
   Rate = 13% per year
   Time = 1 year

2. Principal = $700
   Rate = 19.5% per year
   Time = 3 years

3. Principal = $950
   Rate = 16.5% per year
   Time = 6 months

4. Principal = $500
   Rate = 12% per year
   Time = 3 months

5. Principal = $700
   Rate = 12.5% per year
   Time = 15 months

6. Principal = $450
   Rate = 21.5% per year
   Time = 1 year

Sometimes money is borrowed for a short period of time, for example, a few days.

Example.   Principal = $600

Rate = 15% per year

Time: from 1/1/79 to 1/25/79

Time = 24 days

$I = 600 \times \dfrac{15}{100} \times \dfrac{24}{365}$

$I = \$5.92$

Compute the interest. Round to the nearest cent.

7. Principal: $500
   Rate: 12% per year
   Time: from 1/1/79
   　　　to 1/28/79

8. Principal: $780
   Rate: 15% per year
   Time: from 3/1/79
   　　　to 4/18/79

9. Suppose that you borrowed $500 at 12.5% per year. One month later you paid $100 on your loan. How much of the $100 was interest? How much principal would you still owe?

Installment buying

Tomas wants to buy a guitar that costs $160. Since he doesn't have enough money to pay cash, he has decided to buy it on an **installment plan.** He will make a **down payment** and then pay the balance in regular **monthly payments.**

Since the merchant is really lending Tomas an amount of money, he charges Tomas interest on that amount.

CASH PLAN	INSTALLMENT PLAN
$160	$40 down payment and $11.40 per month for 1 year

$11.40 ← per month
$\times 12$ ← months
2280
1140
$136.80 ← total monthly payments
+40.00 ← down payment
$176.80 ← installment plan cost

   The installment plan costs $16.80 more than paying cash for the guitar. The $16.80 is interest. Before buying something on an installment plan, check to see if you could pay less by borrowing the money from a bank or credit union.

EXERCISES

How much greater than the cash price is the installment price?

1. Drums: $175 cash or $50 down and $11.67 per month for 12 months.

2. Bass guitar: $280 cash or $70 down and $13.77 per month for 18 months.

3. Amplifier: $265.88 cash or $60 down and $37.40 per month for 6 months.

4. Guitar: $475 cash or $100 down and $34.37 per month for 1 year.

5. Andrew bought a $627 stereo set on the installment plan. The down payment was $150.

   a. After paying the down payment, how much did he owe? This amount is the principal of the installment loan.

   b. The first monthly payment was $43.72. Of that payment, $3.98 was interest and the rest was principal. How much was paid on the principal?

   c. After the first payment was made, how much principal was still owed? This is called the **unpaid balance.**

   d. Since the principal during the second month was less, the interest was also less. Of the next $43.72 payment, $3.64 was interest. How much was principal?

   e. After the second payment was made, how much was the unpaid balance?

6. Sarah bought a used car priced at $3400. She paid $1000 down and 30 monthly payments of $120.

   a. What was the total amount of the monthly payments?

   b. What was the principal of the installment loan?

   c. What was the amount of interest?

   ★ d. What was the simple interest rate?

Checking accounts

The basic idea of a checking account is simple. You give the bank some money, called a **deposit.** When you need some of the money, you write a check, which tells the bank how much to take from your account and to whom it is to be paid.

B Person or business to whom the money is *to be paid*

A The *date* the check was written

Carl R. Parker
1525 Oak Street
Sometown USA

No. *874*

January 20 ,19 *83*

Pay to the
Order of *Dennis Morgan*

$ *56 34/100*

Fifty - six and 34/100 Dollars

*National
City Bank*

⑆011205⑉ ⑈743 628⑈

C The *amount* of the check is written two ways to avoid error and possible alteration.

D The *signature* assures the bank that the check is authentic. It can be checked against the signature on file.

The check also acts as a receipt, because the person who receives the money endorses the check (signs his name on the back of the check). This is proof that he received the money.

EXERCISES

Look at the check on page 288. Tell how you would fill in Ⓐ, Ⓑ, Ⓒ, and Ⓓ for each of the following transactions.

1. On January 24, 1983, Mr. Parker took his dog to the Central Animal Clinic for some shots. The shots cost $15.75.

2. On January 25, 1983, Mr. Parker bought a TV set for $695.20 from Nichols Furniture Company.

3. On January 26, 1983, Mr. Parker paid his electric bill by check. The amount was $50.25. The company was Northwest Power Company.

4. On January 26, 1983, Mr. Parker needed $40 in cash. He went to his bank and deposited $157.35. He wrote a check to "cash."

5. Mr. Parker's checkbook has a section in which he keeps a record of his account. Complete each balance.

Check No.	Date	Pay to	Amount	Deposit	Balance	
					$895	38
874	Jan. 20	Dennis Morgan	$56.34		839	04
	Jan. 20			200.00	1039	04
875	Jan. 24	Central Animal Clinic	15.75			
876	Jan. 25	Nichols Furniture Co.	695.20			
877	Jan. 26	Northwest Power	50.25			
878	Jan. 26	Cash	40.00	157.35		

6. The National City Bank charges Mr. Parker a service charge if his balance falls below $200. Did he have to pay a service charge during the time shown in the record above?

7. Why do you think that the bank does not charge for a checking account when the balance stays above $200?

★ 8. Find out whether a local bank charges a service charge. If so, how do they determine how much is charged?

★ 9. List some advantages to having a checking account. Can you think of any disadvantages?

Computers in careers

Often computer programmers write programs that involve branches and loops. Study this flow chart.

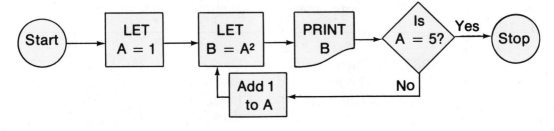

Now study this program to see how the program *branches* at a question, how *loops* are written, and how to tell the computer to skip steps.

```
10   LET A = 1
20   LET B  = A↑2
25   PRINT B
30   IF A = 5 THEN 60
40   LET A = A + 1
50   GØ TØ 20
60   END
```

At line 30 there is a **branch.** The statement tells the computer to skip to line 60 (END) if A = 5. If A is not 5, then the computer goes to the next line, line 40.

Line 40 is a little strange, since it is impossible for a number to *equal* a number 1 greater. This statement tells the computer to add 1 to the number stored in A and then to store that new number back in A. This means that the old value of A is lost, but that's OK since it has already served its purpose.

Line 50 tells the computer to go back to line 20 and do the computation with the new value of A. Lines 20, 25, 30, 40, and 50 form a **loop.** The computer repeats the steps over and over until A = 5. Then it skips to line 60 and stops.

Notice the new words that the computer recognizes:

IF . . . THEN
GØ TØ

EXERCISES

Be the computer. Follow the program.

1. 10   LET A = 1
    20   LET C = 2 * A
    30   PRINT C
    40   IF A = 10 THEN 70
    50   LET A = A + 1
    60   GØ TØ 20
    70   END

2. 100   LET G = 1
    200   LET H = 1
    300   LET I = G + H
    400   PRINT I
    500   IF H = 6 THEN 900
    600   LET G = G + 1
    700   LET H = H + 1
    800   GØ TØ 300
    900   END

3. 100   LET M = 1
    110   LET N = 2 ↑ M
    120   PRINT N
    130   IF N = 32 THEN 160
    140   LET M = M + 2
    150   GØ TØ 110
    160   END

4. 1000   LET A = 1
    2000   LET B = A ↑ 2
    3000   PRINT B
    4000   IF A = 10 THEN 7000
    5000   LET A = A + 1
    6000   GØ TØ 2000
    7000   END

5. 10   LET A = 1
    20   LET C = 3 * A
    30   PRINT C
    40   IF A = 20 THEN 70
    50   LET A = A + 1
    60   GØ TØ 20
    70   END

6. 10   LET A = 1
    20   LET B = 3.14 * (A ↑ 2)
    30   PRINT B
    40   IF A = 5 THEN 80
    60   LET A = A + 1
    70   GØ TØ 20
    80   END

7. Write flow charts for the programs in exercises 1–4.

8. Write a program for this flow chart.

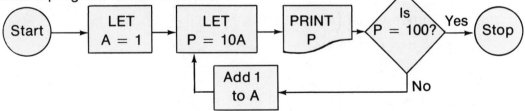

Savings accounts

	Date	Withdrawal	Deposit	Interest	Balance
No. 22357			⚶ VILLAGE SAVINGS BANK		
1 2	1/1/83		$500.00		$500.00
3 4	4/1/83			$6.25	$506.25
5 6	7/1/83			$6.33	$512.58
7 8	10/1/83			$6.41	$518.99
9 10	1/1/84			$6.49	$525.48

You may have a savings account at a bank (or a savings and loan company). If so, you receive interest on the money in your account. This interest is **compound interest** instead of simple interest. This means that the interest is added to the principal at regular intervals and that the principal gets larger and larger. In this example the interest is 5% per year compounded quarterly.

Jan. 1 $500 deposited

April 1 $6.25 interest paid $\left(5\% \times 500 \times \frac{1}{4}\right)$
            $506.25 new principal

July 1 $6.33 interest paid $\left(5\% \times 506.25 \times \frac{1}{4}\right)$
            $512.58 new principal

Oct. 1 $6.41 interest paid $\left(5\% \times 512.58 \times \frac{1}{4}\right)$
            $518.99 new principal

Jan. 1 $6.49 interest paid $\left(5\% \times 518.99 \times \frac{1}{4}\right)$
            $525.48 new principal

How much interest was paid in 1 year?
How much interest would have been paid at 5% simple interest?

EXERCISES

1. Pretend that on January 1 you deposited $1000 in a savings account that pays 6% interest compounded quarterly.

   a. How much interest will your account earn the first quarter?
   b. What will the principal be for the second quarter?
   c. What will the interest be for the second quarter?
   d. What will the principal be for the third quarter?
   e. How much will the third-quarter interest be?
   f. What will be the fourth-quarter principal?
   g. How much will the fourth-quarter interest be?
   h. What will be the total interest earned during the year?
   i. What percent of the original $1000 deposit is the total interest earned?
   j. How much greater is the actual percent earned than the 6% rate used?

This table shows the total interest accumulated when $1000 is on deposit at 6% and at 7% interest, both compounded quarterly.

2. How much interest is earned in the first year at 6%?

3. How much interest is earned in the first 2 years at 6%?

4. How much interest is earned at 6% in the 2nd year? 3rd year? 4th year? 5th year?

Total Amount of Interest
When $1000 Is on Deposit

Year	6% compounded quarterly	7% compounded quarterly
1	$ 61.36	$ 71.86
2	126.49	148.88
3	195.62	241.44
4	268.98	319.93
5	346.85	414.78
. . .	. . .	. . .
10	814.02	1001.60

5. Why does the amount of interest earned increase from year to year?

6. How much more interest is earned in the first year at 7% than at 6%?

7. Suppose you invest $1000 at 7% *simple interest* for 10 years. How much interest would you earn? How much more would you earn at 7% compounded quarterly?

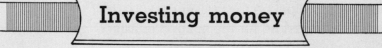

Investing money

There are many ways to invest money. You can earn interest by lending money to the federal government (buying savings bonds) or by lending money to a corporation (buying corporate bonds). You also can become a part-owner of almost any large company by buying shares of stock in the company. As an owner, you will share in the profits of the company.

EXERCISES

1. **a.** A $100 United States Savings Bond cost $50. At the end of 11 years the bond will be worth $100. What is the amount of interest? What is the simple annual interest rate?

   b. If a savings bond is held for less than 5 years, a lower rate of interest is paid. At the end of 1 year a $100 bond is worth $52.25. What is the amount of interest? What is the simple annual interest rate?

2. Jean bought a $1000 bond from a large company. The bond pays 9% interest each year.

   a. How much interest does she receive each year?
   b. The company pays the interest semiannually (every 6 months). How much is Jean paid each 6 months?
   c. The bond matures in 10 years. This means that the company will repay the loan 10 years after she bought the bond. How much interest will she earn in all?

3. Stock prices are given in dollars and eighths of dollars. (An eighth of a dollar is 12.5¢, or $.125.) Suppose one share of stock in General Electronics Company can be bought for $23\frac{3}{8}$ ($23.375). What will 100 shares cost?

4. In each exercise, you are given the price per share of a stock and a number of shares. Compute the total cost.

   a. 100 shares at $18\frac{1}{2}$ per share

   b. 1000 shares at $3\frac{3}{4}$ per share

   c. 50 shares at $47\frac{5}{8}$ per share

   d. 200 shares at $83\frac{7}{8}$ per share

   e. 25 shares at $10\frac{1}{8}$ per share

   f. 43 shares at $112\frac{3}{8}$ per share

5. Suppose that you own 20 shares of Cooper Oil Company stock. The company pays a dividend (part of the profits) of 22¢ per share each quarter. How much would you receive in a year?

6. Suppose that you bought 100 shares of General Electronics at $21\frac{3}{8}$ per share and sold them a year later at $29\frac{1}{8}$. How much did your stock increase in value? (Not all the gain is profit. You must pay a **stock broker** a commission both for buying and for selling stock.)

7. You bought 50 shares of International Motor Company stock at $93\frac{1}{4}$ per share. Two years later it was worth $74\frac{3}{8}$ per share. How much did the stock decrease in value?

8. Suppose that you bought 150 shares of International Industries for $17\frac{5}{8}$ per share plus a 1.5% commission to the stockbroker. One year later you sold the stock for $13\frac{3}{8}$ per share and paid a 1.5% commission on the sale. How much money did you lose on this investment?

Write as a decimal or mixed decimal.

1. $\frac{7}{8}$

2. $\frac{3}{4}$

3. $\frac{3}{2}$

4. $\frac{1}{3}$

5. $\frac{5}{6}$

6. $\frac{5}{12}$

7. $1\frac{1}{4}$

8. $1\frac{3}{5}$

9. $2\frac{1}{2}$

10. $2\frac{3}{4}$

11. $3\frac{3}{8}$

12. $1\frac{2}{3}$

13. 18%

14. 9%

15. 0.5%

16. 0.06%

17. $66\frac{2}{3}$%

18. $9\frac{1}{3}$%

Solve. [pages 274–275]

1. Robert earns $6.85 per hour for a 40-hour week, with time and a half for overtime. How much does he earn in a 44-hour week?

2. Sandy earns $9600 per year plus 7% of all sales above $150,000. What does she earn in a year if her total sales are $175,000?

Solve. [pages 280–281]

3. **a.** The radio regularly sells for $39.95. What is the sale price?
   b. Suppose that there is a 5% sales tax. Compute the total cost of the radio, including the sales tax.

Compute the simple interest for a loan of [pages 284–285]

4. $300 at 10% per year for 2 years.

5. $500 at 8% per year for 3 months.

Solve. [pages 286–289; 292–295]

6. Ms. Kendrick bought a $380 TV set for $100 down and $11.95 per week for 26 weeks. How much extra did it cost her to use the installment plan?

7. Jerry Black had a balance of $216.12 in his checking account. He then wrote checks for $85.15, $26.85, and $50.00 and deposited $89.90. What was his balance then?

8. Alice has $480 in a credit union that pays her $6\frac{1}{2}$% interest compounded semiannually. How much interest will she earn in 1 year?

9. Jon bought a $1000 corporate bond that paid $5\frac{3}{4}$% interest. How much interest was he paid every 6 months?

10. Mrs. Pitkin bought 20 shares of stock that paid a 40¢ quarterly dividend on each share. She paid $25\frac{1}{4}$ per share. How much was her total yearly dividend?

1. Look at the used-car ads in a newspaper and pick out a car you would like to buy.

2. What is the price?

3. Assume that you would have to pay 25% down. What would be your down payment?

4. How much would you still owe?

Monthly Payment to Repay $1 at an Annual Rate of 15%	
Number of Monthly Payments	Amount of Payment
6	$0.17403
9	0.11816
12	0.09026
15	0.07352
18	0.06238
24	0.04848

5. The table at the right can be used to help you find how much the monthly payments would be if you paid 15% yearly interest.

   a. Pick the number of monthly payments you wish to make.
   b. Find the number in the table opposite the number of months you picked.
   c. Multiply that number by the balance you owe. This is the monthly payment.

6. How much would you actually pay for the car?

7. How much more than the cash price would you pay?

Find the pay for 40 hours and add the pay for the 6 hours overtime.

1. A company pays its employees time and a half for all hours over 40 that they work each week. How much should they pay a worker that earns $5.30 an hour and works 46 hours?

20% off $24.60
is the same as
80% of $24.60

2. a. Compute the sale price of the tennis racket.

    b. Compute the total price if there is a 6% sales tax.

Find the simple interest for a loan of

3. $240 at 6% for one year.

$$I = prt$$

Interest = principal ×
rate × time

4. $385 at 8.5% for 2 years.

5. $750 at 9% for 9 months.
    Hint: 9 months is $\frac{3}{4}$ of a year.

6. a. How much is the down payment?

    b. What is the total of the 12 monthly payments?

    c. Give the total installment cost.

The total installment cost is the down payment plus the total of the monthly payments.

Only $45 down and $12.50 a month for 1 year.

Consider an investment of $1000 at an interest rate of 6.5% compounded quarterly for a period of 2 years (8 quarters). Here is a BASIC program that will compute and print the principal at the end of each quarter. Notice that the value of A is used as a **counter.** Statements 10, 60, and 70 tell the computer to count the times that the interest is added to the principal and to stop when the number reaches 8.

```
10   LET A = 1
20   LET P = 1000
30   LET I = P * 0.065 / 4
40   LET P = P + I
50   PRINT P
60   IF A = 8 THEN 90
70   LET A = A + 1
80   GØ TØ 30
90   END
```

1. Be a computer and work through the program given above.

2. Consider an investment of $1 at 7.75% compounded quarterly. Write a program that will compute and print the principal at the end of each quarter for a period of 10 years.

3. Write a program that will compute and print the number of quarters that it will take a principal of $1000 to double at 6.5% compounded quarterly.

299

b c d   a b c d   a b c d   a b c d   a b c d   a b c d

2.

MAJOR CHECKUP
STANDARDIZED FORMAT

5.   6.

b c d   a b c d   a b c d   a b c d   a b c d

8.   9.   10.   11.   12.

Choose the correct letter.

1. The least common multiple of 6 and 9 is

- **a.** 36
- **b.** 3
- **c.** 18
- **d.** none of these

2. Find the circumference. Use 3.14 as an approximation for π.

1.2 m

- **a.** 3.768 m
- **b.** 7.536 m
- **c.** 4.5216 m
- **d.** none of these

3. Give the difference.

$$3\frac{2}{3} - 2\frac{3}{4}$$

- **a.** $1\frac{11}{12}$
- **b.** $1\frac{1}{12}$
- **c.** $\frac{1}{12}$
- **d.** none of these

---

4. Give the product.

$$2\frac{1}{2} \times 1\frac{3}{5}$$

- **a.** 4
- **b.** $\frac{1}{4}$
- **c.** $1\frac{9}{16}$
- **d.** none of these

5. Compute the area.

8 cm   8 cm   6.4 cm   9.6 cm

- **a.** 61.44 cm²
- **b.** 38.4 cm²
- **c.** 30.72 cm²
- **d.** none of these

6. Solve.

$$\frac{5}{n} = \frac{3}{8}$$

- **a.** $4\frac{4}{5}$
- **b.** $\frac{5}{24}$
- **c.** $1\frac{7}{8}$
- **d.** none of these

---

7. Solve.

$$33\frac{1}{3}\% \text{ of } 60 = n$$

- **a.** 40
- **b.** 180
- **c.** 20
- **d.** none of these

8.

B   A   C

Triangle *ABC* is
- **a.** an isosceles triangle
- **b.** an equilateral triangle
- **c.** a scalene triangle
- **d.** none of these

9. Give the total installment cost.
$38.95 down
$34.79 a month for 1 year

- **a.** $456.43
- **b.** $884.88
- **c.** $502.19
- **d.** none of these

---

10. The simple interest for a loan of $600 at 8% a year for 9 months is

- **a.** $48
- **b.** $24
- **c.** $36
- **d.** none of these

11. Laura hiked 0.4 mile in 5 minutes. At that rate, how many miles could she hike in an hour?

- **a.** 2
- **b.** 2.4
- **c.** 4.8
- **d.** none of these

12. David earned $26.10 for working 6 hours. How much did he earn per hour?

- **a.** $4.35
- **b.** $4.40
- **c.** $156.60
- **d.** none of these

300

Positive and Negative Numbers

11

Windchill Factor: ⁻29°

Positive and negative numbers

We can use **positive** and **negative** numbers to measure quantities that have direction.

On one passing play the Richmond Eagles gained 17 yards. A gain of 17 yards can be represented by

$$^{+}\mathbf{17}$$

Read as "positive 17."

On one running play they lost 6 yards. A loss of 6 yards can be represented by

$$^{-}\mathbf{6}$$

Read as "negative 6."

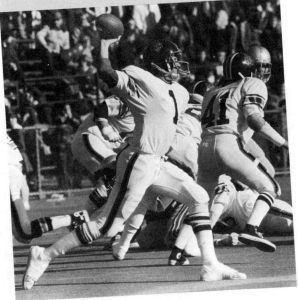

· SPORTS ·

Defense holds Lions to ⁻12 yards rushing in first quarter.

Any time we work with **directed** quantities, we can use positive numbers for quantities with one direction and negative numbers for quantities with the opposite direction.

Positive and negative numbers are shown on the number line below. The numbers in red are called **integers.**

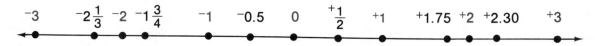

The numbers to the right of 0 are positive.
The numbers to the left of 0 are negative.
The number 0 is neither positive nor negative.

Integers can also represent electrical charges. Imagine containers that have mixtures of positive and negative charges in them. The charges form as many positive-negative pairs as possible. The pairs have no charge. Count the unpaired charges to find the charge in the container.

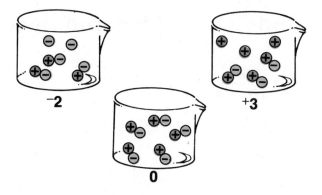

EXERCISES

If ⁻8° represents 8° below zero, then what number would represent

1. 7 degrees above zero?

2. 15 degrees below zero?

If ⁺2$\frac{1}{2}$ represents being 2$\frac{1}{2}$ hours ahead of schedule, then what number would represent

3. 4$\frac{1}{4}$ hours ahead of schedule?

4. 6$\frac{3}{4}$ hours behind schedule?

5. neither ahead of nor behind schedule?

Use integers to represent the charges in these containers.

6.

7.

8.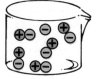

The number line can be used to show the order of positive and negative numbers. A number is less than every number to its right and greater than every number to its left.

$$\overset{\longleftarrow\bullet\quad\bullet\qquad\bullet\quad\bullet\qquad\bullet\qquad\bullet\quad\bullet\qquad\bullet\quad\bullet\qquad\bullet\qquad\bullet\quad\bullet\bullet\longrightarrow}{{}^-3\ \ {}^-2\tfrac{5}{8}\quad {}^-2\ {}^-1.6\quad {}^-1\quad \tfrac{{}^-2}{5}\ \ 0\quad {}^+\tfrac{3}{4}\ {}^+1\ {}^+1.41\quad {}^+2\quad {}^+\tfrac{5}{2}\quad {}^+3\ {}^+3\tfrac{1}{5}}$$

<, =, or >?

9. ⁻2 ● ⁻3

10. ⁺2 ● ⁺3

11. ⁻3 ● ⁺2

12. ⁺3 ● ⁻2

13. ⁺1.41 ● 0

14. ⁻1.6 ● ⁻2$\frac{5}{8}$

15. $\frac{⁺5}{2}$ ● ⁺3$\frac{1}{5}$

16. 0 ● $\frac{⁻2}{5}$

17. $\frac{⁻3}{4}$ ● ⁻0.7

18. ⁺2$\frac{1}{2}$ ● $\frac{⁺5}{2}$

19. $\frac{⁺3}{5}$ ● $\frac{⁺5}{8}$

20. ⁻1.6 ● ⁻1$\frac{1}{2}$

21. $\frac{⁻5}{3}$ ● ⁻1$\frac{2}{3}$

22. $\frac{⁺5}{8}$ ● ⁺0.625

23. ⁻16$\frac{1}{2}$ ● ⁻16.48

24. 0 ● ⁻0.004

Adding positive and negative numbers

To understand how to add, you can think about putting charges together.

EXAMPLE 1. $^+4 + {}^+2 = ?$

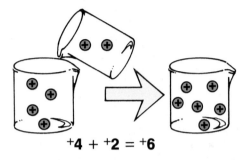

$$^+4 + {}^+2 = {}^+6$$

EXAMPLE 2. $^-2 + {}^-3 = ?$

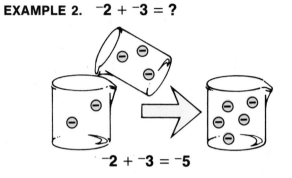

$$^-2 + {}^-3 = {}^-5$$

EXAMPLE 3. $^+5 + {}^-3 = ?$

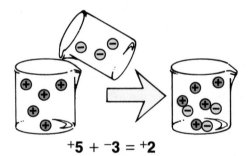

$$^+5 + {}^-3 = {}^+2$$

EXAMPLE 4. $^-5 + {}^+2 = ?$

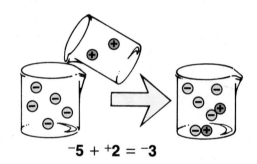

$$^-5 + {}^+2 = {}^-3$$

EXAMPLE 5. $^+4 + {}^-4 = ?$

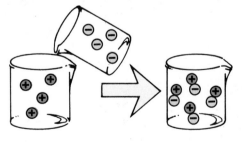

$$^+4 + {}^-4 = 0$$

$^+4$ and $^-4$ are called **opposites,** because their sum is 0.

$^-16$ is the opposite of $^+16$. 0 is its own opposite.

EXERCISES

Give each sum.

1. $^+5 + {}^+2$

2. $^-5 + {}^-2$

3. $^+5 + {}^-2$

4. $^-5 + {}^+2$

5. $^+6 + {}^+8$

6. $^-6 + {}^-8$

7. $^+6 + {}^-8$

8. $^-6 + {}^+8$

9. $^+7 + {}^+5$

10. $^-7 + {}^-5$

11. $^+7 + {}^-5$

12. $^-7 + {}^+5$

13. $^+4 + {}^+6$

14. $^-4 + {}^-6$

15. $^+4 + {}^-6$

16. $^-4 + {}^+6$

17. $^+9 + 0$

18. $^-9 + 0$

19. $^+4 + 0$

20. $^-4 + 0$

21. $^+18 + {}^+12$

22. $^-18 + {}^-12$

23. $^+18 + {}^-12$

24. $^-18 + {}^+12$

25. $^-8 + {}^+7$

26. $^-8 + {}^-7$

27. $^+8 + {}^-7$

28. $^+8 + {}^+7$

29. $^-16 + {}^-15$

30. $^+16 + {}^-15$

31. $^-16 + {}^+15$

32. $^+16 + {}^+15$

33. $\dfrac{^+3}{4} + \dfrac{^-1}{2}$

34. $\dfrac{^+3}{4} + \dfrac{^+1}{2}$

35. $\dfrac{^-3}{4} + \dfrac{^+1}{2}$

36. $\dfrac{^-3}{4} + \dfrac{^-1}{2}$

37. $^-3.8 + {}^+6.9$

38. $0 + \dfrac{^+5}{8}$

39. $^+8.5 + {}^-3.4$

40. $\dfrac{^-7}{4} + 0$

41. $\dfrac{^-3}{8} + \dfrac{^+3}{8}$

42. $\dfrac{^+3}{2} + \dfrac{^-3}{2}$

43. $^-2.4 + {}^+2.4$

44. $\dfrac{^+15}{24} + \dfrac{^-15}{24}$

True or false?

45. The sum of two positive numbers is always positive.

46. The sum of two negative numbers is always positive.

47. The sum of a positive number and a negative number is always positive.

48. The sum of a positive number and a negative number is always negative.

49. The sum of a positive number and a negative number may be positive, negative, or 0.

50. The sum of two opposites is 0.

Give the opposite of each number.

51. $^+6$

52. $^-23$

53. $^+6.2$

54. $\dfrac{^-3}{5}$

55. 0

56. $^+7.082$

305

Subtracting positive and negative numbers

You can understand how to subtract by thinking about taking charges out of a container.

EXAMPLE 1. $^{+}4 - {}^{+}1 = ?$

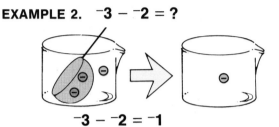

$$^{+}4 - {}^{+}1 = {}^{+}3$$

EXAMPLE 2. $^{-}3 - {}^{-}2 = ?$

$$^{-}3 - {}^{-}2 = {}^{-}1$$

EXAMPLE 3. $^{+}2 - {}^{+}5 = ?$

We do not have 5 ⊕ to take out.

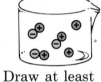

Draw at least 3 ⊕⊖ pairs.

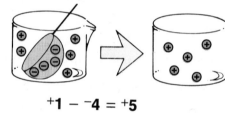

$$^{+}2 - {}^{+}5 = {}^{-}3$$

EXAMPLE 4. $^{+}1 - {}^{-}4 = ?$

We do not have 4 ⊖ to take out.

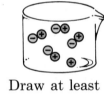

Draw at least 4 ⊕⊖ pairs.

$$^{+}1 - {}^{-}4 = {}^{+}5$$

Addition and subtraction are closely related. Study these examples.

$^{+}6 - {}^{+}3 = {}^{+}3$	$^{-}5 - {}^{-}4 = {}^{-}1$	$^{+}3 - {}^{+}7 = {}^{-}4$	$^{+}3 - {}^{-}8 = {}^{+}11$
$^{+}6 + {}^{-}3 = {}^{+}3$	$^{-}5 + {}^{+}4 = {}^{-}1$	$^{+}3 + {}^{-}7 = {}^{-}4$	$^{+}3 + {}^{+}8 = {}^{+}11$

These examples give us a way to subtract.

To subtract a number, add the opposite. $^{-}7 - {}^{+}4 = {}^{-}7 + {}^{-}4 = {}^{-}11$

306

EXERCISES

Copy and complete.

1. $^+9 - {}^+3 = {}^+9 + {}^-3$
   $= ?$

2. $^-6 - {}^+2 = {}^-6 + {}^-2$
   $= ?$

3. $^+8 - {}^-4 = {}^+8 + {}^+4$
   $= ?$

4. $^-7 - {}^-5 = {}^-7 + {}^+5$
   $= ?$

5. $^-3 - {}^+7 = {}^-3 + ?$
   $= ?$

6. $^+9 - {}^-4 = {}^+9 + ?$
   $= ?$

Give each difference.

7. $^+5 - {}^+8$

8. $^+6 - {}^-2$

9. $^-9 - {}^-5$

10. $^-7 - {}^+4$

11. $^+3 - {}^-8$

12. $^+4 - 0$

13. $^+8 - {}^-3$

14. $^-8 - {}^+3$

15. $^-6 - {}^-2$

16. $0 - {}^-5$

17. $^-9 - {}^+3$

18. $^+6 - {}^-8$

19. $^-12 - {}^-9$

20. $^+15 - {}^+19$

21. $^-13 - {}^+23$

22. $^-25 - {}^-19$

23. $^-16 - {}^+17$

24. $^+15 - {}^-15$

25. $^+\frac{1}{2} - {}^+\frac{1}{4}$

26. $^-\frac{3}{8} - {}^-\frac{1}{4}$

27. $^-\frac{2}{3} - {}^+\frac{5}{6}$

28. $^+3.4 - {}^+2.5$

29. $^-5.6 - {}^+3.8$

30. $^-9.6 - {}^-7.4$

Copy and complete the addition-subtraction boxes. Add across and subtract down.

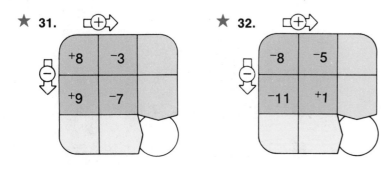

★ 31.

★ 32.

KEEPING SKILLS SHARP

Solve.

1. $x + 18 = 25$

2. $y - 32 = 17$

3. $z + 23 = 49$

4. $56 + t = 87$

5. $51 + t = 51$

6. $r - 29 = 24$

7. $s - 64 = 95$

8. $36 + t = 194$

9. $r + 30 = 51$

10. $n - 62 = 80$

11. $42.6 + m = 94.9$

12. $k - 68.91 = 28.24$

13. $x + 2.67 = 5.94$

14. $y - 3.26 = 4.79$

15. $5.83 + s = 9.72$

16. $c - 2.17 = 8.24$

Practice exercises

Simplify.

1. $^+5 + {}^-8$

2. $^+9 - {}^+5$

3. $0 - {}^-9$

4. $^-6 + {}^+5$

5. $^+3 - {}^-9$

6. $^+7 + {}^+7$

7. $^+8 + {}^-7$

8. $^-6 - {}^-9$

9. $^-4 + {}^-6$

10. $^+5 + {}^-4$

11. $^-2 - {}^-6$

12. $^+8 - {}^+8$

13. $^-15 + {}^+16$

14. $^-19 - {}^-17$

15. $^-15 - {}^+12$

16. $^-9 + {}^-18$

17. $^+16 - {}^+20$

18. $^-23 - {}^+15$

19. $^-32 + {}^+14$

20. $^+23 + {}^+14$

21. $^+11 + {}^-11$

22. $^+16 + {}^-23$

23. $^-15 - {}^+16$

24. $^-16 - {}^-42$

25. $^-14 + {}^-23$

26. $^+17 - {}^+32$

27. $^+45 + {}^+38$

28. $^-19 - 0$

29. $^+23 - {}^-78$

30. $^-95 + {}^+34$

31. $^-62 - {}^-78$

32. $0 + {}^+93$

33. $\dfrac{^+2}{3} - \dfrac{^+5}{8}$

34. $\dfrac{^+1}{2} + \dfrac{^-4}{5}$

35. $\dfrac{^-3}{8} + \dfrac{^-2}{3}$

36. $\dfrac{^+7}{4} - \dfrac{^+3}{2}$

37. $^-2.75 + {}^+4.16$

38. $^-3.14 - {}^-2.65$

39. $^+16.8 - {}^-4.21$

40. $^+39.1 - {}^+42.6$

<, =, or >?

41. $^-5 + {}^-3$ ⬤ $^-4$

42. $^+8 - {}^-2$ ⬤ $^+10$

43. $^-7 - {}^+2$ ⬤ $^-5$

44. $^-4 + {}^-2$ ⬤ $^-5$

45. $^-3 + {}^+6$ ⬤ $^-3$

46. $^-5 - {}^-7$ ⬤ $^-12$

47. $^+5 + {}^-3$ ⬤ $^+6 + {}^-5$

48. $^+8 - {}^-3$ ⬤ $^-3 - {}^+8$

49. $^-8 + {}^+6$ ⬤ $^+6 + {}^-8$

50. $\dfrac{^-3}{4} + \dfrac{^+3}{4}$ ⬤ $\dfrac{^-1}{2} - \dfrac{^-1}{4}$

51. $\dfrac{^+3}{8} - \dfrac{^-2}{5}$ ⬤ $\dfrac{^+3}{8} + \dfrac{^+2}{5}$

52. $^-4.1 + {}^+3.2$ ⬤ $^-4.1 + {}^+3.1$

53. $^+6.21 + {}^-6.21$ ⬤ $^-7.16 + {}^+7.15$

54. $^-6.19 + {}^-7.2$ ⬤ $^+6.28 - {}^-4.1$

55. $^+18.6 - {}^-7.4$ ⬤ $^-10.2 + {}^+8.3$

Temperature formulas

Temperature can be measured in both degrees Celsius and degrees Fahrenheit.

On the Celsius scale, water freezes at 0° and boils at 100°.

On the Fahrenheit scale, water freezes at 32° and boils at 212°.

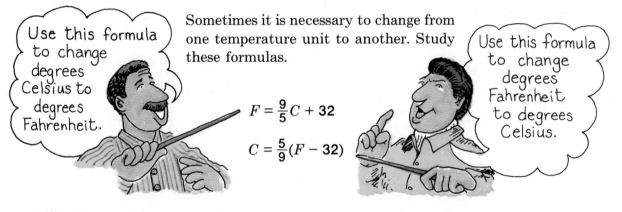

Sometimes it is necessary to change from one temperature unit to another. Study these formulas.

Use this formula to change degrees Celsius to degrees Fahrenheit.

Use this formula to change degrees Fahrenheit to degrees Celsius.

$$F = \frac{9}{5}C + 32$$

$$C = \frac{5}{9}(F - 32)$$

EXAMPLES.

Change 20°C to degrees Fahrenheit.

$$F = \frac{9}{5}C + 32$$

$$F = \frac{9}{5} \times \overset{4}{20} + 32$$
$$\underset{1}{}$$

$$F = 36 + 32 = 68$$

So, 20°C = 68°F.

Change 50°F to degrees Celsius.

$$C = \frac{5}{9}(F - 32)$$

$$C = \frac{5}{9}(50 - 32)$$

$$C = \frac{5}{9}(18) = 10$$

So, 50°F = 10°C.

EXERCISES
Change to degrees Fahrenheit.
1. 50°C   **2.** 18°C   **3.** 0°C   **4.** ⁻12°C

Change to degrees Celsius.
5. 68°F   **6.** 150°F   **7.** ⁻13°F   **8.** 0°F

9. The melting point of gold is 958°C. What is its melting point in degrees Fahrenheit?

10. The melting point of silver is 1761°F. What is its melting point in degrees Celsius?

Multiplying positive and negative numbers

To multiply, you can think of "putting charges in" as positive and "taking charges out" as negative.

EXAMPLE 1. $^+3 \times {}^+2 = ?$

Put in 3 sets of $^+2$ charges.

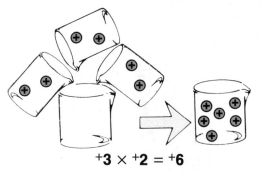

$$^+3 \times {}^+2 = {}^+6$$

EXAMPLE 2. $^+3 \times {}^-2 = ?$

Put in 3 sets of $^-2$ charges.

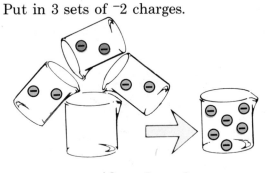

$$^+3 \times {}^-2 = {}^-6$$

EXAMPLE 3. $^-3 \times {}^+2 = ?$

We need to take out 3 sets of $^+2$ charges. So, draw at least 6  pairs.

$$^-3 \times {}^+2 = {}^-6$$

EXAMPLE 4. $^-3 \times {}^-2 = ?$

We need to take out 3 sets of $^-2$ charges. So, draw at least 6 ⊕⊖ pairs.

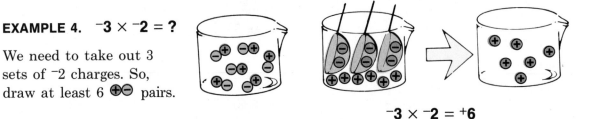

$$^-3 \times {}^-2 = {}^+6$$

These examples give us a way to multiply.

> The product of two numbers with the *same* sign is *positive*.
> The product of two numbers with *different* signs is *negative*.
> The product of any number and 0 is 0.

EXERCISES

Give the product.

1. $^+8 \times {}^+7$ 2. $^-8 \times {}^-7$ 3. $^+8 \times {}^-7$ 4. $^-8 \times {}^+7$

5. $^+5 \times {}^+9$ 6. $^-5 \times {}^-9$ 7. $^+5 \times {}^-9$ 8. $^-5 \times {}^+9$

9. $^-7 \times {}^+3$ 10. $^+5 \times 0$ 11. $^-8 \times 0$ 12. $^-7 \times {}^-9$

13. $^-9 \times {}^+9$ 14. $^+4 \times {}^-8$ 15. $^+7 \times {}^+4$ 16. $^+8 \times {}^-8$

17. $^-6 \times {}^+6$ 18. $^-8 \times {}^-9$ 19. $^+7 \times {}^-9$ 20. $^-6 \times {}^-9$

21. $^-4.2 \times {}^+3$ 22. $^-3.1 \times {}^-2.4$ 23. $^+5.3 \times {}^-2.6$ 24. $^+8 \times {}^+4.3$

25. $0 \times {}^-6.7$ 26. $^+4.2 \times {}^-6$ 27. $^-5.0 \times {}^+3.6$ 28. $^-3.2 \times {}^-1.5$

29. $^+\frac{1}{4} \times {}^+\frac{1}{2}$ 30. $^-\frac{1}{3} \times {}^+\frac{1}{2}$ 31. $^-\frac{3}{4} \times {}^-\frac{2}{3}$ 32. $^+\frac{3}{4} \times {}^-\frac{1}{5}$

33. $^-\frac{1}{6} \times {}^-\frac{2}{3}$ 34. $^-\frac{3}{5} \times {}^+\frac{3}{4}$ 35. $^+\frac{2}{5} \times {}^+\frac{3}{4}$ 36. $^+\frac{5}{9} \times {}^-\frac{3}{4}$

<, =, or >?

37. $^+3 \times {}^-5$ ● $^+15$ 38. $^-6 \times 0$ ● $^+6$ 39. $^-8 \times {}^+6$ ● $^-45$

40. $^-8 \times {}^-5$ ● $^+38$ 41. $^-7 \times {}^+4$ ● $^-25$ 42. $^+6 \times {}^-5$ ● $^-32$

43. ★ **WHO'S PUSHING THE BUTTONS?**

You got into a hotel elevator. You went up 3 floors, down 6 floors, and up 8 floors. You were then at the top floor.

You went down 7 floors, up 2 floors, and down 9 floors. You were then on the first floor. Where did you get on?

311

Dividing positive and negative numbers

You can find a quotient by finding a missing factor. Remember that multiplication and division are related.

EXAMPLE 1. $+36 \div +9 = ?$

$$+9 \times ? = +36 \qquad +9 \times +4 = +36$$

So, $+36 \div +9 = +4$

EXAMPLE 2. $-36 \div +9 = ?$

$$+9 \times ? = -36 \qquad +9 \times -4 = -36$$

So, $-36 \div +9 = -4$

EXAMPLE 3. $-36 \div -9 = ?$

$$-9 \times ? = -36 \qquad -9 \times +4 = -36$$

So, $-36 \div -9 = +4$

EXAMPLE 4. $+36 \div -9 = ?$

$$-9 \times ? = +36 \qquad -9 \times -4 = +36$$

So, $+36 \div -9 = -4$

These examples give us a way to divide.

> The quotient of two numbers with the same sign is positive.
> The quotient of two numbers with different signs is negative.
> The quotient of 0 divided by any nonzero number is 0.

Two numbers are **reciprocals** if their product is $+1$.

$$-8 \times \frac{-1}{8} = +1 \qquad -8 \text{ and } \frac{-1}{8} \text{ are reciprocals.}$$

$$\frac{+2}{3} \times \frac{+3}{2} = +1 \qquad \frac{+2}{3} \text{ and } \frac{+3}{2} \text{ are reciprocals.}$$

Dividing by a number is the same as multiplying by its reciprocal.

$$^-6 \div {}^+2 = {}^-6 \times {}^+\frac{1}{2}$$
$$= {}^-3$$

$$^+\frac{3}{4} \div {}^-\frac{2}{5} = {}^+\frac{3}{4} \times {}^-\frac{5}{2}$$
$$= \frac{^-15}{8}$$
$$= {}^-1\frac{7}{8}$$

EXERCISES
Give each quotient.

1. $^+12 \div {}^-4$ 2. $^-16 \div {}^-2$ 3. $0 \div {}^+3$

4. $^-20 \div {}^+5$ 5. $^-21 \div {}^+3$ 6. $^+24 \div {}^+8$

7. $^+27 \div {}^-3$ 8. $^-36 \div {}^-6$ 9. $^+72 \div {}^-8$

10. $^+81 \div {}^+9$ 11. $^-28 \div {}^-7$ 12. $^-45 \div {}^-9$

13. $^-30 \div {}^-5$ 14. $^+42 \div {}^-7$ 15. $^-32 \div {}^+4$

16. $^+36 \div {}^-9$ 17. $^-54 \div {}^+6$ 18. $^+72 \div {}^+9$

19. $^-6.4 \div {}^-8$ 20. $^-4.0 \div {}^+8$ 21. $^-5.6 \div {}^+0.8$

22. $^+4.8 \div {}^-6$ 23. $^-0.63 \div {}^+0.7$ 24. $^+4.9 \div {}^+7$

Give each quotient. *Hint:* Multiply by the reciprocal.

25. $^+5 \div {}^-7$ 26. $^+3 \div {}^+4$ 27. $^-9 \div {}^+4$

28. $^-\frac{2}{3} \div {}^-\frac{1}{3}$ 29. $^+\frac{2}{5} \div {}^-\frac{1}{4}$ 30. $^+\frac{5}{9} \div {}^-\frac{2}{3}$

31. $^+\frac{3}{8} \div {}^-\frac{1}{2}$ 32. $^-\frac{1}{2} \div {}^+\frac{3}{8}$ 33. $^-\frac{5}{4} \div {}^-\frac{3}{2}$

34. **NAME THAT STATE!**

Crack the code to name each state.

2N2ATOM   2S2N2IWOC

3A2SNKR   4ABLM

2ADEVN   2S2IRMUO

4I4S2PM   2A2INOLUS

Solve.

1. $3a = 27$

2. $5c = 35$

3. $9y = 0$

4. $8t = 104$

5. $4k = 11$

6. $0.3r = 12$

7. $5k = 13$

8. $9n = 16$

9. $3y = 2$

10. $\frac{x}{4} = 5$

11. $\frac{s}{3} = 9$

12. $\frac{m}{7} = 5$

13. $\frac{k}{9} = 11$

14. $\frac{d}{12} = 16$

15. $\frac{n}{15} = 5.4$

16. $\frac{k}{5} = 13$

Practice exercises

From now on, let's agree not to write the raised plus sign when writing a positive number.

Simplify.

1. $(6 + {}^-2) + 5$
2. $({}^-8 - 3) + 4$
3. ${}^-8 - (3 + 4)$

4. $(9 - {}^-2) + 6$
5. $9 - ({}^-2 + 6)$
6. $5 + ({}^-3 + 3)$

7. $(3 \times {}^-2) + 5$
8. $3 \times ({}^-2 + 5)$
9. $4 + ({}^-3 \times 2)$

10. $({}^-8 - 5) \times {}^-4$
11. ${}^-8 - (5 \times {}^-4)$
12. $6 \times ({}^-4 + 1)$

13. $(15 \div {}^-3) + {}^-2$
14. $15 \div ({}^-3 + {}^-2)$
15. $12 \div (4 - 2)$

16. $({}^-6 \times 3) \div 3$
17. $({}^-12 \times 4) \div 4$
18. $({}^-18 \div 6) \times {}^-2$

19. $({}^-5 \times 6) - 8$
20. ${}^-5 \times (6 - 8)$
21. $7 \times ({}^-4 - {}^-3)$

22. $(8 + 2) - (3 + 1)$
23. $({}^-5 - 3) + (6 + {}^-4)$
24. $({}^-2 - {}^-9) + (7 - {}^-4)$

25. $(8 \div 4) + (2 - {}^-7)$
26. $({}^-16 \div 4) - (8 + {}^-2)$
27. $(3 + 8) \times (18 \div {}^-3)$

28. $({}^-15 \div {}^-3) + (21 \div {}^-7)$
29. $({}^-24 \div {}^-6) \times (5 - {}^-1)$
30. $(3 \times {}^-5) - (12 \div {}^-4)$

Complete the paths.

31.   **32.**

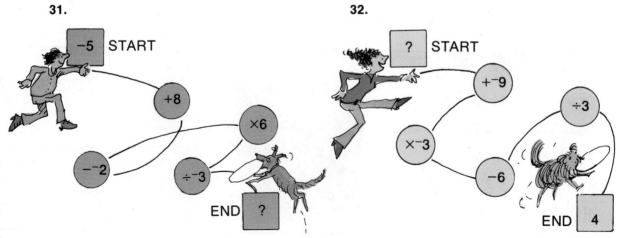

TARGET 10

$(^-5 \times 5) \div ^-3 = ^-25 \div ^-3$
$= 8\frac{1}{3}$

$(8 - ^-6) - 3 = 14 - 3$
$= 11$

-5 -3 5   8 -6 3

JOE

SUSAN

Which student got closer to 10?

Which is closer to 10?

1. a. $(^-8 + ^-3) \times 1$
   b. $6 + (^-4 \div ^-2)$

2. a. $(^-6 + 9) \div ^-2$
   b. $(7 - 4) \times 3$

3. a. $(^-9 \div 2) \times ^-2$
   b. $(^-7 \times ^-7) \div 5$

4. a. $(5 + 2) + 4$
   b. $(^-8 \div ^-2) - ^-5$

5. a. $9 + (^-2 \times 0)$
   b. $(6 \times ^-6) \div ^-4$

6. a. $^-4 \times (5 \div ^-2)$
   b. $(^-6 + 9) \times 3$

Play the game.

1. Divide the class into two teams.

2. Make this set of cards.

-9 -8 -7 -6 -5 -4 -3 -2 -1 0

1 2 3 4 5 6 7 8 9

3. A player from each team picks three cards. Each player builds a number by adding, subtracting, multiplying, or dividing the three numbers. The player who gets closer to 10 earns a point for his team.

4. After all players have played, the team with the greater total wins the game.

Solving addition and subtraction equations

In Chapter 2 you learned to solve equations by adding the same number to both sides or by subtracting the number from both sides. You can still use those methods with positive and negative numbers.

EXAMPLE 1. *Equation:* $t + {}^-9 = {}^-17$

Subtract $^-9$ from both sides: $t + {}^-9 - {}^-9 = {}^-17 - {}^-9$

$$t = {}^-8$$

Check: $^-8 + {}^-9 = {}^-17$ *It checks!*

EXAMPLE 2. *Equation:* $r - 24 = {}^-8$

Add 24 to both sides: $r - 24 + 24 = {}^-8 + 24$

$$r = 16$$

Check: $16 - 24 = {}^-8$ *It checks!*

I got this equation by moving the 7 to the other side and changing the subtraction sign to an addition sign.

$$x - 7 = {}^-4$$
$$x = {}^-4 + 7$$
$$x = 3$$

$$a + {}^-18 = {}^-5$$
$$a = {}^-5 - {}^-18$$
$$a = 13$$

EXERCISES
Copy and finish solving each equation. Check your solutions.

1. $y + 18 = {}^-3$

$y + 18 - 18 = \underline{\,?\,}$

$y = \underline{\,?\,}$

2. $x - 8 = {}^-2$

$x - 8 + 8 = \underline{\,?\,}$

$x = \underline{\,?\,}$

3. $z + {}^-4 = 2$

$z + {}^-4 - {}^-4 = \underline{\,?\,}$

$z = \underline{\,?\,}$

Solve and check.

4. $r + {}^-7 = 9$

5. $x + 19 = {}^-14$

6. $a + {}^-6 = 9$

7. $s + {}^-5 = {}^-3$

8. $v + 8 = {}^-12$

9. $g + {}^-11 = {}^-3$

10. $a + {}^-10 = {}^-5$

11. $z + 6 = {}^-9$

12. $n + {}^-2 = 1$

13. $b - {}^-3 = 8$

14. $c - {}^-9 = 6$

15. $u - {}^-15 = 0$

16. $m - {}^-15 = 6$

17. $f - 6 = {}^-5$

18. $d - 9 = {}^-8$

19. $x - 18 = {}^-2$

20. $z - 12 = 0$

21. $y - {}^-20 = 7$

22. $y - 12 = {}^-30$

23. $n + 19 = {}^-20$

24. $x + 31 = 70$

25. $b + 14 = 12$

26. $c - 9 = {}^-2$

27. $k + {}^-47 = {}^-21$

28. $y + 25 = {}^-34$

29. $n + {}^-6 = 0$

30. $k + 47 = {}^-56$

★ **31.** $y + 2.5 = {}^-3.4$

★ **32.** $n + {}^-0.6 = {}^-1.4$

★ **33.** $k + 4.7 = {}^-5.6$

★ **34.** $y + \frac{{}^-1}{4} = \frac{1}{2}$

★ **35.** $g - \frac{{}^-1}{2} = 0$

★ **36.** $z + \frac{{}^-2}{3} = \frac{5}{6}$

$n + 5 = {}^-3$

Write an equation.
Solve the equation and check your solution in the problem.

37. 5 more than n is ${}^-3$.

38. 9 less than n is 2.

39. $\frac{{}^-2}{3}$ added to n is $\frac{1}{6}$.

40. $\frac{3}{4}$ subtracted from n is $\frac{1}{2}$.

41. n increased by 81 is ${}^-12$.

42. n decreased by 4 is 15.

Solving multiplication and division equations

Remember that you can solve some equations by multiplying or dividing both sides by the same number.

EXAMPLE 1. *Equation:* $\dfrac{m}{-3} = 5$

Multiply both sides by -3: $\quad -3 \times \dfrac{m}{-3} = -3 \times 5$

$$m = -15$$

Check: $\quad \dfrac{-15}{-3} = 5 \qquad$ *It checks!*

EXAMPLE 2. *Equation:* $8y = -4$

Divide both sides by 8: $\quad \dfrac{8y}{8} = \dfrac{-4}{8}$

$$y = \dfrac{-1}{2}$$

Check: $\quad 8 \times \dfrac{-1}{2} = -4 \qquad$ *It checks!*

> I get the same result if I move the 6 to the other side and change the division to multiplication.

$$\dfrac{s}{6} = -3 \qquad\qquad -2n = -12$$

$$s = -3 \times 6 \qquad\qquad n = \dfrac{-12}{-2}$$

$$s = -18 \qquad\qquad n = 6$$

EXERCISES
Copy and finish solving each equation. Check.

1. $-5x = -30$

$$\dfrac{-5x}{-5} = \dfrac{-30}{?}$$

$$x = ?$$

2. $\dfrac{y}{4} = -12$

$$4 \times \dfrac{y}{4} = ? \times -12$$

$$y = ?$$

3. $3m = 10$

$$\dfrac{3m}{3} = \dfrac{10}{?}$$

$$m = ?$$

Solve and check.

4. $\dfrac{y}{-2} = 3$ 5. $\dfrac{y}{4} = 2$ 6. $\dfrac{b}{-9} = {}^-1$

7. $\dfrac{d}{7} = 5$ 8. $\dfrac{b}{3} = {}^-2$ 9. $\dfrac{x}{-6} = 4$

10. $\dfrac{p}{12} = {}^-3$ 11. $\dfrac{k}{10} = 2$ 12. $\dfrac{m}{5} = {}^-6$

13. $^-3t = {}^-15$ 14. $^-4c = 40$ 15. $5c = {}^-35$

16. $^-8z = {}^-80$ 17. $6a = {}^-96$ 18. $^-2q = 28$

19. $11a = 121$ 20. $^-13j = 39$ 21. $12w = {}^-156$

22. $\dfrac{n}{5} = {}^-1.5$ 23. $8t = 96$ 24. $\dfrac{d}{-9} = 54$

25. $2g = 9$ 26. $^-4u = 18$ 27. $\dfrac{r}{-6} = 82$

28. $4r = 0.32$ 29. $\dfrac{f}{-3} = {}^-7.8$ 30. $^-3s = 0.57$

31. $\dfrac{v}{21} = \dfrac{^-1}{2}$ 32. $^-6s = \dfrac{2}{3}$ 33. $\dfrac{h}{15} = \dfrac{3}{5}$

Write an equation.
Solve your equation and check your solution in the problem.

34. n divided by $^-2$ is 5.

35. n multiplied by $^-4$ is $^-48$.

36. n decreased by 8 is $^-4$.

37. n increased by 15 is 11.

38. 14 times a number n is $\dfrac{1}{2}$.

39. $^-0.72$ subtracted from n is 2.09.

40. **HEADS OR TAILS?**

A fish is 12 inches long. The head is as long as the tail. If the head were twice as long, the head plus the tail would be as long as the body. How long is the head? The tail? The body?

Give the answer in simplest form.

1. $\dfrac{1}{8} + \dfrac{3}{4}$

2. $3 + \dfrac{1}{2}$

3. $\dfrac{5}{6} + \dfrac{2}{9}$

4. $\dfrac{7}{8} - \dfrac{1}{4}$

5. $1 - \dfrac{3}{8}$

6. $\dfrac{3}{2} - \dfrac{2}{3}$

7. $\dfrac{1}{6} \times \dfrac{3}{4}$

8. $\dfrac{5}{3} \times \dfrac{3}{10}$

9. $\dfrac{5}{8} \times \dfrac{8}{5}$

10. $1 \div \dfrac{2}{3}$

11. $\dfrac{7}{8} \div \dfrac{3}{4}$

12. $\dfrac{5}{2} \div \dfrac{5}{4}$

13. $\dfrac{5}{6} + \dfrac{3}{8}$

14. $\dfrac{5}{6} - \dfrac{3}{8}$

15. $\dfrac{5}{6} \times \dfrac{3}{8}$

16. $\dfrac{5}{6} \div \dfrac{3}{8}$

319

Solving two-step equations

I am thinking of a number. If I multiply it by 5 and then subtract 23, I get 14. What is the number?

You can find the number by writing an equation and solving it.

$$5y - 23 = 14$$

To solve the equation, get an equation with y all by itself on one side of the equal sign.

First add 23
to both sides: $\quad 5y - 23 + 23 = 14 + 23$

$$5y = 37$$

Divide both
sides by 5: $\quad \dfrac{5y}{5} = \dfrac{37}{5}$

$$y = \dfrac{37}{5}$$

Check: $\quad 5\left(\dfrac{37}{5}\right) - 23 \overset{?}{=} 14 \quad$ *It checks!*

EXAMPLE 1.

Equation:	$3x + 11 = {}^-25$
Subtract 11:	$3x + 11 - 11 = {}^-25 - 11$
	$3x = {}^-36$
Divide by 3:	$\dfrac{3x}{3} = \dfrac{{}^-36}{3}$
	$x = {}^-12$
Check:	$3({}^-12) + 11 \overset{?}{=} {}^-25$

SHORTCUT

EXAMPLE 2.

Equation:	$\dfrac{w}{{}^-4} + 3 = 6$
Subtract 3:	$\dfrac{w}{{}^-4} + 3 - 3 = 6 - 3$
	$\dfrac{w}{{}^-4} = 3$
Multiply by ${}^-4$:	${}^-4 \times \dfrac{w}{{}^-4} = {}^-4 \times 3$
	$w = {}^-12$
Check:	$\dfrac{{}^-12}{{}^-4} + 3 \overset{?}{=} 6$

EXAMPLE 3.

$$\dfrac{z}{3} - 5 = {}^-4$$

$$\dfrac{z}{3} = {}^-4 + 5$$

$$\dfrac{z}{3} = 1$$

$$z = 3 \times 1$$

$$z = 3 \qquad \text{Check: } \dfrac{3}{3} - 5 \overset{?}{=} {}^-4$$

EXERCISES

Copy and finish solving each equation.
Check your solution.

1. $3y - 14 = {}^-2$

$3y - 14 + 14 = {}^-2 + ?$

$3y = ?$

$\dfrac{3y}{3} = \dfrac{12}{?}$

$y = ?$

2. $4t + 9 = 1$

$4t + 9 - 9 = 1 - ?$

$4t = ?$

$\dfrac{4t}{4} = \dfrac{{}^-8}{?}$

$t = ?$

3. ${}^-6n - 8 = 10$

${}^-6n - 8 + 8 = 10 + ?$

${}^-6n = ?$

$\dfrac{{}^-6n}{{}^-6} = \dfrac{18}{?}$

$n = ?$

4. $8r + 3 = {}^-5$

5. $5y - 2 = {}^-7$

6. ${}^-4k + {}^-12 = 0$

7. $\dfrac{n}{6} + 3 = {}^-5$

$\dfrac{n}{6} + 3 - 3 = {}^-5 - ?$

$\dfrac{n}{6} = ?$

$6 \times \dfrac{n}{6} = ? \times {}^-8$

$n = ?$

8. $\dfrac{s}{3} - 5 = 7$

$\dfrac{s}{3} - 5 + 5 = 7 + ?$

$\dfrac{s}{3} = ?$

$3 \times \dfrac{s}{3} = ? \times 12$

$s = ?$

9. $\dfrac{d}{{}^-4} - {}^-2 = 3$

$\dfrac{d}{{}^-4} - {}^-2 + {}^-2 = 3 + ?$

$\dfrac{d}{{}^-4} = ?$

${}^-4 \times \dfrac{d}{{}^-4} = ? \times 1$

$d = ?$

10. $\dfrac{j}{3} + 7 = {}^-2$

11. $\dfrac{k}{{}^-2} + {}^-5 = 8$

12. $\dfrac{x}{5} - 4 = {}^-7$

Solve.

13. $9y + 20 = 2$

14. $\dfrac{x}{4} + 2 = {}^-5$

15. $\dfrac{k}{7} - 4 = 6$

16. $\dfrac{m}{{}^-3} + {}^-7 = 5$

17. ${}^-8y + 2 = {}^-14$

18. $3y - 5 = 7$

19. $7y - 5 = {}^-5$

20. $\dfrac{y}{3} - {}^-4 = {}^-1$

21. $\dfrac{r}{{}^-8} + 6 = 0$

22. $\dfrac{t}{{}^-2} - 12 = 15$

23. ${}^-4y + {}^-12 = {}^-4$

24. $2y - {}^-8 = 16$

25. ${}^-4y + 19 = 3$

26. $\dfrac{z}{{}^-5} - 14 = {}^-18$

27. $\dfrac{n}{{}^-2} - {}^-10 = {}^-8$

28. $\dfrac{w}{6} + {}^-11 = {}^-10$

★ **29.** $5x + 3 = {}^-14$

★ **30.** $9y - 13 = 0$

31. $123x - 1648 = 197$

32. $\dfrac{g}{{}^-26} + 57 = 110$

33. $0.31s + 0.57 = 2.22$

Practice exercises

Compute.

1. $6 + {}^-4$
2. ${}^-8 - {}^-2$
3. $5 - 3$
4. $9 - 14$

5. ${}^-3 \times 6$
6. ${}^-15 \div {}^-5$
7. ${}^-12 + {}^-15$
8. ${}^-24 \times {}^-2$

9. $46 \times {}^-5$
10. $46 - {}^-5$
11. $13 + {}^-18$
12. ${}^-6 \times {}^-12$

13. ${}^-48 \div {}^-8$
14. $24 \div {}^-3$
15. $45 \div 9$
16. $45 \times {}^-9$

17. $57 - 94$
18. ${}^-38 - {}^-26$
19. ${}^-18 + 26$
20. $36 \times {}^-6$

21. ${}^-3 + 7 - {}^-4$
22. $7 - 4 \times {}^-2$
23. $(7 - 4) \times {}^-2$

24. ${}^-5 \times {}^-2 \times 3$
25. ${}^-4 + 6 \div {}^-2$
26. $({}^-4 + 6) \div {}^-2$

27. ${}^-24 \div 6 \times 4$
28. $5 - (8 + {}^-3)$
29. $(5 - 8) + {}^-3$

30. ${}^-30 - 6 \div 3$
31. $8 \times {}^-6 + 1$
32. $8 \times ({}^-6 + 1)$

Solve.

33. ${}^-2x = {}^-24$
34. $\frac{y}{{}^-2} = {}^-24$
35. $b + {}^-2 = {}^-24$

36. $n - {}^-2 = {}^-24$
37. $3m = {}^-15$
38. $5x = 30$

39. $7a = {}^-7$
40. $\frac{m}{3} = {}^-7$
41. ${}^-12 + a = {}^-15$

42. $2a + 6 = 24$
43. $3x + 4 = {}^-17$
44. $5m - 3 = 32$

45. ${}^-3x + 7 = {}^-11$
46. ${}^-2y - 5 = {}^-17$
47. $\frac{a}{{}^-1} + 6 = {}^-5$

48. ${}^-4y + 2 = 22$
49. $\frac{e}{4} - 7 = 42$
50. $3t - {}^-6 = {}^-6$

51. $8p = 8$
52. $5t + 10 = 0$
53. $\frac{x}{4} + 7 = 3$

54. $y - {}^-5 = 5$
55. $2a - 7 = {}^-1$
56. $\frac{t}{{}^-3} + 6 = 0$

57. ${}^-6n - 9 = {}^-3$
58. ${}^-1x = 4$
59. ${}^-1y + 6 = 2$

Problem solving

First write an equation. Then solve the equation and check your solution.

1. Sarah has 52 records. She has 19 more records than Alice. How many records does Alice have?
   Let n = number of Alice's records.

   Equation: $n + 19 = 52$

2. Four girls have 8 of the "top twenty" singles. They would like to play the "top twenty" at a school party. If the 4 girls share equally, how many records will each have to buy?

3. Mary has 3 times as many records as she had a year ago. She now has 51 records. How many did she have a year ago?

4. Kim sold 13 of her records. She then had 39. How many did she have before she sold the records?

5. The girls played 8 singles and 1 LP in 45 minutes. The LP took 21 minutes. What was the average time per record for the singles?

6. Mary bought some singles that were on sale for $.69 each. She spent a total of $5.07. The sales tax was $.24. How many records did she buy?

7. Sarah bought 15 records for $3.75 at a garage sale. If each record cost the same amount, how much did she pay for each record?

8. Kim is selecting records for the first 60 minutes of the party. She has selected a 15-minute LP. If the singles average 3 minutes apiece, how many singles should she select?

Graphing pairs of positive numbers

48° North Latitude
30° West Longitude

A pair of numbers (latitude and longitude) are used to locate any point on the earth. We also use pairs of numbers to locate points in a plane. Here is how we use pairs of positive numbers.

The point shown is the **graph** of the **ordered pair** (5, 3).

Since the first number of the ordered pair is 5, you start at the origin and count five spaces *to the right*. Then you count *up 3,* because 3 is the second number of the pair. The point has **coordinates** (5, 3).

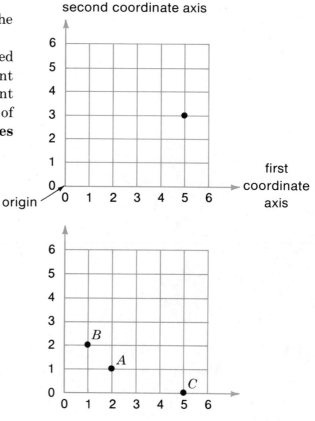

second coordinate axis

first coordinate axis

origin

The coordinates of point *A* are (2, 1).
The coordinates of point *B* are (1, 2).
The coordinates of point *C* are (5, 0).

EXERCISES

Give the coordinates of

1. point A 2. point B

3. point C 4. point D

5. point E 6. point F

7. point G 8. point H

9. point I 10. point J

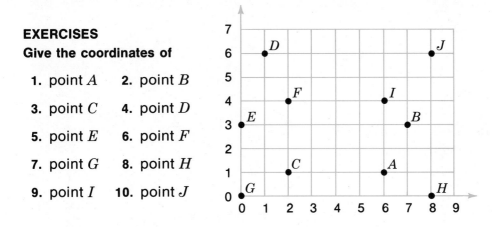

Draw a pair of axes on a piece of graph paper.
Locate these points. Label each with its letter.

11. A:(3, 8)

12. B:(8, 3)

13. C:(1, 1)

14. D:(0, 4)

15. E:(4, 0)

16. F:(2, 3)

17. G:(3, 2)

18. H:(0, 0)

19. I:$\left(4, \frac{1}{2}\right)$

20. J:$\left(2\frac{1}{2}, 5\right)$

21. K:$\left(2\frac{3}{4}, \frac{1}{4}\right)$

22. L:(1.5, 2.5)

Draw another pair of axes.

23. Draw the square with these vertices:
(2, 1), (6, 1), (6, 5), and (2, 5).

24. What are the midpoints of the sides of the square?

25. Join the midpoints of the sides to form a new square.

26. What are the midpoints of the sides of the new square?

27. Guess the coordinates of the midpoint of the segment that
joins (3, 1) and (5, 5). Check your guess.

28. ⭐ GET THE POINT?

Make a small dot anywhere on a piece of unlined paper.
Now on another piece of unlined paper the same size make a
dot in the *same* place. You may use a ruler, protractor, or compass. You cannot place one piece of paper on top of the other
except to check your work.

How many different ways can you find to do this?

Graphs

Imagine being on a ship that is sailing at a constant rate of 4 kilometers per hour. This graph shows the relationship between the sailing time in hours and the distance sailed in kilometers.

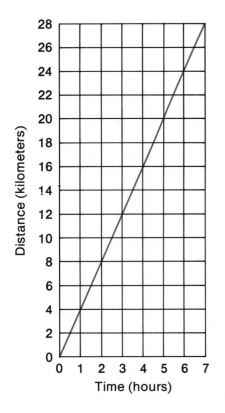

EXERCISES
Use the graph above to answer the questions.

1. How far would you sail in 3 hours?

2. How far would you sail in 6.5 hours?

3. How long would it take you to sail 10 km?

4. How long would it take you to sail 19 km?

The higher you are above the surface of the ocean, the farther away the horizon is. This graph shows how the two distances are related.

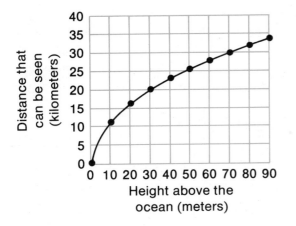

Distance that can be seen (kilometers)

Height above the ocean (meters)

5. How far could you see if you were 20 meters above the ocean?

6. If the top of the mast of the Santa Maria was 30 meters above the ocean, how far could a sailor at the top of the mast see?

7. How many meters above the ocean would you have to be to be able to see 30 kilometers?

If an object is dropped from the top of the mast of the ship, it falls faster and faster until it strikes the water. This graph shows how far an object will fall in a given number of seconds.

8. How far will an object fall in 1 second? In 2 seconds? How much farther does it fall in the second second than in the first second?

9. How far will an object fall in 6 seconds? In 7 seconds? How far will it fall during the 7th second? How much farther does it fall during the 7th second than it does during the 1st second?

10. About how long does it take an object to fall 80 meters? 160 meters?

11. A sailor is in the rigging 30 meters above the surface of the water. If he fell, how long would it take him to reach the water?

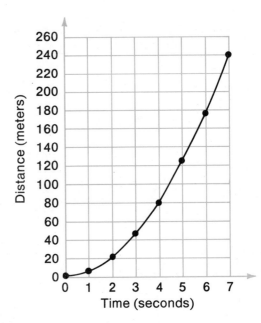

Distance (meters)

Time (seconds)

The coordinate plane

In this graph, the first and second coordinate axes include negative numbers. This allows us to graph pairs of positive and negative numbers.

The coordinates for point P are ($^-$4, 3). The coordinates for point Q are ($^-$2, $^-$3). What are the coordinates for point R? For point S?

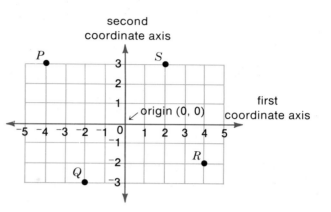

EXERCISES

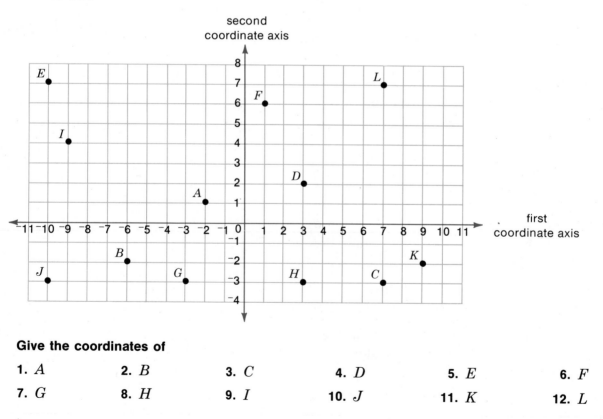

Give the coordinates of

1. A	**2.** B	**3.** C	**4.** D	**5.** E	**6.** F
7. G	**8.** H	**9.** I	**10.** J	**11.** K	**12.** L

Graph the following ordered pairs. Label each with its coordinates.

13. $(3, ^-6)$ **14.** $(4, ^-2)$ **15.** $(^-3, ^-1)$ **16.** $(2, ^-4)$

17. $(^-3, 5)$ **18.** $(^-2, ^-2)$ **19.** $(^-3, 0)$ **20.** $(^-4, 4)$

21. $\left(4, \frac{1}{2}\right)$ **22.** $\left(\frac{1}{2}, ^-3\right)$ **23.** $\left(^-5, 2\frac{1}{2}\right)$ **24.** $\left(3\frac{1}{2}, ^-1\right)$

25. Here are some ordered pairs in which the second coordinate is twice the first.

$(^-2, ^-4)$, $(^-1, ^-2)$, $\left(\frac{^-1}{2}, ^-1\right)$

a. List 7 more such ordered pairs.
b. Graph all 10 ordered pairs.
c. Do the points "line up"?

26. a. List 10 ordered pairs such that the second coordinate is the square of the first.
b. Graph the ordered pairs.
c. Do the points "line up"?

second coordinate axis

(graph showing triangle with vertices (2, 1), (4, 5), (6, 1))

first coordinate axis

★ **27.** Copy the triangle on graph paper. Now draw the triangle that you get if you

a. multiply the first coordinate of each point by $^-1$ and keep the same second coordinate.
b. multiply both coordinates of each point by $^-1$.
c. multiply the second coordinate of each point by $^-1$ and keep the same first coordinate.
d. add 6 to the first coordinate of each point and keep the same second coordinate.
e. add $^-5$ to both coordinates of each point.
f. add $^-4$ to the second coordinate of each point and keep the same first coordinate.

Estimate to find the two incorrect answers.

1. a. $2.8 \times 7.5 = 21$

  b. $5.6 \times 0.25 = 0.140$

  c. $24.1 \div 3.6 = 66.9$

  d. $8.67 \div 4.25 = 2.04$

Multiply or divide. Round each quotient to the nearest hundredth.

2. 7.6×0.43

3. 6.7×3.4

4. 0.82×0.4

5. 0.3×0.2

6. 1.23×4.06

7. $4.3\overline{)28.71}$

8. $0.6\overline{)5.33}$

9. $0.28\overline{)1.44}$

10. $6\overline{)38.1}$

11. $1.7\overline{)0.643}$

329

Problem solving

Students on a track team keep records of their training progress.

1. Alice kept this broken-line graph of her progress in the 100-meter dash.

   a. What was her time after 1 week of training?
   b. By how many seconds did she improve her time over the 8 weeks?
   c. Each time shown on the graph is the average time of 3 dashes. At the end of the seventh week, Alice's first dash was 12.2 seconds and her second dash was 12.5 seconds. What was the time of her third dash?

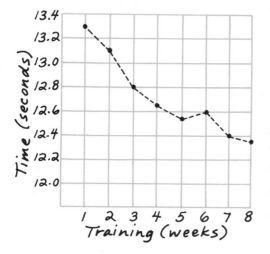

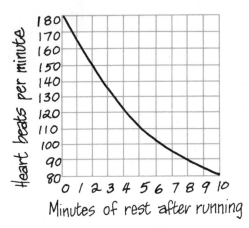

Heart beats per minute — Minutes of rest after running

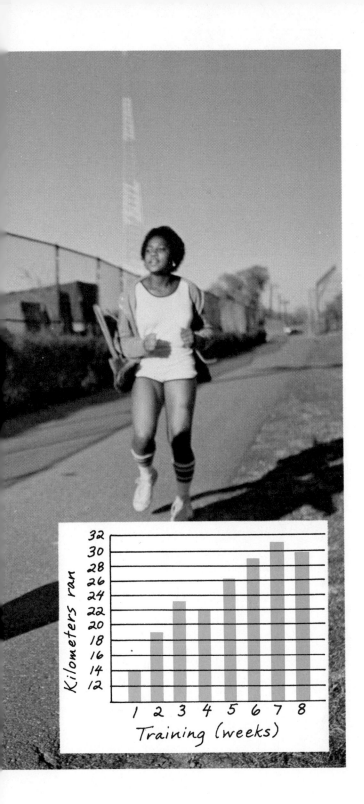

Kilometers ran — Training (weeks)

2. Ruth made this graph of how fast her heartbeat returns to normal after running.

   a. What was her heart rate immediately after running?

   b. About how long did she rest before her heart rate was 140?

   c. By what percent did her heart rate decrease after two minutes of rest?

   d. How many minutes did she rest before her heart rate decreased by $33\frac{1}{3}\%$?

3. Sarah kept this bar graph of the kilometers she ran each week during training.

   a. How many kilometers did she run during the first week?

   b. How many kilometers did she run during the first 4 weeks?

   c. How much farther did she run during the second 4-week period?

   d. By what percent did she increase her distance from the fourth week to the fifth week?

Give each sum. [pages 304–305, 308]

1. $^-3 + {}^+8$
2. $^+5 + {}^+7$
3. $^-8 + {}^-5$
4. $^+7 + {}^-10$

Give each difference. [pages 306–308]

5. $^-3 - {}^+4$
6. $^+5 - {}^-6$
7. $^+8 - {}^+9$
8. $^-6 - {}^-1$

Give each product. [pages 310–311]

9. $^-5 \times {}^+8$
10. $^-3 \times {}^-6$
11. $^+7 \times {}^+4$
12. $^+9 \times {}^-2$

Give each quotient. [pages 312–313]

13. $^+20 \div {}^-4$
14. $^-15 \div {}^+5$
15. $^-24 \div {}^-6$
16. $^+49 \div {}^+7$

Solve. [pages 316–322]

17. $x + {}^-5 = 6$
18. $y - 8 = {}^-5$
19. $^-4a = 20$
20. $5n = {}^-35$
21. $\frac{p}{3} = 6$
22. $6t - {}^-3 = 27$

Write an equation and solve. [page 323]

23. John has 76 stamps in his collection. He has 4 times as many stamps as Marcia. How many stamps does Marcia have in her collection?

24. Bill bought 101 stamps. He put the same number of stamps on each of 8 pages of his album and had 5 left over. How many stamps did he put on each page?

Give the coordinates of
[pages 324–325, 328–329]

25. point A.
26. point B.
27. point C.
28. point D.

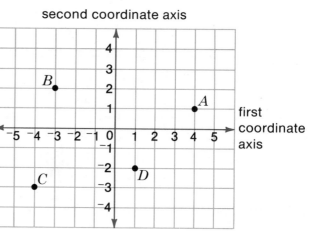

second coordinate axis

first coordinate axis

332

CHAPTER PROJECT

The year's high for a share of Bank of Virginia stock was $27\frac{1}{4}$, or $27.25.

The year's low for a share of this stock was $8.75.

DAILY STOCK QUOTATIONS

Year High	Year Low	Stocks		Div.	Day High	Day Low	Close	Net Chg.
36½	22	Bk of NY		2.20	24½	24	24½	+ ¼
27¼	8¾	Bk of Va		.88	9⅛	9	9⅛	+ ⅜
57¼	29½	BankTr		3	31	30⅝	30⅞	+ ⅛
34	17¾	BarbOil		.80e	19	19	19	– ¼
24¼	9⅝	BardCR		.20	10	9⅝	9⅝	– ¼
22¾	2¼	BarnM		2.79e	4½	4⅛	4½	+ ⅜
10¼	6⅜	BasicInc		.40	6½	6¼	6½	– ⅛
30	24¾	Basic	pf	2.50	24¾	24¾	24¾	. . .
15¼	10¾	BatesMf		.20	12¼	12⅛	12⅛	– ¼
19½	14¾	BatesMf pf	1		15⅞	15¾	15¾	. . .
22¼	4⅝	BathInd		.40	6⅜	6	6⅛	– ⅜
45	17¾	BauschL		.60	26¼	25¼	25⅜	– ⅝
48⅝	24⅛	BaxtLab		.17	26	24¾	25	– ¾
6	4½	BaykCig		.32	4⅝	4½	4½	. . .
28⅞	10	Bearing		.32	11⅛	11	11⅛	+ ⅛
23⅜	12¾	BeatFds		.72	12⅞	12⅛	12⅝	– ¼
40	16	Beckmn		.50	19⅛	18	18½	– ⅝
21¾	16¼	Beker		.28	17⅞	17	17¾	+ ¼
18½	9½	BelcoP		.77t	11	10¾	11	+ ⅛

The day's net change (the difference between yesterday's closing price and today's closing price) was $^{+}\frac{3}{8}$. That means that the price of each share of stock gained, or went up, $\frac{3}{8}$ of a dollar, or $37\frac{1}{2}$¢. Notice that some stocks had a negative net change. That means that the price of the stock lost, or went down, that day.

1. What was the day's high for a share of Bank of Virginia? The day's low? At what price was the stock selling when the market closed?

2. Select eight stocks from the list above. Pretend that you own 100 shares of each of the eight stocks. Compute your loss or gain from the quotations given above.

3. Select 10 stocks that are listed on the New York Stock Exchange. Pretend that you own 100 shares of each stock. For one week, compute the total dollar net change of your 1000 shares of stock.

333

$^-7 + {}^+2 = {}^-5$

Give each sum.

1. $^+4 + {}^-6$ 2. $^-3 + {}^-2$ 3. $^-5 + {}^+8$

4. $^+7 + {}^-7$ 5. $^-5 + {}^-6$ 6. $^-6 + {}^+2$

To subtract a number, add its opposite.
$$^-8 - {}^+3 = {}^-8 + {}^-3$$
$$= {}^-11$$

Give each difference.

7. $^-4 - {}^+1$ 8. $^-6 - {}^-2$ 9. $^+9 - {}^+8$

10. $^+8 - {}^-5$ 11. $^-8 - {}^-8$ 12. $^-3 - {}^+7$

If the signs are the same, the product or quotient is positive.
$$^+6 \times {}^+3 = {}^+18$$
$$^-16 \div {}^-2 = {}^+8$$

If the signs are different, the product or quotient is negative.
$$^-9 \times {}^+4 = {}^-36$$
$$^+21 \div {}^-7 = {}^-3$$

Give each product.

13. $^+5 \times {}^+7$ 14. $^-3 \times {}^-9$ 15. $^+6 \times {}^-4$

16. $^-8 \times 0$ 17. $^-5 \times {}^+4$ 18. $^-6 \times {}^-7$

Give each quotient.

19. $^-42 \div {}^+6$ 20. $^+48 \div {}^+8$ 21. $^+56 \div {}^-7$

22. $^-27 \div {}^-9$ 23. $^+40 \div {}^+5$ 24. $^-54 \div {}^+9$

$$6y - 3 = {}^-27$$
$$6y = {}^-24$$
$$y = {}^-4$$

Solve.

25. $y + 8 = 3$ 26. $w - {}^-2 = 6$

27. $^-3k = 21$ 28. $\frac{n}{2} = 8$

29. $4p - 2 = {}^-30$ 30. $^-5x - 5 = 15$

To graph an ordered pair:

Start at $(0, 0)$. Move right or left for the first number. Move up or down for the second number.

Give the coordinates of

31. point A.

32. point B.

33. point C.

34. point D.

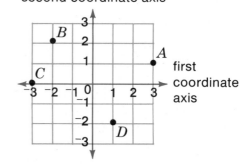

CHAPTER CHALLENGE

Mathematical sentences that contain these symbols
are called *inequalities*.

<	>	≤	≥	≠
is less than	is greater than	is less than or equal to	is greater than or equal to	is not equal to

This inequality has many solutions: $2y < {}^-8$

In fact, every number less than $^-4$ is a solution.

You can show all of the solutions on a number-line graph.

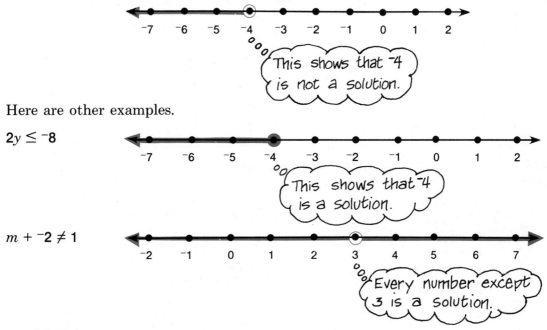

Here are other examples.

$2y \leq {}^-8$

$m + {}^-2 \neq 1$

EXERCISES

Make graphs to show solutions to these inequalities.

1. $g - 3 < {}^-1$

2. $r + 4 > {}^-1$

3. $t + 3 \geq 2$

4. $x + {}^-2 < 2$

5. $3a \leq 9$

6. $2b > {}^-4$

7. $\frac{c}{5} < 0$

8. $\frac{m}{2} \neq {}^-2$

9. $2t + 1 \leq 7$

a b c d
2.
a b c d
a b c d
a b c d
8.
a b c d
9.
a b c d
10.
a b c d
11.
a b c d
5.
a b c d
6.
a b c
12.
a b c

MAJOR CHECKUP
STANDARDIZED FORMAT

Choose the correct letter.

1. Divide. $0.36\overline{)8.294}$
Round the quotient to
the nearest hundredth.

    a. 23.03
    b. 23.04
    c. 230.49
    d. none of these

2. Give the prime
factorization for 72.

    a. 9×8
    b. $2^2 \times 3^3$
    c. $2^4 \times 3$
    d. none of these

3. Give the sum.

$$2\frac{3}{4} + 1\frac{1}{6}$$

    a. $3\frac{11}{12}$
    b. $4\frac{11}{12}$
    c. $3\frac{2}{5}$
    d. none of these

4. Give the quotient.

$$\frac{3}{5} \div \frac{5}{3}$$

    a. 1
    b. $2\frac{7}{9}$
    c. $\frac{9}{25}$
    d. none of these

5. Find the surface area.

1 m
5 m
4 m

    a. 20 m²
    b. 29 m²
    c. 58 m²
    d. none of these

6. Solve.

$$\frac{7}{x} = \frac{10}{16}$$

    a. 4.375
    b. 22.85
    c. 11.2
    d. none of these

7. Which figure has a
point of symmetry?

    a. equilateral
triangle
    b. square
    c. regular
pentagon
    d. none of these

8. A parka that regularly
sells for $65.79 is on
sale for 25% off. What
is the sale price?

    a. $16.45
    b. $43.86
    c. $49.34
    d. none of these

9. Give the difference.

$$^-3 - {}^-7$$

    a. $^-4$
    b. $^+4$
    c. $^-10$
    d. $^+10$

10. Solve.

$$^-2n + 4 = 10$$

    a. $^-3$
    b. $^-7$
    c. $^-12$
    d. none of these

11. How many minutes long
is 1 week?

    a. 2520
    b. 5040
    c. 7200
    d. none of these

12. Dody is 52 km from
Elba. Dody is 3.7 km closer
to Elba than Faro is. How
far is Faro from Elba?

    a. 48.3 km
    b. 49.7 km
    c. 55.7 km
    d. none of these

Probability and Statistics

12

Give the ratio.

1. red marbles to marbles

2. blue marbles to marbles

3. yellow marbles to marbles

4. red marbles to not-red marbles

5. blue marbles to not-blue marbles

6. not-yellow marbles to yellow marbles

Equally likely outcomes

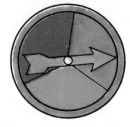

Event
Spinning this spinner

If you spin this spinner, there are 3 possible outcomes. Since the "chance" of getting each outcome is the same, we say that the outcomes are **equally likely.**

Event
Tossing this coin

There are two equally likely outcomes, "heads" and "tails."

Now think about combining the events, that is, first spinning the spinner and then flipping the coin. We can use a **tree diagram** to show the outcomes.

Event
Spinning the spinner
and then
flipping the coin

Tree Diagram of Outcomes

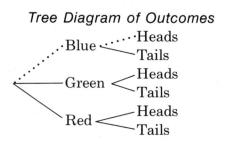

Notice that each "branch" of the tree diagram shows a possible outcome. For example, the dotted branch shows the outcome "spinning blue" **and then** "flipping heads."

A Basic Counting Principle

> If a first event has m outcomes and if a second event has n outcomes, then the first event followed by the second event has $m \times n$ outcomes.

From the example we have

Outcomes for spinning spinner		Outcomes for flipping coin		Total number of outcomes
3	×	2	=	6

EXERCISES

First tell how many outcomes there are for an event. Then tell whether the outcomes are equally likely.

1. Tossing the number cube (The outcome is the number of dots on the top face.)

2. Spinning the spinner

3. Without looking, picking a marble from the bag

4. Tossing the paper cup

Draw a tree diagram that shows all possible outcomes. Then tell whether the outcomes are equally likely.

5. *Event*
Picking a card and then tossing the number cube

6. *Event*
Picking a card and then flipping the coin

7. How many outcomes are there for the event flipping a coin and then tossing a number cube? Are the outcomes equally likely?

8. Sarah has 3 sweaters and 4 pairs of slacks. How many different sweater-slacks outfits does she have?

★ 9. How many 5-digit license plates can be made? Assume that 0 can be the first digit.

Probability

When you spin the spinner, there are 4 equally likely outcomes. The **probability** of each outcome is $\frac{1}{4}$.

$$P(\text{red}) = \frac{1}{4} \quad \begin{array}{l} \leftarrow \text{Number of "red" outcomes} \\ \leftarrow \text{Total number of outcomes} \end{array}$$

Read as "probability of red equals $\frac{1}{4}$."

Here are some other probabilities:

$$P(\text{blue}) = \frac{1}{4} \qquad P(\text{not blue}) = \frac{3}{4}$$

$$P(\text{red } or \text{ green}) = \frac{2}{4} = \frac{1}{2}$$

The probability of an impossible event is 0.

$$P(\text{brown}) = 0$$

> If an event has m equally likely outcomes, then the probability of one of the outcomes is $\frac{1}{m}$.

Notice the words *equally likely* in the sentence above. Let's consider an event where the outcomes are not equally likely.

Event

Picking a marble from the bag

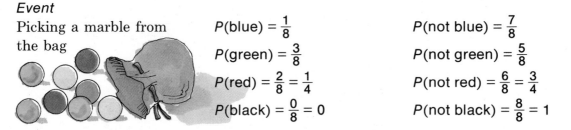

$$P(\text{blue}) = \frac{1}{8} \qquad P(\text{not blue}) = \frac{7}{8}$$

$$P(\text{green}) = \frac{3}{8} \qquad P(\text{not green}) = \frac{5}{8}$$

$$P(\text{red}) = \frac{2}{8} = \frac{1}{4} \qquad P(\text{not red}) = \frac{6}{8} = \frac{3}{4}$$

$$P(\text{black}) = \frac{0}{8} = 0 \qquad P(\text{not black}) = \frac{8}{8} = 1$$

Notice that the probability of the last outcome is 1. If an outcome is *certain* to occur, then the probability of that outcome is 1.

EXERCISES

Give each probability.

Event

Picking a marble from the bag

1. P(blue)
2. P(not blue)
3. P(not green)
4. P(red)
5. P(yellow)
6. P(not yellow)

Event

Tossing a number cube

7. P(1)
8. P(6)
9. P(odd number)
10. P(4 *or* 6)
11. P(number greater than 6)

Event

Picking a card from a deck of cards of the first 50 counting numbers

12. P(even number)
13. P(number greater than 40)
14. P(multiple of 5)
15. P(number less than 36)
16. P(1-digit number)
17. P(square number)

Complete.

18. If the probability of an outcome is $\frac{5}{8}$, then the outcome is ___more/less___ likely to happen than not to happen.

19. If the probability of an outcome is $\frac{1}{4}$, then the outcome is ___more/less___ likely to happen than not to happen.

Solve.

20. Suppose that 12 red marbles and 18 white marbles are placed in a bag and thoroughly mixed. If one marble is picked, what is the probability that it is red? That it is white?

Give each sum in simplest form.

1. $2 + 4\frac{1}{3}$

2. $3\frac{1}{2} + 2\frac{1}{4}$

3. $4\frac{1}{2} + 5\frac{1}{3}$

4. $1\frac{7}{8} + 2\frac{3}{4}$

5. $5\frac{3}{5} + 2\frac{4}{5}$

6. $6\frac{1}{2} + 7\frac{2}{3}$

7. $8\frac{3}{8} + 3\frac{3}{4}$

8. $9\frac{3}{4} + 4\frac{2}{3}$

9. $12\frac{5}{8} + 10\frac{5}{6}$

10. $14\frac{3}{4} + 11\frac{2}{5}$

11. $15\frac{1}{8} + 11\frac{3}{4}$

12. $20\frac{2}{3} + 31\frac{5}{6}$

13. $24\frac{3}{4} + 19\frac{3}{4}$

14. $22\frac{4}{5} + 21\frac{1}{2}$

15. $17\frac{3}{4} + 2\frac{5}{6}$

16. $19\frac{3}{8} + 14\frac{5}{8}$

Probability—independent and dependent events

Now let's consider a first event followed by a second event.

First Event
Picking a marble

Second Event
Flipping a coin

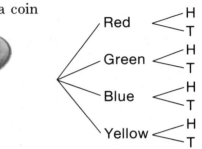

Notice that $P(\text{red}) = \frac{1}{4}$, $P(\text{H}) = \frac{1}{2}$,

and $P(\text{red and then H}) = \frac{1}{8}$

> If the probability of an outcome of a first event is $\frac{1}{m}$ and the probability of an outcome of a second event is $\frac{1}{n}$, then the probability of the first outcome followed by the second outcome is $\frac{1}{m} \times \frac{1}{n}$, or $\frac{1}{mn}$.

From the example above, we have

$$P(\text{red and then H}) = \frac{1}{4} \times \frac{1}{2} = \frac{1}{8}$$

The two events described above are **independent** events, since the outcome of the first event does not affect the outcome of the second event.

Two events such that the outcome of the first affects the outcome of the second are called **dependent** events.

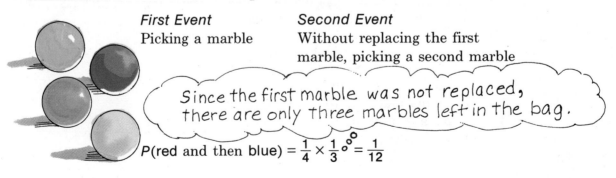

First Event
Picking a marble

Second Event
Without replacing the first marble, picking a second marble

Since the first marble was not replaced, there are only three marbles left in the bag.

$P(\text{red and then blue}) = \frac{1}{4} \times \frac{1}{3} = \frac{1}{12}$

EXERCISES
Give each probability.

First Event
Picking a marble

Second Event
Tossing a
number cube

1. *P*(red and then 5)

2. *P*(not red and then 4)

3. *P*(blue and then not 2)

4. *P*(not green and then not odd)

---

5. *P*(green and then green)

6. *P*(blue and then not blue)

7. *P*(not yellow and then red)

8. *P*(yellow and then not red)

First Event
Spinning this spinner

Second Event
Spinning this spinner

First Event: Picking a card

Second Event: Without replacing the
first card, picking a
second card

9. *P*(and then)

10. *P*(a four-sided figure and then)

11. *P*(a red card and then a black card)

12. *P*(a non-black card and then)

There are 52 playing cards in a full deck.

First Event
Picking a card
from a full deck
of playing cards

Second Event
Without replacing the
first card, picking a
second card

★ 13. *P*(heart and then heart)

★ 14. *P*(4 and then 6)

★ 15. *P*(king and then king)

★ 16. *P*(heart and then club)

Sample space

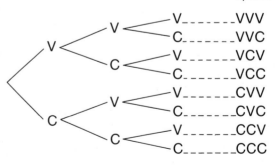

Every customer who buys an ice-cream cone is given a Flavor Match card. When the card is rubbed, the word VANILLA or CHOCOLATE appears on each of the three boxes. The words are equally likely to appear.

What is the probability of getting a winning card? To find the probability of getting a winning card, it is helpful to first list the **sample space** (the set of all possible outcomes of an event is called the sample space of the event). The sample space is shown in this tree diagram.

Look at the sample space. Two of the 8 outcomes have flavors that are all the same.

P(all flavors the same) $= \frac{2}{8} = \frac{1}{4}$

So the probability of getting a winning card is $\frac{1}{4}$.

Sample Space

```
                      V--------VVV
              V <
                      C--------VVC
        V <
                      V--------VCV
              C <
                      C--------VCC
  <
                      V--------CVV
              V <
                      C--------CVC
        C <
                      V--------CCV
              C <
                      C--------CCC
```

EXERCISES

Refer to the same space on the preceding page. What is the probability of getting

1. VANILLA exactly once?

2. CHOCOLATE exactly twice?

3. VANILLA at least once?

4. CHOCOLATE in the first two boxes?

5. Think about tossing these number cubes.

The outcome shown can be represented by the number pair (1, 4).

a. Copy and complete this table.

Number on red die

	1	2	3	4	5	6
1				(1, 4)		
2						
3						
4						
5						
6						

Number on blue die

b. How many outcomes are in the sample space?

6. Refer to your sample space in exercise 5 to find the following probabilities.

a. *P*(doubles)
b. *P*(not doubles)
c. *P*(sum of 2)
d. *P*(sum of 12)
e. *P*(sum of 7)
f. *P*(not sum of 7)

7. Think about a family that has 3 children.

a. List the sample space. Use *BGG* to represent a boy as the oldest child, a girl as the middle child, and a girl as the youngest child.
b. Assume that the probability of the birth of a boy is the same as the probability of the birth of a girl. What is the probability that there are 2 boys and 1 girl in the family?
c. What is the probability that the children are *not* all boys or all girls?

★ 8. These five marbles are placed in a bag.

Then two marbles are picked, one after the other.

a. Make a tree diagram of the sample space.
b. What is the probability that the red marble will be picked?
c. What is the probability that the green marble will not be picked?

345

Odds

The **odds** in favor of an outcome is the ratio of the number of ways the outcome *can* occur to the number of ways that the outcome *cannot* occur.

Event
Spinning this spinner

The odds in favor of spinning a 2 are

$$\frac{1}{7}$$

$\nearrow$ number of ways that outcome can occur
$\searrow$ number of ways that outcome cannot occur

Read as "one to seven."

The odds against spinning a 2 are

$$\frac{7}{1}$$

$\nearrow$ number of ways that outcome cannot occur
$\searrow$ number of ways that outcome can occur

If the odds in favor of an outcome are $\frac{a}{b}$, then the odds against the outcome are $\frac{b}{a}$.

Other examples:

The odds in favor of spinning green are $\frac{3}{5}$.

The odds in favor of spinning red are $\frac{4}{4} = \frac{1}{1}$.

The odds against spinning a multiple of 3 are $\frac{6}{2} = \frac{3}{1}$.

The odds against spinning a number less than 4 are $\frac{5}{3}$.

EXERCISES

Compute each probability or odds.

Event

Picking one marble

1. *P*(red)   2. *P*(not red)
3. Odds in favor of picking red
4. *P*(blue)   5. *P*(not blue)
6. Odds in favor of picking blue
7. Odds against picking blue

Event

Tossing the number cube

8. *P*(5)   9. *P*(not 5)
10. *P*(2 or 3)   11. Odds in favor of 5
12. Odds against 5
13. Odds in favor of an even number
14. Odds against an even number

Event

Picking one card

15. *P*(green)
16. *P*(triangle)
17. Odds in favor of a square
18. Odds in favor of a circle
19. Odds against red

Event

Picking one card

★ 20. Odds in favor of an even number
★ 21. Odds against a prime number
★ 22. Odds in favor of a multiple of 3 or a multiple of 4
★ 23. Odds in favor of a number less than 7

(whole numbers 1 through 24)

★ 24. Odds against a number greater than 16

Give each difference in simplest form.

1. $4\frac{3}{8} - 2$

2. $5\frac{2}{3} - 1\frac{1}{3}$

3. $6\frac{3}{4} - 2\frac{1}{2}$

4. $8\frac{1}{2} - 3\frac{1}{3}$

5. $6 - 3\frac{1}{2}$

6. $4\frac{1}{4} - 2\frac{3}{4}$

7. $9\frac{1}{3} - 4\frac{1}{2}$

8. $8\frac{1}{8} - 3\frac{5}{16}$

9. $12\frac{2}{3} - 3\frac{3}{4}$

10. $18\frac{1}{4} - 12\frac{5}{6}$

11. $19\frac{1}{2} - 11\frac{3}{8}$

12. $24\frac{3}{4} - 12\frac{7}{8}$

13. $26\frac{9}{10} - 18\frac{1}{2}$

14. $28\frac{1}{5} - 15\frac{3}{4}$

15. $24\frac{3}{4} - 23\frac{9}{10}$

16. $30\frac{1}{2} - 18\frac{5}{6}$

347

Sampling to estimate probabilities

Some students were asked to find what percent of the entire student body play a musical instrument. Of course, they could have checked with each student. But that would have taken too long. Instead, they decided to take a **sample** of the student population and then estimate the percent from their sample.

Their sample had to be representative of the population (the entire student body). It had to be large enough and had to be **unbiased.** For their sample to be unbiased, each member of the student body had to have an equally likely chance of being selected. For their sample they chose the first 80 students to enter the school.

From their sample they predicted the percent of the student body that play a musical instrument.

number who
play an instrument

number in
sample

$$\frac{49}{80} = \frac{x}{100}$$

$$80x = 4900$$
$$x = 61.25$$

They estimated that about 61% of the student body play a musical instrument. Of a student population of 480, they predicted that 61% of 480, or about 293, play a musical instrument.

Below are the results of another sample taken by the students.

1. How many students in the sample like WMS best?

2. Which station is the most popular?

3. How many students are in the sample?

4. What percent like KGB best? Round your answer to the nearest percent.

5. On the basis of the sample, how many students of a student population of 480 like KGB best? Round your answer to the nearest whole number.

6. On the basis of the sample, predict how many of the 480 students like WMS best.

7. Predict how many students of the student body do not like WBW best.

8. Predict how many students in the school like either KGB or WBW best.

9. If they had asked one more student for his favorite radio station, what would you guess the answer would have been? Can you be sure?

★ 10. Take a sample of your student body to find out what percent prefer your favorite radio station. Use your sample to estimate how many students in your school agree with your choice.

11. ★ **HEAD OVER HEELS**

20 students were surveyed. 12 students said they liked doing forward flips and 9 students said they liked doing backward flips. The survey showed that 4 students liked doing both kinds of flips. How many students did not like either kind of flip?

Presenting data—graphs

Statistics is a branch of mathematics that involves collecting data, analyzing the data, and then making inferences (drawing probable conclusions) from the data.

Graphs provide a visual organization of data. The data listed in the table below are represented on two different kinds of graphs: a bar graph and a broken-line graph.

Population Density of the United States	
Year	Population per square mile
1880	16.9
1890	21.2
1900	25.6
1910	31.0
1920	35.6
1930	41.2
1940	44.2
1950	42.6
1960	50.6
1970	57.4
1980	64.0

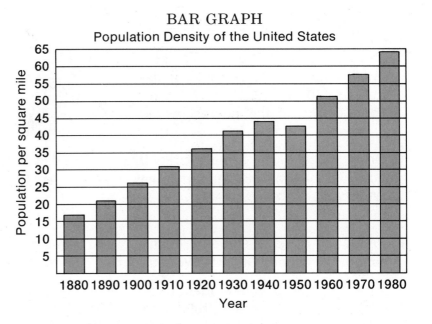

BAR GRAPH
Population Density of the United States

EXERCISES
Study the three ways in which the population density was presented.

1. Which is the most accurate?

2. Which is probably the least accurate?

3. Which do you think is least attractive?

4. Which do you think is the most attractive?

5. Could the bar graph have been made so that the population density could be read to the nearest tenth of a person? How?

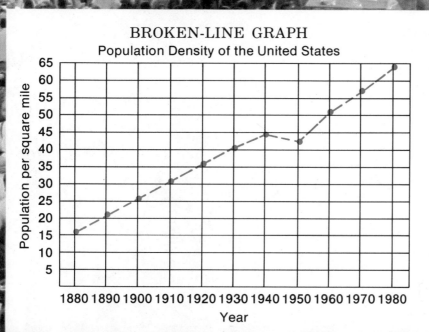

BROKEN-LINE GRAPH
Population Density of the United States

Give each product in simplest form.

1. $2 \times 4\frac{1}{2}$

2. $2\frac{1}{3} \times 7$

3. $1\frac{1}{3} \times 1\frac{1}{2}$

4. $3\frac{1}{3} \times 3$

5. $2\frac{2}{3} \times 3\frac{1}{2}$

6. $6 \times 3\frac{1}{3}$

7. $3\frac{3}{4} \times 4\frac{1}{4}$

8. $2\frac{1}{2} \times 2\frac{1}{2}$

9. $1\frac{2}{3} \times 4\frac{3}{5}$

10. $1\frac{1}{5} \times 4\frac{3}{8}$

11. $2\frac{1}{2} \times 3$

12. $3\frac{2}{3} \times 4\frac{1}{2}$

13. $4\frac{2}{3} \times 3\frac{1}{3}$

14. $5\frac{1}{4} \times 3\frac{1}{2}$

15. $4\frac{3}{4} \times 2\frac{2}{3}$

16. $2\frac{2}{3} \times \frac{3}{8}$

6. Look at the broken-line graph. Is it possible that the population density in 1965 was 60 persons per square mile? Why or why not? Does the broken-line graph really tell you anything about the population density of any years except those that are listed?

7. From a magazine or newspaper, cut out a graph. Construct a different kind of graph that shows the same information.

★ 8. Find out your school's daily attendance for each day of the past two full weeks. Show the daily attendance on a bar graph and on a broken-line graph.

Presenting data—graphs

The **tally** below shows the results of the election for the student council.

Election Tally	
Andrews	ЖТ ЖТ ЖТ ЖТ I
Carter	ЖТ ЖТ ЖТ ЖТ ЖТ I
Howey	ЖТ ЖТ ЖТ ЖТ ЖТ ЖТ ЖТ I
Manning	ЖТ ЖТ ЖТ
Sanchez	ЖТ ЖТ ЖТ ЖТ II

The school election committee made this **pictograph** of the election results and placed it on a school bulletin board.

Election Results	
Andrews	👤👤👤👤👤👤👤
Carter	👤👤👤👤👤👤👤👤
Howey	👤👤👤👤👤👤👤👤👤👤
Manning	👤👤👤👤👤
Sanchez	👤👤👤👤👤👤👤
	Each 👤 stands for 3 votes.

352

On another bulletin board they posted this **circle graph** of the results. The example below shows how they constructed the circle graph.

number of votes for Andrews $\longrightarrow$

total number of $\longrightarrow$ votes

$$\frac{21}{120} = \frac{x}{100}$$

$$120x = 2100$$
$$x = 17.5$$

Andrews got 17.5% of the votes. 17.5% of 360° is 63°. They marked off an angle of 63° in the circle.

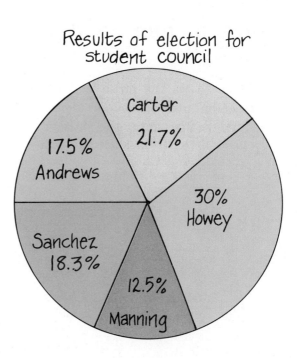

Results of election for student council

Carter 21.7%

17.5% Andrews

30% Howey

Sanchez 18.3%

12.5% Manning

EXERCISES

Refer to the pictograph to answer the following questions.

1. How many votes does each 👤 stand for?

2. Who got the most votes?

3. Who got the fewest votes?

4. How many votes did Andrews get?

5. Estimate the number of votes that Carter got.

6. How many students voted in the election?

Refer to the circle graph to answer the following questions.

7. How many candidates were there?

8. Who got the most votes?

9. Who got the fewest votes?

10. What percent of the votes did Sanchez get?

11. What percent of the votes did the top two "vote getters" get?

12. Can you tell just by looking at the circle graph how many students voted for Manning?

★ 13. **a.** List your six favorite songs.
   b. Take a survey. Have each of your friends pick the song from your list that he or she likes best.
   c. Show the results on a circle graph.

Mean, median, and mode

The table shows the pulse rate (heartbeats per minute) of some students. To help analyze the data, the pulse rates have been listed from least to greatest.

NAME	PULSE RATE	ORDERED RATES
ADAMS, A.	81	
ALLEN, J.	71	61
BORWICK, A.	76	62
BURNER, G.	80	65
CALLON, A.	82	68
COOKE, C.	86	69
DAVIS, F.	83	70
DRIVERS, R.	78	71
FALLON, C.	62	72
HOWARDS, F.	78	74
JACKSON, H.	70	75
JOHNSON, N.	72	76
LAVENTI, B.	81	77
LOGAN, D.	68	78
MARSHALL, G.	77	78
NEEDHAM, R.	78	78
OSLEY, J.	75	78
PARKER, N.	61	80
ROGERS, D.	69	81
SWEETMAN, W.	84	81
TROTTER, L.	78	82
TULMAN, M.	74	83
WALLACE, K.	65	84
		86

The **range** is the difference between the largest and smallest numbers.

$86 - 61 = 25$
The range is 25.

The **mean,** or average, is the sum of all the numbers divided by the number of numbers.

$$\begin{array}{r} 75.17 \\ 23\overline{)1729.00} \end{array}$$
Rounded to the nearest tenth, the mean is 75.2.

The **median** is the middle number. To find the median of an even number of numbers, average the two middle numbers.

The median is 77.

The **mode** is the number (or numbers) that occur most often.

The mode is 78.

354

EXERCISES

Find the range of each set of numbers.

1. 16, 23, 18, 19, 17, 21

2. 83.4, 86.9, 81.5, 90.3, 87.4

3. Compute the mean to the nearest tenth.

   59, 62, 71, 53, 74, 60, 57, 68, 75

4. Compute the mean to the nearest cent.

   $42.15, $38.75, $46.29, $50.18, $51.65, $43.83

Find the median. Remember that you average the two middle numbers if you have an even number of numbers.

5. 18, 14, 23, 19, 20, 17, 16, 24, 20, 21, 20

6. 152, 157, 150, 162, 159, 163, 158, 160

7. What is the mode of the data in exercise 5?

Mean, median, or mode?

8. Half the numbers in a set of data are less than the _?_ and half are greater.

9. The _?_ is always a number in the set.

10. The median and _?_ may not be numbers in the set.

11. Some sets of numbers do not have a _?_.

12. **a.** You and your classmates take your pulse rates. Record your name along with your pulse rate on the chalkboard.
    b. Order the data.
    c. Determine the range, the mean, the median, and the mode.

★ 13. Find seven whole numbers that range from 17 to 25 and have a median of **22**, a mode of **23**, and a mean of 21.

★ 14. NO SPEEDING!

Ms. Brown drove 100 kilometers from A to B at 60 kilometers per hour. Then she drove the 100 kilometers from B to A at 40 kilometers per hour. What was her average speed for the round trip? (The answer is not 50 kilometers per hour.)

355

Frequency distribution

The scores of a mathematics test can be recorded in a table. Such a table is called a **frequency distribution.** It tells how many students received each of the listed scores.

From the table we can compute the mean. First multiply each test score by its frequency. Adding all these products gives the total number of points. To find the number of students, add the frequencies. Then divide the total number of points by the number of students.

Test Score	Frequency	Number of Points
72	//	144
73	/	73
74	/	74
75		0
76		0
77	ЖЖ /	462
78	//	156
79	/	79
80	//	160
81	/	81
82	////	328
83	//	166
84		0
85	//	170
86	/	86
87		0
88	///	264
89	/	89
90	/	90
91		0
92	/	92

A **histogram** is a special kind of bar graph that is used to show frequency. The data given above are shown in this histogram. Notice that all the intervals (72–74, 75–77, 78–80, etc.) are equal.

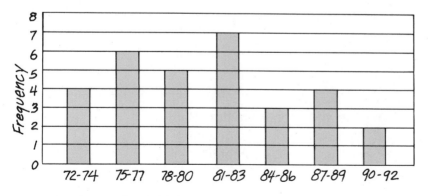

EXERCISES

For exercises 1–8, use the data on page 356.

1. How many students got a score of 82?

2. How many scored 80 or above?

3. Compute the mean score to the nearest tenth. *Hint:* Divide the total number of points by the number of students.

4. What is the median?

5. Find the mode.

6. Give the range.

7. Can you tell from the histogram alone whether any student got a score of 75? Why or why not?

Use the data below for exercises 8–13.

Time for 50-meter dash in seconds	Frequency
7	//
8	////
9	ⅢⅢ ⅢⅢ
10	ⅢⅢ //
11	ⅢⅢ
12	///
13	/
14	/

8. How many ran the 50-meter dash?

9. Which time is the mode?

10. What is the range of times?

11. What is the mean time?

12. What is the median time?

13. Make a histogram of the frequency distribution.

Give each quotient in simplest form.

1. $1\frac{1}{4} \div 1\frac{1}{4}$

2. $5 \div 1\frac{1}{2}$

3. $9\frac{1}{2} \div 3\frac{1}{2}$

4. $3\frac{3}{4} \div 3$

5. $8\frac{1}{2} \div 2\frac{1}{8}$

6. $4\frac{3}{8} \div 2$

7. $8\frac{3}{4} \div 2\frac{1}{2}$

8. $16\frac{3}{4} \div 2\frac{1}{8}$

9. $0 \div 4\frac{1}{3}$

10. $12\frac{3}{5} \div 4\frac{1}{10}$

11. $9\frac{3}{4} \div 2\frac{1}{8}$

12. $6\frac{2}{3} \div 1\frac{1}{6}$

Misleading statistics

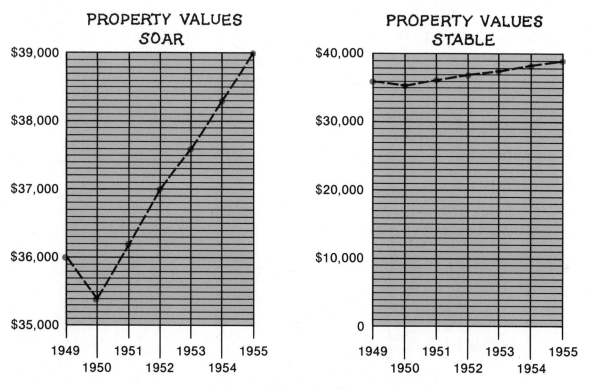

Average Price of a Home

EXERCISES

1. Answer these questions using the first graph.
   a. What was the average price of a home in 1949?
   b. What was the average price of a home in 1955?
   c. What was the increase in price over that period?
   d. What was the percent of increase?

2. Answer the 4 questions in exercise 1 using the second graph.

3. Do the graphs show the same information?

4. Do the pictures suggest the same idea?

5. Can the first graph be misleading?

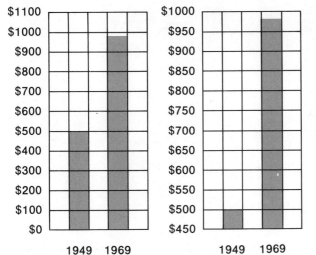

Average Tax on a Home

6. Do both bar graphs to the left show the same information?

7. Which graph do you think shows better the relationship between average tax on a home in 1949 and average tax on a home in 1969? Why?

The average yearly income of the residents on Oak Circle is $42,000.

Oak-Circle Residents' Yearly Incomes	
Smith	$200,000
Jones	$20,000
White	$15,000
Perez	$15,000
Chin	$15,000
Cooper	$15,000
Shultz	$12,000

8. The mean, median, and mode are all used as "averages." Which one is the salesman using?

9. Do you believe that the salesman's claim describes the neighbors' incomes accurately?

10. What would be a better average to use? Why?

11. If you had to pick an "average" salary for this group, would you pick the mean, median, or mode?

Yearly Salary	
Sanchez (owner)	$175,000
Porter (foreman)	$24,000
Pride (laborer)	$13,000
Goza (laborer)	$12,000
Lee (laborer)	$11,500
Starz (laborer)	$10,000
Hyde (laborer)	$10,000

Complete. [pages 338–341]

Event

Picking a marble
from the bag

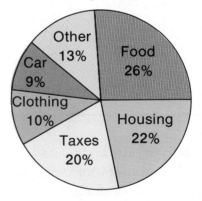

1. P(green) = ?

2. P(blue) = ?

3. P(red) = ?

4. P(not green) = ?

5. P(red or blue) = ?

6. P(yellow) = ?

Give the probability. [pages 342–343]

First Event

Picking a card

Second Event

Flipping the coin

7. P(square and then heads)

8. P(circle and then tails)

9. P(not a triangle and then heads)

**Answer these questions about the circle
graph.** [pages 350–353]

10. What is the greatest percent spent
for?

11. What percent is spent on taxes?

12. The family income is $24,000 per
year. How much is spent per year on
clothing?

Family Budget

Other
13%

Car
9%

Food
26%

Clothing
10%

Housing
22%

Taxes
20%

**Give the range, the mean, the median,
and the mode.** [pages 354–355]

13. 5, 6, 7, 8, 9

14. 13, 8, 11, 13, 17, 19

15. 10.3, 8.4, 9.6, 8.4, 7.5, 11.4, 8.2

How many students of average height, lying head to toe, are needed to stretch from Los Angeles to New York City?

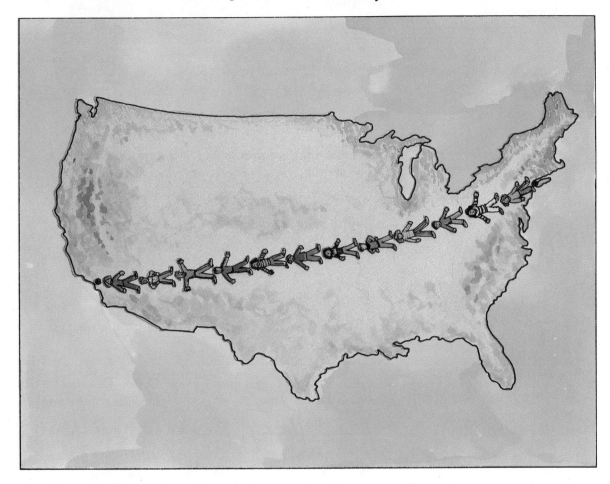

1. Select 20 students at random.

2. Measure their heights to the nearest centimeter.

3. Compute the average height.

4. Use your average to answer the question.
   Hint: The distance from Los Angeles to New York City is 4683.8 kilometers.

The probability of spinning green is $\frac{1}{2}$.

$P(\text{green}) = \frac{1}{2}$

$P(\text{green and then red})$

$= \frac{1}{2} \times \frac{1}{6}$

$= \frac{1}{12}$

Give each probability.

1. $P(\text{green})$
2. $P(\text{red})$
3. $P(\text{not green})$
4. $P(\text{not red})$
5. $P(\text{green or blue})$
6. $P(\text{green or red})$

Remember that the probability of a sure outcome is 1. The probability of an impossible outcome is 0.

7. $P(\text{yellow})$ 8. $P(\text{not yellow})$
9. $P(\text{red and then green})$
10. $P(\text{green and then blue})$

The **range** is the difference between the greatest and the smallest numbers.

The **mean** is the average.

The **median** is the middle number.

The **mode** is the number that occurs most often.

The table shows the weekly allowance (to the nearest dollar) of some students.

WEEKLY ALLOWANCE			
(rounded to the nearest dollar)			
5	4	5	3
3	6	2	4
5	3	1	2
2	4	0	5
1	2	8	1
3	3	3	0
3	5	7	2
2	7	2	6
2	4	4	3
0	0	2	6

11. Order the data from smallest to largest.
12. What is the range?
13. What is the mean allowance?
14. What is the median allowance?
15. What is the mode?

Suppose that this spinner is a fair spinner—that is, that the probability of its stopping on any one of the digits is $\frac{1}{10}$.

We could generate random digits by spinning the spinner and recording (in order) the digits on which the spinner stops.

Since a fair spinner is difficult to construct, we will use the following random digits, which have been generated by another device.

200 Random Digits*

49487	52802	28667	62058	87822	14704	18519	17889	45869	14454
29480	91539	46317	84803	86056	62812	33584	70391	77749	64906
25252	97738	23901	11106	86864	55808	22557	23214	15021	54268
02431	42193	96960	19620	29188	05863	92900	06836	13433	21709

This list of random digits can be used to select unbiased samples. For example, suppose that 83 students want to go to the state basketball final game, but their school is allowed only 15 tickets. The school could randomly select 15 of the 83 students by assigning a 2-digit number to each student (00, 01, 02, . . . , 10, 11, . . . , 80, 81, 82) and then, starting in the first row of the table, selecting 2-digit numbers. The students with the first 15 numbers may buy tickets.

49   48   75   28   02   28   66   76   20   58   87 . . .

↑ duplicate

↑ Ignore. There is no student with this number.

How could a table of random digits be used to make these selections?

1. Randomly divide a group of 80 students into 2 equally large groups.

2. Randomly assign 90 students to 6 groups of 9 students.

3. Randomly pick 60 students from a group of 720 students.

4. Randomly select 100 homes from a city of 12,250 homes for a TV survey.

5. The selection in exercise 1 also could have been made by tossing a coin. What is another way of making the selection in exercise 2?

* Reprinted by permission of the Rand Corporation.

	a b c d		a b c d	a b c d	a b c d		a b c d		a b
1.	⬜⬜⬜⬜	2.	⬜⬜⬜⬜	⬜⬜⬜⬜	⬜⬜⬜⬜	5.	⬜⬜⬜⬜	6.	⬜⬜

MAJOR CHECKUP
STANDARDIZED FORMAT

	a b c d		a b c d	a b c d	a b c d		a b c d		a b
7.	⬜⬜⬜⬜	8.	⬜⬜⬜⬜	9. ⬜⬜⬜⬜	10. ⬜⬜⬜⬜	11.	⬜⬜⬜⬜	12.	⬜⬜

Choose the correct letter.

1. Divide. Round the quotient to the nearest hundredth.

$0.19\overline{)3.74}$

- **a.** 19.684
- **b.** 19.68
- **c.** 196.8
- **d.** none of these

2. 2.84 kg = $\underline{?}$ g

- **a.** 284
- **b.** 28.4
- **c.** 2840
- **d.** none of these

3. Multiply.

$\frac{4}{9} \times \frac{3}{8}$

- **a.** $1\frac{5}{27}$
- **b.** $\frac{27}{32}$
- **c.** 6
- **d.** none of these

4. The area of this trapezoid is

10 m, 13 m, 15 m, 12 m, 24 m

- **a.** 204 m²
- **b.** 288 m²
- **c.** 62 m
- **d.** none of these

5. The ratio of prime-number cards to composite-number cards is

6 7 8 9 10

- **a.** 1 : 4
- **b.** 2 : 3
- **c.** 2 : 5
- **d.** none of these

6. What is the percent of discount?

$24 $15

- **a.** $37\frac{1}{2}\%$
- **b.** 60%
- **c.** $62\frac{1}{2}\%$
- **d.** none of these

7. The simple interest for a loan of $800 at 12% a year for 3 years is

- **a.** $288
- **b.** $28.80
- **c.** $24
- **d.** none of these

8. Solve.

$^-3n + 6 = {}^-9$

- **a.** 1
- **b.** $^-1$
- **c.** 5
- **d.** none of these

9. The probability of spinning a number less than 6 and then flipping heads is

- **a.** $\frac{3}{8}$
- **b.** $\frac{9}{8}$
- **c.** $\frac{5}{16}$
- **d.** none of these

10. The median of 4, 9, 5, 8, and 9 is

- **a.** 7
- **b.** 8
- **c.** 9
- **d.** none of these

11. What fraction of a yard is 8 inches?

- **a.** $\frac{2}{9}$
- **b.** $\frac{2}{3}$
- **c.** $\frac{1}{4}$
- **d.** none of these

12. Leon bought 3 pens for 19¢ each and 3 pads for $1.05 each. How much more did he spend for pads than pens?

- **a.** $3.72
- **b.** $2.58
- **c.** 86¢
- **d.** none of these

Indirect Measurement —Similar and Right Triangles

13

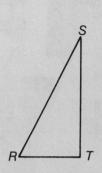

Complete each pair of corresponding parts for the congruent fitting.

1. $\overline{AB} \leftrightarrow \underline{\ ?\ }$
2. $\overline{BC} \leftrightarrow \underline{\ ?\ }$
3. $\overline{CA} \leftrightarrow \underline{\ ?\ }$
4. $\angle A \leftrightarrow \underline{\ ?\ }$
5. $\angle B \leftrightarrow \underline{\ ?\ }$
6. $\angle C \leftrightarrow \underline{\ ?\ }$

Solve.

7. $\frac{3}{n} = \frac{12}{20}$
8. $\frac{n}{6} = \frac{8}{10}$
9. $\frac{7}{3} = \frac{n}{5}$
10. $\frac{4}{7} = \frac{9}{n}$

Similar figures

These two photographs have the same shape. They are **similar**.

Two figures that have the same shape are called **similar figures.**

These two triangles are similar.

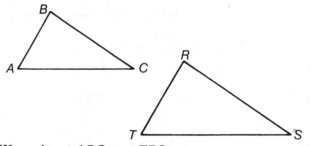

We write $\triangle ABC \sim \triangle TRS$
and say "Triangle *ABC* is similar to triangle *TRS*."

EXERCISES
Do the two figures look similar?

1.

2.

3.

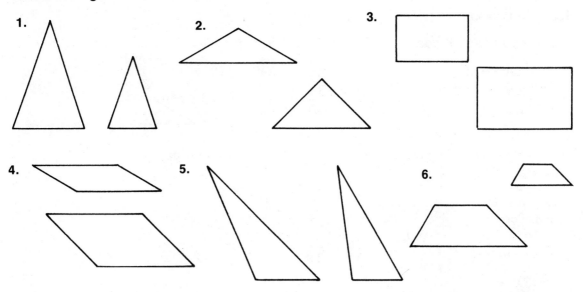

4.

5.

6.

These two triangles are similar.

7. Is $\angle D \cong \angle U$?

8. Is $\angle E \cong \angle V$?

9. Is $\angle F \cong \angle W$?

What is the ratio of

10. the length of $\overline{DE}$ to the length of $\overline{UV}$?

11. the length of $\overline{DF}$ to the length of $\overline{UW}$?

12. Guess the ratio of the length of $\overline{EF}$ to the length of $\overline{VW}$.

13. a. On graph paper, draw a pair of similar triangles.
b. List all pairs of congruent angles.
c. Compare the lengths of the sides that are opposite congruent angles. Are the ratios equal?

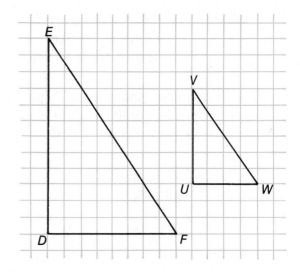

Similar polygons

Here are two similar triangles.

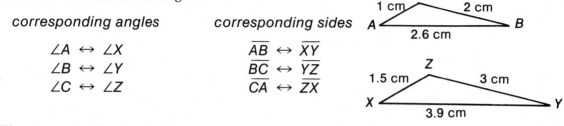

corresponding angles	corresponding sides
$\angle A \leftrightarrow \angle X$	$\overline{AB} \leftrightarrow \overline{XY}$
$\angle B \leftrightarrow \angle Y$	$\overline{BC} \leftrightarrow \overline{YZ}$
$\angle C \leftrightarrow \angle Z$	$\overline{CA} \leftrightarrow \overline{ZX}$

The corresponding angles are congruent and the corresponding sides are in the same ratio.

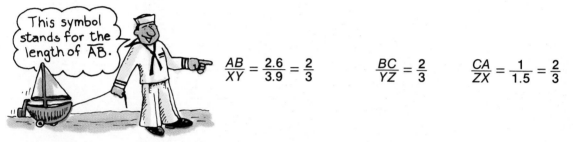

This symbol stands for the length of $\overline{AB}$.

$$\frac{AB}{XY} = \frac{2.6}{3.9} = \frac{2}{3} \qquad \frac{BC}{YZ} = \frac{2}{3} \qquad \frac{CA}{ZX} = \frac{1}{1.5} = \frac{2}{3}$$

Since all three ratios are equal, the corresponding sides are said to be **proportional.**

> In similar polygons, the corresponding angles are congruent and the corresponding sides are proportional.

These two triangles are similar. Since similar triangles have proportional sides, we can solve a proportion to find the length x.

$$\frac{x}{20} = \frac{9}{15}$$
$$15x = 180$$
$$x = 12$$

The length x is 12 m.

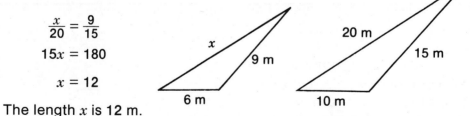

What are some other proportions that you could solve to find the length x?

EXERCISES

The two polygons in each exercise are similar. Solve a proportion to find the missing length. Round each answer to the nearest tenth unit.

1.
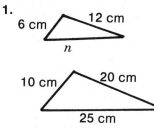
6 cm   12 cm
n

10 cm   20 cm
25 cm

2.
9 m
8 m
12 m
4.5 m
n   4 m

3.

6.8 m
3.8 m   1.6 m
5.6 m

8.4 m
5.7 m
2.4 m
n

4.
21.15 km
n
22.95 km

28.20 km
12.40 km
30.6 km

The two polygons in each exercise are similar. Find both missing lengths. Round each answer to the nearest tenth unit.

★ 5.
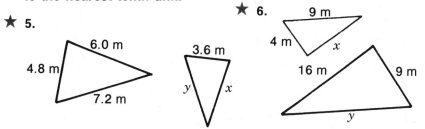
6.0 m
4.8 m
7.2 m

3.6 m
y   x

★ 6.
9 m
4 m
x

16 m   9 m
y

★ 7. a. Get a protractor and draw two triangles that have congruent corresponding angles.
  b. Measure the sides. Are they proportional?

KEEPING SKILLS SHARP

Solve.

1. $x + 6 = {}^-15$

2. $x - 4 = 9$

3. $3x = {}^-12$

4. $4x = 20$

5. $2x + 3 = 13$

6. ${}^-3x + 4 = 1$

7. $5x - 19 = {}^-4$

8. $4x - {}^-2 = 26$

9. $5x + 5 = 0$

10. ${}^-3x - 2 = 10$

11. $9x + 16 = {}^-2$

12. $4x - 2 = {}^-2$

13. $3x + 9 = 3$

14. ${}^-2x + 3 = 11$

15. $4x - 6 = {}^-2$

16. ${}^-3x - 5 = {}^-8$

More about similar polygons

Here is a quick way to check whether two triangles are similar:

If the corresponding angles of two triangles are congruent, then the triangles are similar.

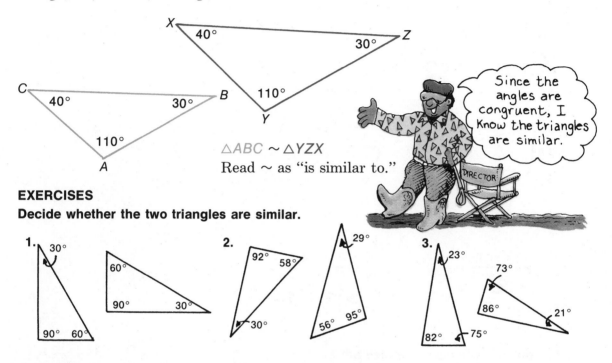

$\triangle ABC \sim \triangle YZX$

Read ~ as "is similar to."

EXERCISES

Decide whether the two triangles are similar.

Remember that the sum of the angle measures of a triangle is 180°. In these exercises you are given two of the angles. Find the third. (There are 60 minutes in 1 degree; 60′ = 1°.)

4. 90°, 30°   5. 90°, 45°   6. 60°, 60°   7. 50°, 38°

8. 110°, 35°   9. 145°, 27°   ★ 10. 27°18′, 59°17′ ★ 11. 93°16′, 46°19′

12. △ABC has a 50° angle and a 70° angle. △XYZ also has a 50° angle and a 70° angle. Are the triangles similar?

13. a. Suppose that two right triangles also have 45° angles. Are they similar?

    b. Suppose that two right triangles also have 30° angles. Are they similar?

Find the missing angle measures.

14.

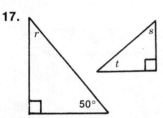

15.

16.

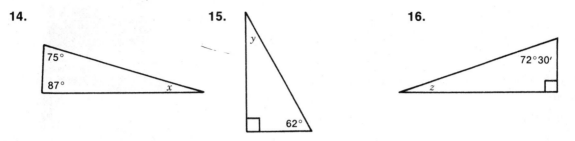

The two right triangles are similar.
Find the missing angle measures.

17.

18.

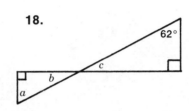

19.

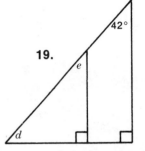

★ **20. a.** Are corresponding angles of these two rectangles congruent?
  b. Are the corresponding sides proportional?
  (Are these ratios equal: $\frac{AB}{MN}$, $\frac{BC}{NO}$, $\frac{CD}{OP}$, $\frac{AD}{MP}$?)
  c. Are the rectangles similar?

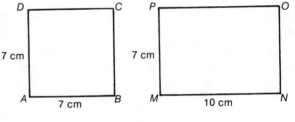

★ **21. a.** Are corresponding sides of the two parallelograms proportional?
  b. Are the corresponding angles congruent?
  c. Are the parallelograms similar?

★ **True or false?**

22. All equilateral triangles are similar.

23. All right triangles are similar.

24. All rectangles are similar.

25. All parallelograms are similar.

26. All squares are similar.

27. All isosceles triangles are similar.

Indirect measurement

Similar triangles can be used to find lengths that would be difficult to measure directly. Below, you are shown how indirect measurement can be used to find the height of the flagpole.

The triangle made by the meterstick and its shadow is similar to the triangle made by the flagpole and its shadow. John found the height of the flagpole by solving this proportion.

$$\frac{h}{100} = \frac{306}{68}$$

$$68 \times h = 100 \times 306$$

$$h = 450$$

So the height of the flagpole is 450 cm, or 4.50 m.

EXERCISES

First read the problem carefully and study the sketch.
Then solve the problem.

1. A building casts a 150-meter shadow. At the same time, a man 2 meters tall casts a 3-meter shadow. How tall is the building?

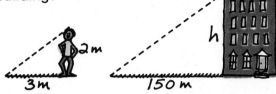

2. A tree casts a 30.5-meter shadow. At the same time a meterstick casts a 1.6-meter shadow. How tall is the tree?

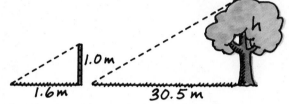

Make your own sketches for exercises 3 and 4.

3. A meterstick casts a shadow that is 0.35 meter long. At the same time, a water tank casts a shadow that is 24.80 meters long. About what is the height of the water tank?

4. A utility pole casts a shadow that is 24.50 meters long. The shadow of a meterstick that is stood upright 22.50 meters from the pole ends at the same point. Find the height of the utility pole.

★ 5. A backpacking club wants to measure the distance across a lake. The club made the measurements recorded in the sketch and used similar triangles to find the distance across the lake. Why are the triangles similar? How far is it across the lake?

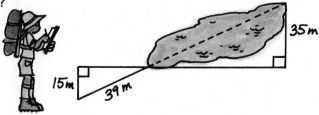

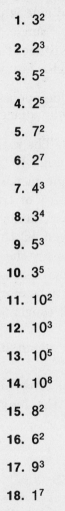

KEEPING SKILLS
SHARP

Give the standard
numeral.

1. 3^2

2. 2^3

3. 5^2

4. 2^5

5. 7^2

6. 2^7

7. 4^3

8. 3^4

9. 5^3

10. 3^5

11. 10^2

12. 10^3

13. 10^5

14. 10^8

15. 8^2

16. 6^2

17. 9^3

18. 1^7

Tangent ratios

All three of these right triangles are similar. Why?

The red side is called the **side opposite** the 30° angle. The blue side is called the **side adjacent** to the 30° angle. Since the triangles are similar, their ratios of

$$\frac{\text{side opposite (30° angle)}}{\text{side adjacent (30° angle)}}$$

are equal. The ratio of the side opposite an acute angle to the side adjacent to the acute angle in a *right* triangle is called the **tangent** of the angle. (The longest side of the triangle, shown here in black, is not used in the tangent ratio.) We could measure the sides and divide to find the approximate ratio. However, to save time and to be more accurate, we can use a table of tangent ratios.

$$\tan 30° \approx 0.58$$

We can use the tangent ratios to help us compute the lengths of sides of right triangles.

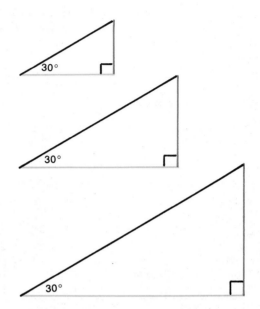

Some tangent ratios
tan 5° ≈ 0.09
tan 10° ≈ 0.18
tan 15° ≈ 0.27
tan 20° ≈ 0.36
tan 25° ≈ 0.47
tan 30° ≈ 0.58
tan 35° ≈ 0.70
tan 40° ≈ 0.84
tan 45° = 1.00
tan 50° ≈ 1.19
tan 55° ≈ 1.43
tan 60° ≈ 1.73
tan 65° ≈ 2.14
tan 70° ≈ 2.75
tan 75° ≈ 3.73
tan 80° ≈ 5.67
tan 85° ≈ 11.43

EXAMPLES.

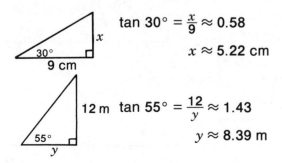

$$\tan 30° = \frac{x}{9} \approx 0.58$$
$$x \approx 5.22 \text{ cm}$$

$$\tan 55° = \frac{12}{y} \approx 1.43$$
$$y \approx 8.39 \text{ m}$$

EXERCISES

Name the side opposite the given angle and the side adjacent to the given angle.

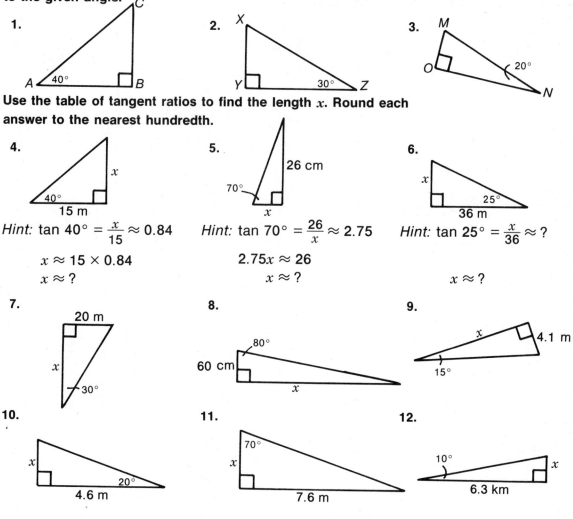

1.

2.

3.

Use the table of tangent ratios to find the length x**. Round each answer to the nearest hundredth.**

4.

Hint: $\tan 40° = \dfrac{x}{15} \approx 0.84$

$x \approx 15 \times 0.84$

$x \approx ?$

5.

26 cm

Hint: $\tan 70° = \dfrac{26}{x} \approx 2.75$

$2.75x \approx 26$

$x \approx ?$

6.

36 m

Hint: $\tan 25° = \dfrac{x}{36} \approx ?$

$x \approx ?$

7.

8.

9.

10.

11.

12.

Solve. *Hint:* **First draw a picture. Round each answer to the nearest hundredth.**

★ **13.** A hot-air balloon is directly over a ballpark that is 10 kilometers from where the balloon was launched. A sighting from the point where it was launched shows the balloon to be 30° above horizontal. How high is the balloon over the ballpark?

★ **14.** How far from a 300-meter cliff would you have to stand in order to look directly at the top by sighting 70° above horizontal?

Practice exercises

Use similar triangles to find the length x.
Round to the nearest tenth.

1.

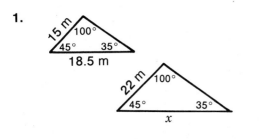

2.

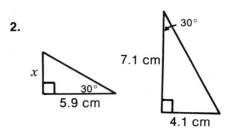

3.

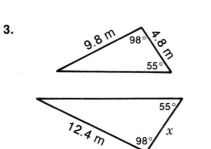

4.

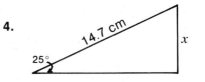

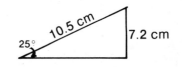

5.

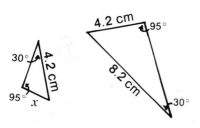

6.

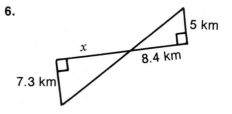

★ **7.**

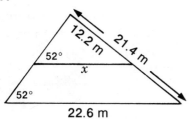

★ **8.**

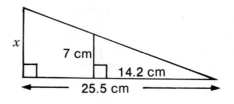

Use the table of tangent ratios to find the length x.
Round your answer to the nearest hundredth.

9.

30°
5.6 cm
x

10.

8.2 m
40°
x

11.

4.2 km
50°
x

12.

20°
12.8 m
x

13.

60°
6 cm
x

14.

30°
12.8 m
x

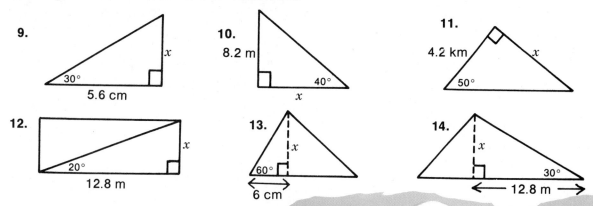

Solve.

15. An airplane flying at an altitude of 8.4 km sights a flashing beacon. The angle of depression for the sighting is 20°. How far will the airplane have to fly to be directly over the beacon?

★ 16. An airplane is sighted from a control tower. The airplane is 18.2 km from a point directly over the tower. The tower is 80 m high. The angle of elevation is 15°. What is the altitude of the airplane?

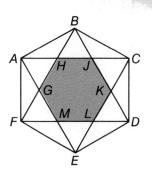

17. ★ **HEXED FRACTION**

Hexagon *MLKJHG* and hexagon *ABCDEF* are regular hexagons. What fraction of the area of hexagon *ABCDEF* is hexagon *MLKJHG*?

Square roots

Ancient mathematicians thought about numbers in geometric terms. So when they multiplied a number by itself, they thought about finding the area of a square. That is the reason we still talk about **squaring** numbers.

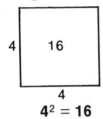

$$4^2 = 16$$

We say, "4 squared is 16."

We also say, "The square root of 16 is 4."

This is a short way of writing the last sentence.

$$\sqrt{16} = 4$$

Here are some more examples:

$$7^2 = 49 \qquad 10^2 = 100 \qquad 1.2^2 = 1.44$$
$$\sqrt{49} = 7 \qquad \sqrt{100} = 10 \qquad \sqrt{1.44} = 1.2$$

EXERCISES
Simplify.

1. $\sqrt{36}$ 2. $\sqrt{9}$ 3. $\sqrt{25}$ 4. $\sqrt{64}$ 5. $\sqrt{1}$

6. $\sqrt{81}$ 7. $\sqrt{196}$ 8. $\sqrt{256}$ 9. $\sqrt{4}$ 10. $\sqrt{361}$

11. $\sqrt{144}$ 12. $\sqrt{400}$ 13. $\sqrt{169}$ 14. $\sqrt{225}$ 15. $\sqrt{121}$

16. $\sqrt{2.25}$ 17. $\sqrt{2.89}$ 18. $\sqrt{1.69}$ 19. $\sqrt{1.96}$ 20. $\sqrt{3.24}$

Some square roots have only decimal approximations. The divide-and-average method is one way to find a decimal approximation of a square root. Study this example.

EXAMPLE. Find $\sqrt{32}$ to the nearest tenth.

Step 1. Estimate $\sqrt{32}$.

$\sqrt{25} = 5$

$\sqrt{32} = ?$

$\sqrt{36} = 6$

$\sqrt{32}$ is between 5 and 6. We will try 5.6.

Step 2. Divide 32 by 5.6.

$$
\begin{array}{r}
5.71 \\
5.6\overline{)32.000} \\
-28\ 0 \\
\hline
4\ 00 \\
-3\ 92 \\
\hline
80
\end{array}
$$

$\sqrt{32}$ is between 5.6 and 5.7.

Step 3. Average 5.6 and 5.7.

$$\frac{5.6 + 5.7}{2} = 5.65$$

Step 4. Divide 32 by 5.65.

$$
\begin{array}{r}
5.66 \\
5.65\overline{)32.0000} \\
-28\ 25 \\
\hline
3\ 750 \\
-3\ 390 \\
\hline
3600
\end{array}
$$

$\sqrt{32}$ is between 5.65 and 5.66.

$\sqrt{32} = 5.7$ to the nearest tenth.

True or false?

21. $\sqrt{2}$ is between 1 and 2.

22. $\sqrt{3}$ is between 1 and 2.

23. $\sqrt{5}$ is between 1 and 2.

24. $\sqrt{5}$ is between 2 and 3.

25. $\sqrt{5}$ is between 2.2 and 2.3.

26. $\sqrt{5}$ is between 2.3 and 2.4.

27. $\sqrt{5}$ is between 2.22 and 2.23.

28. $\sqrt{5}$ is between 2.23 and 2.24.

Use the divide-and-average method.
Give an approximation to the nearest tenth.

29. $\sqrt{7}$ 30. $\sqrt{12}$ 31. $\sqrt{50}$ 32. $\sqrt{68}$ 33. $\sqrt{75}$

34. $\sqrt{90}$ 35. $\sqrt{110}$ 36. $\sqrt{160}$ 37. $\sqrt{218}$ 38. $\sqrt{236}$

Right triangles

The sides of right triangles have special names. The side opposite the right angle, the longest side, is called the **hypotenuse.** The other two sides are called the **legs.**

In this lesson you will explore an interesting property of right triangles.

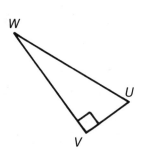

EXERCISES

Which side is the hypotenuse?

1.

2.

3.

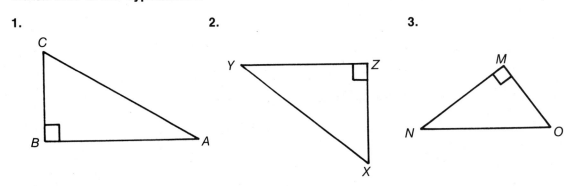

Which sides are the legs?

4.

5.

6.

Complete.

Look for a pattern.

7.

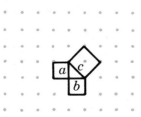

The area of the square on

a. leg a is ⟨?⟩.
b. leg b is ⟨?⟩.
c. the hypotenuse is ⟨?⟩.

8.

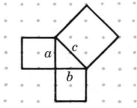

The area of the square on

a. leg a is ⟨?⟩.
b. leg b is ⟨?⟩.
c. the hypotenuse is ⟨?⟩.

9.

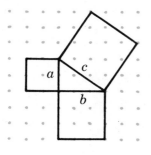

The area of the square on

a. leg a is ⟨?⟩.
b. leg b is ⟨?⟩.
c. the hypotenuse is ⟨?⟩.

10.

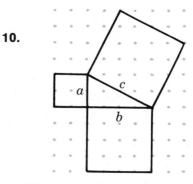

The area of the square on

a. leg a is ⟨?⟩.
b. leg b is ⟨?⟩.
c. the hypotenuse is ⟨?⟩.

11. a. Use a protractor and carefully draw a right triangle.
  b. Measure the sides to the nearest millimeter.
  c. Square the length of the hypotenuse.
  d. Square the lengths of the legs.
  e. Add the squares of the legs.
  f. How does the sum compare to the square of the hypotenuse?
  g. Draw another right triangle and repeat steps a–f.

The Rule of Pythagoras

Ancient mathematicians discovered this remarkable fact about right triangles:

The area of the square drawn on the hypotenuse is equal to the sum of the areas of the squares drawn on the legs.

This fact is called the **Rule of Pythagoras.** It is often stated like this:

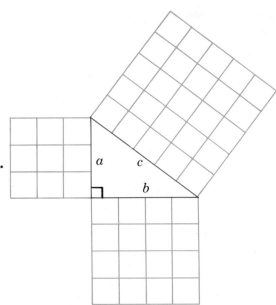

In a right triangle the square of the hypotenuse is equal to the sum of the squares of the legs:

$$a^2 + b^2 = c^2$$

We can use the Rule of Pythagoras to compute the length of a side of a right triangle when we know the lengths of the other two sides.

EXAMPLE 1.

$$a^2 + b^2 = c^2$$
$$7^2 + 9^2 = c^2$$
$$49 + 81 = c^2$$
$$130 = c^2$$
$$\sqrt{130} = c$$

7 cm
c
9 cm

EXAMPLE 2.

$$a^2 + b^2 = c^2$$
$$6^2 + b^2 = 15^2$$
$$36 + b^2 = 225$$
$$b^2 = 189$$
$$b = \sqrt{189}$$

15 m
6 m
b

In Example 1 we have found that the length of the hypotenuse is exactly $\sqrt{130}$ cm. When we need a decimal approximation, we can use a calculator or the divide-and-average method.

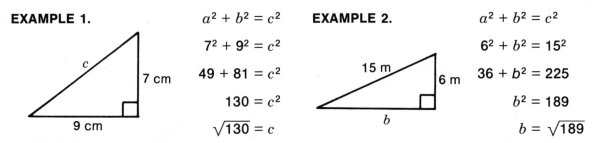

Guess and divide.

$$\begin{array}{r} 11.8 \\ 11\overline{)130} \end{array}$$

Average divisor and quotient.

$$\frac{11 + 11.8}{2} = 11.4$$

Divide.

$$\begin{array}{r} 1\,1.40 \\ 11.4\overline{)130.0\,0} \end{array}$$

The answer to the nearest tenth is 11.4.

EXERCISES

Find the missing length.

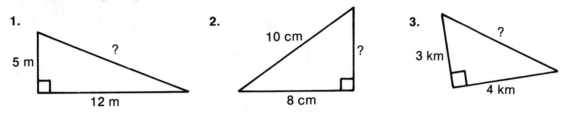

1.

5 m

?

12 m

2.

10 cm

?

8 cm

3.

?

3 km

4 km

Find the missing length. Leave square roots in exact form.

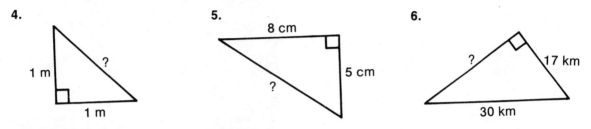

4.

1 m

?

1 m

5.

8 cm

5 cm

?

6.

?

17 km

30 km

Find the missing length. Give the decimal value correct to the nearest tenth unit.

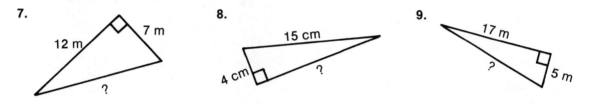

7.

12 m

7 m

?

8.

15 cm

4 cm

?

9.

17 m

?

5 m

Solve. *Hint:* **First draw a picture.**

10. A ladder that is 13 meters long is placed against a wall. The base of the ladder is 5 meters from the wall. How high on the wall does the ladder reach?

11. A plane flies over a control tower at a height of 8 km. An observer on the ground is 15 km from the control tower. How far is the plane from the observer?

12. An empty lot that Al uses as a short-cut is a 30-meter square. How much shorter is his walk diagonally across the lot compared to what his walk along two of its sides would be?

★ **13.** A flower garden is shaped like an equilateral triangle. It measures 12 meters on a side. What is its area? *Hint:* First find its height to the nearest tenth meter.

383

Problem solving

1. The Wilsons bought a used sailboat for $48,950. They paid for it by making a down payment of $18,000 and borrowing the rest of the money at a local bank for 3 years. If they paid 18% simple interest, how much did the boat cost, including interest?

2. It was estimated that the value of the boat would depreciate (lose value) by 9.5% of the sale price during the first year. What would be the value of the boat after one year?

3. The cost for keeping the boat tied up at the dock during the boating season is $65 per meter. Their boat is 12 meters long. How much is the seasonal cost for tying up their boat?

4. During the winter the boat can be stored inside or outside. Inside storage costs $62 per meter and outside storage costs $25 per meter. How much more is the cost of inside storage of this boat? (See exercise 3.)

5. The first year the Wilsons had the boat they had 94 hours of maintenance work done on it. The work cost them $30 per hour. The insurance for the boat was $1500. How much did the Wilsons spend altogether on maintenance work and insurance?

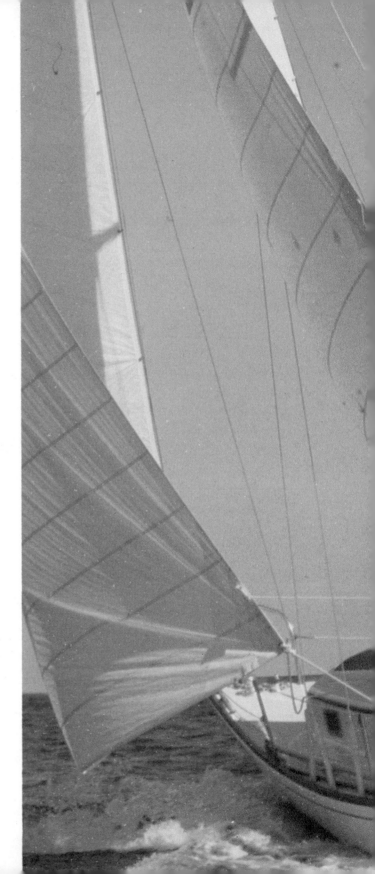

To sail against the wind, a sailboat has to follow a zigzag course. Below are some courses that the Wilsons sailed. The numbers are distances in kilometers.

Compute the distance of each "red" course. Round your answer to the nearest 0.1 kilometer. (You may need the tangent table on page 374.)

7.

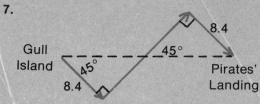

6.

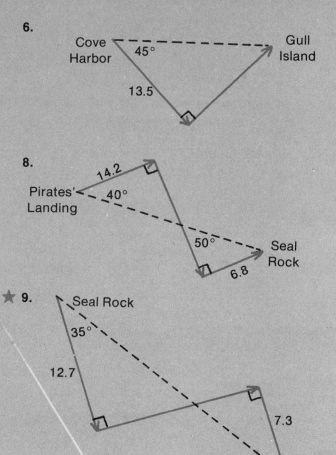

8.

9.

Do the two figures look similar? [pages 366–367]

1.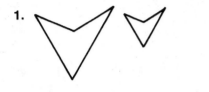

2.

3.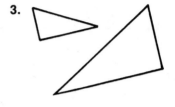

These two figures are similar.
Complete each sentence. [pages 366–369]

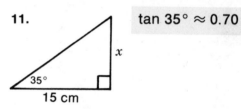

4. $\angle A \cong$?

5. $\angle B \cong$?

6. $\angle C \cong$?

7. $\dfrac{AB}{MN} \cong \dfrac{?}{NO}$

8. $\dfrac{AB}{MN} \cong \dfrac{?}{OM}$

9. $\dfrac{NO}{AC} \cong \dfrac{MN}{?}$

The two right triangles are similar.
Find the length x. [pages 372–373, 376]

10.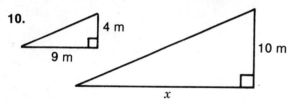

4 m

9 m

10 m

x

Use the table of tangents to find the length x. [pages 374–375, 377]

11.

tan 35° ≈ 0.70

x

35°

15 cm

Simplify. [page 378]

12. $\sqrt{16}$

13. $\sqrt{81}$

14. $\sqrt{0.64}$

Give an approximation to the nearest tenth. [page 379]

15. $\sqrt{17}$

16. $\sqrt{54}$

Use the Rule of Pythagoras to find the missing length.
[pages 380–383]

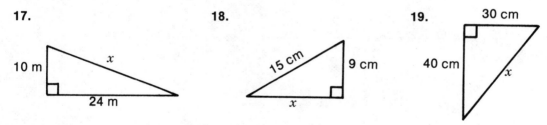

17.

10 m

x

24 m

18.

15 cm

9 cm

x

19.

30 cm

40 cm

x

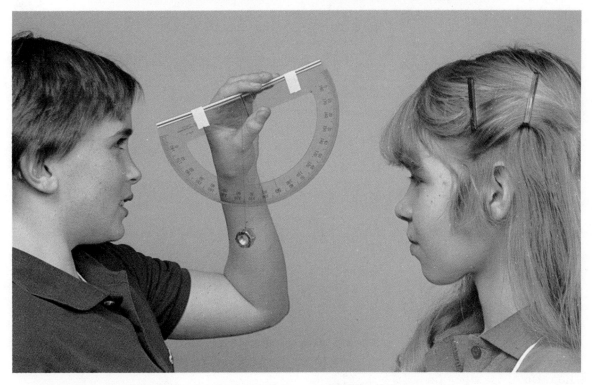

1. Choose a partner. Get a large protractor, a drinking straw, some tape, a string, and a weight. Make the instrument pictured above.

2. The following steps tell you how to use your instrument and a table of tangent ratios to measure the heights of trees, flagpoles, buildings, etc. (You can find the table of tangents in many high school mathematics textbooks.)

   a. Sight through the straw and have your partner read the angle of elevation (shown above in red).

   b. Measure the distance from the base of the object to the point where you sighted.

   c. First use a table of tangents to find the distance x shown in the sketch. Then add the distance d from the ground that you took the sighting.

In similar polygons the corresponding angles are congruent and the corresponding sides are proportional.

Here are two similar polygons.

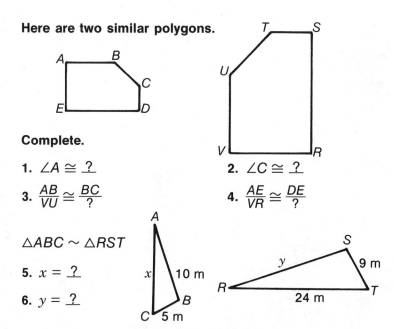

Complete.

1. $\angle A \cong$ <u>?</u>

2. $\angle C \cong$ <u>?</u>

3. $\dfrac{AB}{VU} \cong \dfrac{BC}{?}$

4. $\dfrac{AE}{VR} \cong \dfrac{DE}{?}$

If the corresponding angles of two triangles are congruent, then the triangles are similar.

$\triangle ABC \sim \triangle RST$

5. $x =$ <u>?</u>

6. $y =$ <u>?</u>

The tangent of an acute angle in a right triangle is the ratio of the side opposite the angle to the side adjacent to the angle.

Use the table of tangent ratios to find the length x. Round answers to the nearest hundredth.

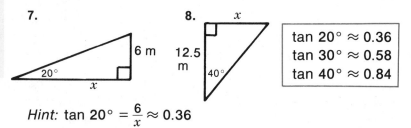

7.

6 m

$20°$

x

8.

x

12.5 m

$40°$

| tan 20° ≈ 0.36 |
| tan 30° ≈ 0.58 |
| tan 40° ≈ 0.84 |

Hint: $\tan 20° = \dfrac{6}{x} \approx 0.36$

Rule of Pythagoras

In a right triangle the square of the hypotenuse is equal to the sum of the squares of the legs.

c b $a^2 + b^2 = c^2$ a

Find the missing length.

9.

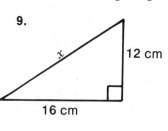

x

12 cm

16 cm

10.

10 cm

26 cm

y

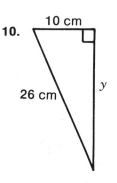

The example shows how to find the approximate measure of an acute angle of a right triangle when you know the length of each leg.

Step 1. Write tan $\angle A$ correct to 4 decimal places.

$$\tan \angle A = \frac{16}{20}$$

$$= 0.8000$$

16 m
20 m
A

Step 2. Locate 0.8000 in the table of tangents.

38°	0.7813
$\angle A$	0.8000
39°	0.8098

Step 3. By comparing the tangents, decide which angle measure is closer.

38°	0.7813
$\angle A$	0.8000
39°	0.8098

0.0187

0.0098

Since 0.8000 is closer to 0.8098 than to 0.7813, $\angle A$ is closer to 39° than to 38°.

$$\angle A \approx 39°$$

Find the approximate measure of $\angle A$.

1.
5 cm
7 cm
A

2.
9 m
11 m
A

3.
6 m
10 m
A

4.
4.8 m
7.2 m
A

5.
2.4 m
9.3 m
A

6.
A
11.3 km
3.8 km

angle	tangent
1°	0.0175
2°	0.0349
3°	0.0524
4°	0.0699
5°	0.0875
6°	0.1051
7°	0.1228
8°	0.1405
9°	0.1584
10°	0.1763
11°	0.1944
12°	0.2126
13°	0.2309
14°	0.2493
15°	0.2679
16°	0.2867
17°	0.3057
18°	0.3249
19°	0.3443
20°	0.3640
21°	0.3839
22°	0.4040
23°	0.4245
24°	0.4452
25°	0.4663
26°	0.4877
27°	0.5095
28°	0.5317
29°	0.5543
30°	0.5774
31°	0.6009
32°	0.6249
33°	0.6494
34°	0.6745
35°	0.7002
36°	0.7265
37°	0.7536
38°	0.7813
39°	0.8098
40°	0.8391
41°	0.8693
42°	0.9004
43°	0.9325
44°	0.9657
45°	1.0000

MAJOR CHECKUP
STANDARDIZED FORMAT

Choose the correct letter.

1. $6.8 \div 10^3 = \underline{?}$

    a. 0.68
    b. 0.068
    c. 0.0068
    d. none of these

2. $\dfrac{\frac{2}{3}}{\frac{5}{9}} = \underline{?}$

    a. $1\frac{1}{5}$
    b. $2\frac{7}{10}$
    c. $\frac{5}{6}$
    d. none of these

3. Find the volume. Use 3.14 as an approximation for π.

8 cm   3 cm

    a. 75.36 cm³
    b. 28.26 cm³
    c. 226.08 cm³
    d. none of these

4. Solve. Round the answer to the nearest tenth.
$$\frac{7}{2} = \frac{37}{n}$$

    a. 10.6
    b. 10.4
    c. 9.1
    d. none of these

5. A parallelogram has how many lines of symmetry?

    a. 1
    b. 2
    c. 4
    d. none of these

6. Find the installment price of a radio that can be bought for $19 down and monthly payments of $6.72 for 1 year.

    a. $99.64
    b. $234.72
    c. $80.64
    d. none of these

7. Solve.
$$^-4n - 8 = 12$$

    a. 1
    b. $^-1$
    c. $^-5$
    d. none of these

8. *Event:* Picking a card from ten cards numbered 1 through 10.

P(prime number) $= \underline{?}$

    a. $\frac{2}{5}$ **b.** $\frac{1}{2}$
    c. $\frac{3}{5}$ **d.** $\frac{3}{10}$

9.

15 m   30°   6 m   10 m   30° x

$x = \underline{?}$

    a. 4 m
    b. 5 m
    c. 8 m
    d. none of these

10.

25 m x 24 m

$x = \underline{?}$

    a. 10 m
    b. 7 m
    c. 1 m
    d. none of these

11. A recipe for 12 rolls uses $3\frac{1}{2}$ cups of flour. How much flour would be used for 8 rolls?

    a. 28 cups   **b.** $5\frac{1}{4}$ cups
    c. $2\frac{1}{3}$ cups   **d.** none of these

12. Kate spent $1.50 for 3 pens and a pad. Each pen cost 27¢. How much was the pad?

    a. 69¢   **b.** 41¢
    c. 23¢   **d.** none of these

Skill Test

1	Add any two decimals	3.68 + 2.59		42.8 + 7.6	
		47.3 + 9.86		1.509 + 0.94	

2	Subtract any two decimals	6.02 − 1.88		7.58 − 3.6	
		56.5 − 2.7		83.4 − 2.97	

3	Multiply any two decimals	4.73 $\times$ 0.9	15.6 $\times$ 0.24	1.2 $\times$ 0.08	4.825 $\times$ 4.02

4	Divide a decimal by a whole number	$8\overline{)0.416}$	$9\overline{)21.33}$	$57\overline{)121.41}$	$34\overline{)28.39}$

5	Divide any two decimals	$0.8\overline{)1.64}$	$0.05\overline{)3.1}$	$4.1\overline{)15.17}$	$0.83\overline{)3.4943}$

6	Divide and round to the nearest hundredth	$0.6\overline{)43.1}$	$0.8\overline{)2.67}$	$0.43\overline{)0.87}$	$1.23\overline{)81.67}$

7	Multiply a decimal by a power of 10	4.63×10^2	0.526×10^3
		5.7×10^2	0.975×10^4

8	Divide a decimal by a power of 10	$35.8 \div 10^2$	$267.0 \div 10^3$
		$82.17 \div 10^3$	$0.02 \div 10^2$

9	Write a large number in scientific notation	Write in scientific notation.	
		59,638	291,783
		4287.9	639,478.25

10	Give the prime factorization of a number	**Give the prime factorization.** 35 42 50 81			

11	Give the GCF and the LCM of two numbers	**Give the GCF and the LCM.** 2,3 6,8 8,16 12,18			

12	Simplify an expression	$3 + 2 \times 5$ $8 + 6 \div 2 \times 3$	$7 \times (5 - 3) + 1$ $4 \times 9 - (2 + 1)$		

13	Find an equivalent fraction	$\frac{3}{4} = \frac{?}{12}$ $\frac{8}{5} = \frac{?}{40}$	$\frac{5}{7} = \frac{?}{35}$ $\frac{5}{8} = \frac{?}{40}$		

14	Write a fraction in lowest terms	$\frac{12}{18} = \underline{?}$	$\frac{45}{81} = \underline{?}$	$\frac{15}{25} = \underline{?}$	$\frac{54}{72} = \underline{?}$

15	Change a fraction to a decimal	$\frac{2}{5} = \underline{?}$	$\frac{5}{8} = \underline{?}$	$\frac{3}{11} = \underline{?}$	$\frac{11}{9} = \underline{?}$

16	Change a decimal to a fraction	$0.6 = \underline{?}$	$0.25 = \underline{?}$	$1.5 = \underline{?}$	$0.625 = \underline{?}$

17	Compare fractions	**< or >?** $\frac{3}{8} \bullet \frac{5}{8}$	$\frac{2}{3} \bullet \frac{3}{5}$	$\frac{5}{7} \bullet \frac{5}{9}$	$\frac{4}{9} \bullet \frac{3}{7}$

18	Add fractions	$\frac{1}{4} + \frac{3}{8}$	$\frac{1}{5} + \frac{2}{3}$	$\frac{1}{9} + \frac{2}{3}$	$\frac{1}{4} + \frac{3}{10}$

19	Subtract fractions	$\frac{9}{10} - \frac{3}{5}$	$\frac{3}{4} - \frac{2}{3}$	$\frac{1}{2} - \frac{1}{8}$	$\frac{3}{4} - \frac{1}{6}$

20	Change a mixed number to a fraction	$3\frac{1}{2} = \underline{?}$	$2\frac{2}{3} = \underline{?}$	$4\frac{3}{4} = \underline{?}$	$5\frac{7}{8} = \underline{?}$
21	Change a mixed number to a decimal	$1\frac{2}{5} = \underline{?}$	$2\frac{3}{4} = \underline{?}$	$1\frac{9}{10} = \underline{?}$	$2\frac{3}{8} = \underline{?}$
22	Change a decimal to a mixed number	$4.6 = \underline{?}$ $3.125 = \underline{?}$	$6.75 = \underline{?}$ $2.08 = \underline{?}$		
23	Change a fraction to a mixed number	$\frac{5}{2} = \underline{?}$	$\frac{10}{3} = \underline{?}$	$\frac{15}{4} = \underline{?}$	$\frac{35}{8} = \underline{?}$
24	Add mixed numbers	$13\frac{1}{4}$ $+5\frac{1}{3}$	$10\frac{2}{3}$ $+3\frac{1}{4}$	$5\frac{2}{3}$ $+7\frac{1}{3}$	$18\frac{2}{3}$ $+9\frac{3}{4}$
25	Subtract mixed numbers	$13\frac{1}{4}$ $-7\frac{1}{6}$	$10\frac{2}{3}$ $-6\frac{1}{5}$	$5\frac{1}{2}$ $-1\frac{3}{4}$	$12\frac{2}{3}$ $-7\frac{3}{4}$
26	Multiply fractions	$\frac{2}{3} \times \frac{4}{7}$	$\frac{6}{7} \times \frac{5}{3}$	$\frac{3}{5} \times \frac{5}{8}$	$\frac{12}{16} \times \frac{4}{3}$
27	Divide fractions	$\frac{3}{2} \div \frac{5}{4}$	$\frac{2}{3} \div \frac{4}{5}$	$\frac{3}{4} \div \frac{3}{8}$	$\frac{2}{5} \div \frac{3}{7}$
28	Multiply mixed numbers	$2\frac{1}{2} \times 3\frac{1}{4}$ $5\frac{2}{3} \times 2\frac{3}{4}$	$2\frac{4}{5} \times 3\frac{1}{8}$ $6\frac{5}{7} \times 2\frac{4}{5}$		

29	Divide mixed numbers	$5\frac{3}{4} \div 1\frac{1}{4}$ $4\frac{1}{2} \div 1\frac{1}{2}$	$7\frac{4}{5} \div 2\frac{1}{4}$ $3\frac{2}{3} \div 2\frac{3}{5}$
30	Solve a proportion	$\frac{6}{5} = \frac{n}{25}$ $\frac{9}{n} = \frac{3}{2\frac{2}{3}}$	$\frac{n}{9} = \frac{6}{4\frac{1}{2}}$ $\frac{6}{3\frac{1}{2}} = \frac{8}{n}$
31	Change a percent to a fraction or a mixed number	$25\% = \underline{?}$ $87.5\% = \underline{?}$	$180\% = \underline{?}$ $66\frac{2}{3}\% = \underline{?}$
32	Change a fraction to a percent	$\frac{1}{2} = \underline{?}$ $\frac{5}{8} = \underline{?}$ $\frac{5}{6} = \underline{?}$ $\frac{7}{4} = \underline{?}$	
33	Change a decimal to a percent	$0.08 = \underline{?}$ $0.75 = \underline{?}$ $3.21 = \underline{?}$ $0.06\frac{1}{4} = \underline{?}$	
34	Change a percent to a decimal	$20\% = \underline{?}$ $33\frac{1}{3}\% = \underline{?}$	$37.5\% = \underline{?}$ $160\% = \underline{?}$
35	Find a percent of a number	20% of $65 = n$ 9.2% of $48 = n$	$66\frac{2}{3}\%$ of $81 = n$ $6\frac{3}{4}\%$ of $125 = n$
36	Find the number when a percent is given	40% of $n = 24$ 8.5% of $n = 3.23$	$33\frac{1}{3}\%$ of $n = 19$ 16.5% of $n = 4.125$

37	Find the percent	$n\%$ of 24 = 12	$n\%$ of 150 = 37.5
		$n\%$ of 55 = 22	$n\%$ of 42 = 58

38	Compare positive and negative numbers	**< or >?**			
		$^-9$ ● $^-4$	0 ● $\frac{^-2}{3}$	17 ● $^-23$	$\frac{^-5}{8}$ ● $\frac{^-3}{4}$

39	Add positive and negative numbers	$^+7 + {}^+4$	$\frac{^-2}{3} + \frac{^+1}{3}$	$^+9 + {}^-6$	$\frac{^-3}{4} + \frac{^-3}{2}$

40	Subtract positive and negative numbers	$^+8 - {}^+12$	$\frac{^-5}{8} - \frac{^+1}{2}$	$^+15 - {}^-8$	$\frac{^-3}{5} - \frac{^-3}{4}$

41	Multiply positive and negative numbers	$^+7 \times {}^+9$	$\frac{^+2}{3} \times \frac{^-3}{5}$	$^-6 \times {}^+7$	$\frac{^-3}{2} \times \frac{^-1}{2}$

42	Divide positive and negative numbers	$^+24 \div {}^+8$	$^-64 \div {}^+16$	$^+8 \div \frac{^-1}{2}$	$\frac{^-3}{4} \div \frac{^-5}{2}$

43	Find the square root of a number	**Give the square root of each number.**			
		36	81	169	1.44

44	Find a decimal approximation of a square root	**Give a decimal approximation rounded to the nearest tenth.**			
		$\sqrt{18}$	$\sqrt{50}$	$\sqrt{110}$	$\sqrt{275}$

Extra Practice

Set 1   Write the standard numeral.

1. eight thousand

2. five thousand one hundred twenty-four

3. forty-two thousand, nine hundred six

4. nineteen thousand, seven hundred fifty-three

5. three hundred twenty-eight thousand, six hundred seventy-six

6. five million, two hundred twelve thousand, four hundred thirty-seven

7. two hundred forty-two million, six thousand, two hundred eighty-three

8. five billion, two hundred twenty million, two hundred eleven thousand, sixty-six

9. twenty-four billion, nine hundred forty million, five thousand, eighty-two

10. seven trillion, one hundred thirty-four million, two hundred thousand, twenty

Set 2   Round each number to the nearest thousand, ten thousand, and million.

1. 8,834,527
2. 3,509,601
3. 29,498,937
4. 49,762,403
5. 312,291,742
6. 233,035,555
7. 456,621,384
8. 789,125,246

Set 3   Add.

1. 39 +89	2. 356 +84	3. 589 +73	4. 7218 +356	5. 9077 +4227	6. 5881 +3619
7. 42 68 +68	8. 91 93 +49	9. 78 86 +35	10. 52 97 +38	11. 23 65 +59	12. 75 74 +89
13. 338 729 +74	14. 656 30 +82	15. 529 476 +54	16. 183 691 +215	17. 706 938 +455	18. 534 827 +333

Set 4   Subtract.

1.	74 −25	2.	62 −37	3.	80 −43	4.	759 −163	5.	842 −256	6.	673 −459

7.	7284 −3162	8.	5916 −2448	9.	6217 −3485	10.	801 −345	11.	705 −277	12.	903 −658

13.	600 −158	14.	900 −219	15.	700 −307	16.	8001 −468	17.	7002 −3708	18.	5000 −2164

Set 5   Multiply.

1.	352 ×6	2.	398 ×6	3.	805 ×7	4.	1864 ×5	5.	6955 ×8	6.	4780 ×9

7.	65 ×53	8.	34 ×48	9.	48 ×34	10.	583 ×29	11.	714 ×51	12.	927 ×64

13.	5174 ×221	14.	4382 ×325	15.	6153 ×417	16.	2916 ×628	17.	4381 ×482	18.	7255 ×526

Set 6   Multiply.

1.	521 ×40	2.	438 ×30	3.	652 ×60	4.	594 ×200	5.	827 ×300	6.	981 ×500

7.	791 ×240	8.	654 ×320	9.	436 ×560	10.	921 ×309	11.	882 ×207	12.	439 ×406

13.	3241 ×502	14.	7583 ×620	15.	2965 ×340	16.	4708 ×506	17.	9213 ×708	18.	6458 ×950

Set 7   Divide.

1. $9\overline{)347}$ 2. $8\overline{)605}$ 3. $3\overline{)636}$ 4. $6\overline{)308}$ 5. $7\overline{)289}$

6. $3\overline{)2593}$ 7. $4\overline{)6474}$ 8. $5\overline{)5806}$ 9. $6\overline{)4352}$ 10. $7\overline{)3746}$

11. $59\overline{)2130}$ 12. $78\overline{)4150}$ 13. $85\overline{)5720}$ 14. $93\overline{)6790}$ 15. $86\overline{)7400}$

16. $74\overline{)2600}$ 17. $68\overline{)3652}$ 18. $73\overline{)4680}$ 19. $92\overline{)7500}$ 20. $84\overline{)3490}$

Set 8 Divide.

1. $2\overline{)615}$ 2. $3\overline{)623}$ 3. $5\overline{)652}$ 4. $6\overline{)634}$ 5. $4\overline{)835}$

6. $23\overline{)2440}$ 7. $18\overline{)5570}$ 8. $26\overline{)3649}$ 9. $31\overline{)6300}$ 10. $17\overline{)5440}$

11. $54\overline{)7026}$ 12. $47\overline{)2360}$ 13. $63\overline{)5057}$ 14. $81\overline{)7300}$ 15. $26\overline{)2689}$

16. $159\overline{)9560}$ 17. $127\overline{)8906}$ 18. $241\overline{)16,900}$ 19. $318\overline{)19,100}$ 20. $429\overline{)25,828}$

Set 9 For 72.839501, give the digit that is in the

1. ones place   2. tens place   3. tenths place   4. thousandths place
5. ten-thousandths place   6. millionths place
7. hundred-thousandths place   8. hundredths place

Set 10 Round each number to the nearest tenth, hundredth, and thousandth.

1. 34.8936   2. 56.4858   3. 0.9608   4. 26.75164   5. 17.0996
6. 5.45395   7. 39.84902   8. 9.97964   9. 34.4998   10. 4.3052

Set 11 < or >?

1. 48.2 ● 48.3   2. 5.90 ● 5.39   3. 0.800 ● 0.799
4. 46.89 ● 47.31   5. 6.390 ● 6.382   6. 493.4 ● 489.8
7. 264.28 ● 272.22   8. 89.990 ● 10.099   9. 72.958 ● 73.094
10. 853.95 ● 835.95   11. 52.1638 ● 52.1368   12. 168.749 ● 168.579
13. 2984.31 ● 2983.41   14. 835.822 ● 843.262   15. 9873.42 ● 9783.42

Set 12 Add.

1. $\begin{array}{r} 7.65 \\ +3.82 \\ \hline \end{array}$ 2. $\begin{array}{r} 0.374 \\ +0.296 \\ \hline \end{array}$ 3. $\begin{array}{r} 5.08 \\ +0.39 \\ \hline \end{array}$ 4. $\begin{array}{r} 82.05 \\ +27.96 \\ \hline \end{array}$ 5. $\begin{array}{r} 58.48 \\ +6.97 \\ \hline \end{array}$ 6. $\begin{array}{r} 4.637 \\ +3.29 \\ \hline \end{array}$

7. 37.5 + 64.7   8. 13.3 + 5.69   9. 2.76 + 52   10. 5.07 + 0.288
11. 36.8 + 8.37   12. 8.79 + 0.493   13. 283 + 0.762   14. 9.53 + 4.96
15. 0.265 + 5.86   16. 98.7 + 4.86   17. 0.254 + 6.48 18. 0.0584 + 0.737

Set 13   Subtract.

1. 72.1
  −50.9
	2. 0.516
	  −0.384
		3. 8.26
		  −4.19
			4. 39.85
			  −27.59
				5. 7.098
				  −5.65
					6. 8.62
					  −5.837

7. 37.5 − 8.3   8. 6.29 − 3.2   9. 538 − 4.75   10. 70.1 − 3.2
11. 83.7 − 4.47   12. 98 − 51.9   13. 6.4 − 6.27   14. 50 − 43.8
15. 0.4 − 0.377   16. 60.7 − 3.92   17. 5.8 − 0.387   18. 0.62 − 0.008

Set 14   Multiply.

1. 45 ×0.6	2. 85 ×0.8	3. 4.5 ×0.5	4. 4.5 ×0.9	5. 0.45 ×0.7	6. 45 ×0.04
7. 0.52 ×18	8. 9.3 ×6.4	9. 7.4 ×0.35	10. 0.26 ×1.4	11. 5.8 ×2.9	12. 45 ×2.5
13. 3.84 ×1.91	14. 56.5 ×5.32	15. 81.3 ×27.3	16. 7.02 ×5.82	17. 51.8 ×6.45	18. 6.24 ×9.03

Set 15   Multiply.

1. 5.2 ×0.03	2. 0.48 ×0.02	3. 0.59 ×0.06	4. 3.4 ×0.05	5. 0.74 ×0.07	6. 2.9 ×0.09
7. 8.12 ×3.2	8. 67.4 ×2.8	9. 0.521 ×0.16	10. 0.380 ×0.24	11. 0.482 ×0.53	12. 39.5 ×0.64
13. 2.95 ×8.12	14. 0.596 ×2.38	15. 5.17 ×4.35	16. 0.462 ×34.2	17. 3.91 ×12.8	18. 73.8 ×42.7

Set 16   Divide. Round each quotient to the nearest hundredth.

1. $38\overline{)7.53}$ 2. $49\overline{)0.891}$ 3. $90\overline{)3.64}$ 4. $14\overline{)7.34}$ 5. $25\overline{)56.92}$

6. $57\overline{)0.548}$ 7. $68\overline{)4.82}$ 8. $26\overline{)2.96}$ 9. $53\overline{)0.834}$ 10. $69\overline{)0.78}$

11. $71\overline{)32.6}$ 12. $66\overline{)9.326}$ 13. $32\overline{)7.31}$ 14. $48\overline{)6.05}$ 15. $57\overline{)3.52}$

16. $85\overline{)53.4}$ 17. $94\overline{)89.1}$ 18. $83\overline{)0.729}$ 19. $79\overline{)0.92}$ 20. $42\overline{)3.11}$

Set 17 Divide.

1. $0.4\overline{)1.48}$
2. $0.06\overline{)1.458}$
3. $0.7\overline{)1.141}$
4. $0.005\overline{)0.0139}$

5. $0.03\overline{)2.52}$
6. $0.2\overline{)14.12}$
7. $0.08\overline{)0.28}$
8. $0.006\overline{)0.48}$

9. $0.013\overline{)0.0975}$
10. $4.6\overline{)3.91}$
11. $0.51\overline{)3.1977}$
12. $7.2\overline{)2.1888}$

13. $0.027\overline{)0.837}$
14. $0.68\overline{)47.6}$
15. $3.8\overline{)20.52}$
16. $0.15\overline{)0.0012}$

17. $0.257\overline{)1.1822}$
18. $18.2\overline{)45.5}$
19. $3.14\overline{)189.97}$
20. $4.06\overline{)3.3292}$

Set 18 Divide. Round each quotient to the nearest hundredth.

1. $0.9\overline{)7.96}$
2. $0.04\overline{)0.245}$
3. $0.8\overline{)0.643}$
4. $0.03\overline{)0.928}$
5. $0.2\overline{)0.368}$

6. $0.7\overline{)0.2341}$
7. $0.09\overline{)3.826}$
8. $0.004\overline{)0.8543}$
9. $0.002\overline{)2.963}$
10. $0.05\overline{)4.321}$

11. $0.32\overline{)43.52}$
12. $5.6\overline{)2.007}$
13. $0.64\overline{)741.8}$
14. $2.8\overline{)0.4352}$
15. $1.3\overline{)3.896}$

16. $6.14\overline{)281.03}$
17. $7.38\overline{)5.961}$
18. $92.4\overline{)43.75}$
19. $3.86\overline{)517.4}$
20. $1.24\overline{)29.63}$

Set 19 Multiply.

1. 5.62×10
2. 33.4×100
3. 0.5962×1000
4. 3.854×100
5. 0.326×100
6. 4.85×1000
7. 0.423×100
8. 52.6×10
9. 85.5×100
10. 74.3×10
11. 6.5811×1000
12. 0.3596×100

Set 20 Divide.

1. $38.25 \div 10$
2. $51.06 \div 100$
3. $473.8 \div 1000$
4. $9.142 \div 10$
5. $826.4 \div 100$
6. $592.6 \div 10$
7. $378.2 \div 1000$
8. $714.2 \div 100$
9. $638.4 \div 10$
10. $109.8 \div 1000$
11. $8.164 \div 100$
12. $3.42 \div 1000$

Set 21 Multiply.

1. 5.638×10^2
2. 2.917×10^1
3. 0.438×10^3
4. 2.635×10^4
5. 0.7189×10^3
6. 0.9544×10^5
7. 0.82936×10^4
8. 4.256×10^6
9. 87.2×10^4
10. 3.71×10^3
11. 0.6×10^3
12. 5.004×10^5

Set 22 Divide.

1. $974.1 \div 10^2$
2. $83.59 \div 10^3$
3. $725.39 \div 10^1$
4. $2639 \div 10^4$
5. $3251 \div 10^5$
6. $846.57 \div 10^4$
7. $5.361 \div 10^3$
8. $72.81 \div 10^2$
9. $38 \div 10^3$
10. $4.16 \div 10^1$
11. $0.7 \div 10^2$
12. $0.02 \div 10^4$

Set 23 Write in scientific notation.

1. 59,174
2. 316,529
3. 7,582,154
4. 82,356,514
5. 753,081
6. 6,054,197
7. 87,150,938
8. 597,346,195
9. 386.2
10. 7596.4
11. 594.8
12. 7165.34
13. 59.6
14. 735.81
15. 9674.3
16. 58365.0

Set 24 Give the prime factorization.

1. 6
2. 21
3. 14
4. 25
5. 18
6. 30
7. 40
8. 45
9. 8
10. 32
11. 10
12. 16
13. 27
14. 57
15. 64
16. 15
17. 52
18. 60
19. 24
20. 12
21. 50
22. 51
23. 68
24. 72

Set 25 Give the greatest common factor (GCF) and the least
common multiple (LCM).

1. 2, 5
2. 4, 8
3. 3, 9
4. 5, 3
5. 4, 6
6. 4, 7
7. 3, 21
8. 3, 8
9. 7, 6
10. 4, 9
11. 6, 14
12. 2, 10
13. 18, 12
14. 12, 16
15. 16, 8
16. 8, 12
17. 10, 15
18. 9, 10
19. 24, 20
20. 15, 20
21. 16, 6
22. 25, 15
23. 18, 10
24. 36, 16

Set 26 Simplify.

1. $3 \times 9 - 2$
2. $12 + 8 \div 2$
3. $24 \div 6 - 2$
4. $36 \div 6 \times 3$
5. $35 - 10 - 3$
6. $18 \div 6 \div 3$
7. $3 \times (8 + 4)$
8. $(24 + 16) \div 8$
9. $24 \times (15 - 13)$
10. $12 + 6 \div 2 + 4$
11. $(12 + 6) \div 2 + 4$
12. $12 + 6 \div (2 + 4)$
13. $57 - (6 + 9) \times 3$
14. $57 - 6 + 9 \times 3$
15. $(57 - 6) + 9 \times 3$
16. $8 \times 7 - 5 \times 6$

Set 27 Solve.

1. $n + 18 = 37$
2. $n + 28 = 52$
3. $n + 74 = 105$
4. $n + 29 = 95$
5. $n + 28 = 108$
6. $n + 37 = 111$
7. $25 + n = 62$
8. $32 + n = 109$
9. $n - 23 = 38$
10. $n - 35 = 67$
11. $n - 23 = 74$
12. $n - 42 = 25$
13. $n - 56 = 42$
14. $n - 59 = 53$
15. $n - 64 = 48$
16. $n - 37 = 73$
17. $n + 25 = 49$
18. $n - 25 = 49$
19. $n + 36 = 74$
20. $n - 36 = 74$

Set 28 Solve.

1. $3n = 27$
2. $5n = 65$
3. $8n = 72$
4. $7n = 77$
5. $9n = 126$
6. $10n = 160$
7. $12n = 156$
8. $20n = 180$
9. $\frac{n}{3} = 9$
10. $\frac{n}{9} = 5$
11. $\frac{n}{6} = 8$
12. $\frac{n}{8} = 5$
13. $\frac{n}{12} = 9$
14. $\frac{n}{3} = 15$
15. $\frac{n}{8} = 15$
16. $\frac{n}{15} = 16$
17. $6n = 36$
18. $\frac{n}{6} = 36$
19. $10n = 130$
20. $\frac{n}{10} = 130$

Set 29 Solve.

1. $5n - 9 = 11$
2. $\frac{n}{3} + 4 = 25$
3. $9n - 15 = 21$
4. $15 + 2n = 33$
5. $4n + 24 = 24$
6. $\frac{n}{5} - 25 = 35$
7. $6n - 2 = 46$
8. $7n + 6 = 13$
9. $12 + 4n = 64$
10. $13 + \frac{n}{2} = 25$
11. $6n + 8 = 44$
12. $19 + 3n = 43$
13. $\frac{n}{4} - 6 = 10$
14. $\frac{n}{6} + 12 = 12$
15. $12n - 24 = 0$
16. $4n + 5 = 13$
17. $12 + 4n = 44$
18. $7 + 5n = 47$
19. $\frac{n}{8} - 12 = 44$
20. $25 + 9n = 34$

Set 30 Complete.

1. 7.2 cm = $\underline{?}$ mm
2. 8.4 m = $\underline{?}$ dm
3. 3 mm = $\underline{?}$ cm
4. 6.8 dm = $\underline{?}$ m
5. 3.8 dm = $\underline{?}$ m
6. 6 mm = $\underline{?}$ cm
7. 5 m = $\underline{?}$ dm
8. 12.8 cm = $\underline{?}$ mm
9. 19.8 cm = $\underline{?}$ dm
10. 3.8 m = $\underline{?}$ dm
11. 14.9 cm = $\underline{?}$ dm
12. 14.3 cm = $\underline{?}$ mm
13. 7.4 dm = $\underline{?}$ m
14. 15.9 cm = $\underline{?}$ dm
15. 9.5 cm = $\underline{?}$ mm
16. 9 dm = $\underline{?}$ m
17. 9.25 dm = $\underline{?}$ cm
18. 5.3 m = $\underline{?}$ dm
19. 36.4 km = $\underline{?}$ m
20. 0.91 km = $\underline{?}$ m
21. 0.575 km = $\underline{?}$ m
22. 8.56 m = $\underline{?}$ cm
23. 0.3 m = $\underline{?}$ mm
24. 78.6 m = $\underline{?}$ km

Set 31   Give the perimeter or circumference.

Use 3.14 as an approximation for π.

1.

4.8 cm

4.8 cm

2.

3.2 cm

9.4 cm

3. 5 m   13 m

12 m

4.

8.0 m   4.8 m

6.4 m

5.

4.8 cm

6.

11 cm

Set 32   Complete.

1. 2 L = ? mL
4. 5000 mL = ? L
7. 3 kL = ? L
10. 3600 L = ? kL

2. 3.4 L = ? mL
5. 2500 mL = ? L
8. 1.6 kL = ? L
11. 1250 L = ? kL

3. 0.26 L = ? mL
6. 568 mL = ? L
9. 0.9 kL = ? L
12. 796 L = ? kL

Set 33   Complete.

1. 4 g = ? mg
4. 3000 mg = ? g
7. 5 kg = ? g
10. 4200 g = ? kg

2. 5.8 g = ? mg
5. 1600 mg = ? g
8. 2.4 kg = ? g
11. 1640 g = ? kg

3. 0.74 g = ? mg
6. 725 mg = ? g
9. 0.8 kg = ? g
12. 598 g = ? kg

Set 34   Complete.

1. 5 ft = ? in.
4. 1 mi = ? ft
7. 4 lb = ? oz
10. 1000 lb = ? T
13. 24 qt = ? gal

2. 4 yd = ? ft
5. 60 ft = ? yd
8. 2 T = ? lb
11. 8 c = ? pt
14. 12 qt = ? c

3. 1 mi = ? yd
6. 60 in. = ? ft
9. 144 oz = ? lb
12. 12 pt = ? qt
15. 6 gal = ? pt

Set 35   Compute.

1.   4 ft 5 in.
   + 2 ft 9 in.

2.   6 ft 9 in.
   + 3 ft 8 in.

3.   9 yd 2 ft
   + 2 yd 2 ft

4.   2 yd 2 ft 8 in.
   + 1 yd 1 ft 7 in.

5.   6 ft 2 in.
   − 2 ft 8 in.

6.   8 yd 1 ft
   − 3 yd 2 ft

7.   5 ft
   − 3 ft 7 in.

8.   9 yd 2 ft 6 in.
   − 3 yd 2 ft 8 in.

9. 1 ft 2 in.
   × 5

10. 3 ft 4 in.
   × 6

11. 4 yd 2 ft
   × 3

12. 1 yd 2 ft 10 in.
   × 4

13. 2)3 ft 4 in.

14. 3)4 yd

15. 4)10 ft 8 in.

16. 2)8 yd 1 ft 6 in.

Set 36 Copy and complete.

1. $\dfrac{1}{2} = \dfrac{?}{4}$ 2. $\dfrac{1}{3} = \dfrac{?}{9}$ 3. $\dfrac{2}{3} = \dfrac{?}{12}$ 4. $\dfrac{8}{10} = \dfrac{4}{?}$ 5. $\dfrac{1}{4} = \dfrac{6}{?}$

6. $\dfrac{7}{8} = \dfrac{21}{?}$ 7. $\dfrac{3}{2} = \dfrac{15}{?}$ 8. $\dfrac{6}{8} = \dfrac{?}{4}$ 9. $\dfrac{1}{2} = \dfrac{?}{10}$ 10. $\dfrac{2}{5} = \dfrac{?}{10}$

11. $\dfrac{1}{3} = \dfrac{3}{?}$ 12. $\dfrac{3}{5} = \dfrac{?}{15}$ 13. $\dfrac{1}{2} = \dfrac{3}{?}$ 14. $\dfrac{2}{3} = \dfrac{10}{?}$ 15. $\dfrac{1}{3} = \dfrac{5}{?}$

16. $\dfrac{12}{10} = \dfrac{?}{5}$ 17. $\dfrac{1}{2} = \dfrac{4}{?}$ 18. $\dfrac{3}{8} = \dfrac{15}{?}$ 19. $\dfrac{3}{2} = \dfrac{6}{?}$ 20. $\dfrac{5}{6} = \dfrac{30}{?}$

Set 37 Write in lowest terms.

1. $\dfrac{2}{4}$ 2. $\dfrac{3}{12}$ 3. $\dfrac{2}{6}$ 4. $\dfrac{6}{16}$ 5. $\dfrac{4}{10}$ 6. $\dfrac{9}{6}$ 7. $\dfrac{10}{16}$ 8. $\dfrac{3}{9}$

9. $\dfrac{16}{18}$ 10. $\dfrac{18}{12}$ 11. $\dfrac{4}{8}$ 12. $\dfrac{15}{12}$ 13. $\dfrac{3}{6}$ 14. $\dfrac{18}{16}$ 15. $\dfrac{4}{12}$ 16. $\dfrac{5}{20}$

17. $\dfrac{9}{24}$ 18. $\dfrac{6}{12}$ 19. $\dfrac{12}{15}$ 20. $\dfrac{6}{24}$ 21. $\dfrac{15}{10}$ 22. $\dfrac{5}{10}$ 23. $\dfrac{15}{24}$ 24. $\dfrac{24}{36}$

Set 38 Change to a decimal.

1. $\dfrac{1}{2}$ 2. $\dfrac{1}{3}$ 3. $\dfrac{1}{4}$ 4. $\dfrac{1}{8}$ 5. $\dfrac{1}{6}$ 6. $\dfrac{1}{7}$ 7. $\dfrac{1}{9}$ 8. $\dfrac{5}{6}$

9. $\dfrac{5}{8}$ 10. $\dfrac{5}{3}$ 11. $\dfrac{3}{4}$ 12. $\dfrac{3}{2}$ 13. $\dfrac{3}{3}$ 14. $\dfrac{2}{3}$ 15. $\dfrac{4}{7}$ 16. $\dfrac{11}{8}$

17. $\dfrac{7}{4}$ 18. $\dfrac{7}{2}$ 19. $\dfrac{7}{9}$ 20. $\dfrac{9}{8}$ 21. $\dfrac{5}{4}$ 22. $\dfrac{5}{2}$ 23. $\dfrac{4}{3}$ 24. $\dfrac{2}{9}$

Set 39 Change to a fraction in lowest terms.

1. 0.75   2. 0.7   3. 0.5   4. 0.375   5. 0.08   6. 0.72   7. 0.1

8. 0.65   9. 0.2   10. 0.02   11. 0.4   12. 0.01   13. 0.125   14. 0.57

Set 40 <, =, or >?

1. $\dfrac{5}{12} \bullet \dfrac{1}{2}$ 2. $\dfrac{1}{2} \bullet \dfrac{1}{3}$ 3. $\dfrac{2}{3} \bullet \dfrac{3}{2}$ 4. $\dfrac{1}{5} \bullet \dfrac{1}{4}$ 5. $\dfrac{5}{6} \bullet \dfrac{3}{4}$

6. $\dfrac{5}{8} \bullet \dfrac{2}{3}$ 7. $\dfrac{6}{16} \bullet \dfrac{3}{8}$ 8. $\dfrac{15}{18} \bullet \dfrac{5}{6}$ 9. $\dfrac{3}{4} \bullet \dfrac{6}{8}$ 10. $\dfrac{3}{8} \bullet \dfrac{1}{3}$

11. $\dfrac{5}{6} \bullet \dfrac{7}{8}$ 12. $\dfrac{1}{2} \bullet \dfrac{5}{9}$ 13. $\dfrac{15}{6} \bullet \dfrac{5}{2}$ 14. $\dfrac{6}{10} \bullet \dfrac{3}{5}$ 15. $\dfrac{5}{3} \bullet \dfrac{5}{4}$

16. $\dfrac{5}{9} \bullet \dfrac{2}{3}$ 17. $\dfrac{5}{6} \bullet \dfrac{5}{8}$ 18. $\dfrac{5}{2} \bullet \dfrac{7}{4}$ 19. $\dfrac{3}{4} \bullet \dfrac{4}{3}$ 20. $\dfrac{9}{5} \bullet \dfrac{5}{9}$

Set 41 **Give each sum in lowest terms.**

1. $\frac{2}{3}+\frac{1}{4}$ 2. $\frac{1}{2}+\frac{3}{8}$ 3. $\frac{2}{5}+\frac{1}{10}$ 4. $\frac{4}{9}+\frac{1}{6}$ 5. $\frac{2}{5}+\frac{1}{4}$ 6. $\frac{3}{5}+\frac{1}{3}$

7. $\frac{1}{2}+\frac{1}{6}$ 8. $\frac{5}{8}+\frac{1}{6}$ 9. $\frac{3}{8}+\frac{1}{3}$ 10. $\frac{3}{5}+\frac{2}{15}$ 11. $\frac{3}{10}+\frac{1}{4}$ 12. $\frac{5}{12}+\frac{1}{4}$

13. $\frac{5}{12}+\frac{3}{8}$ 14. $\frac{1}{2}+\frac{2}{9}$ 15. $\frac{3}{10}+\frac{1}{6}$ 16. $\frac{1}{2}+\frac{1}{12}$ 17. $\frac{5}{9}+\frac{1}{9}$ 18. $\frac{7}{15}+\frac{1}{3}$

Set 42 **Give each difference in lowest terms.**

1. $\frac{2}{3}-\frac{1}{4}$ 2. $\frac{1}{2}-\frac{3}{8}$ 3. $\frac{2}{5}-\frac{1}{10}$ 4. $\frac{4}{9}-\frac{1}{6}$ 5. $\frac{2}{5}-\frac{1}{4}$ 6. $\frac{3}{5}-\frac{1}{3}$

7. $\frac{1}{2}-\frac{1}{6}$ 8. $\frac{5}{8}-\frac{1}{6}$ 9. $\frac{3}{8}-\frac{1}{3}$ 10. $\frac{3}{5}-\frac{2}{15}$ 11. $\frac{3}{10}-\frac{1}{4}$ 12. $\frac{5}{12}-\frac{1}{4}$

13. $\frac{5}{12}-\frac{3}{8}$ 14. $\frac{1}{2}-\frac{2}{9}$ 15. $\frac{3}{10}-\frac{1}{6}$ 16. $\frac{1}{2}-\frac{1}{12}$ 17. $\frac{5}{9}-\frac{1}{9}$ 18. $\frac{7}{15}-\frac{1}{3}$

Set 43 **Change to a fraction.**

1. $2\frac{1}{3}$ 2. $4\frac{3}{5}$ 3. $3\frac{1}{8}$ 4. $7\frac{2}{3}$ 5. $3\frac{1}{5}$ 6. $2\frac{5}{6}$ 7. $1\frac{4}{9}$

8. $3\frac{7}{10}$ 9. $2\frac{3}{8}$ 10. $1\frac{1}{2}$ 11. $3\frac{5}{12}$ 12. $4\frac{4}{15}$ 13. $5\frac{1}{4}$ 14. $8\frac{7}{8}$

Set 44 **Change to a decimal.**

1. $2\frac{1}{4}$ 2. $1\frac{4}{5}$ 3. $3\frac{7}{10}$ 4. $5\frac{3}{4}$ 5. $2\frac{7}{8}$ 6. $4\frac{1}{2}$ 7. $3\frac{7}{25}$

8. $4\frac{9}{20}$ 9. $7\frac{2}{3}$ 10. $5\frac{7}{9}$ 11. $3\frac{5}{6}$ 12. $1\frac{5}{12}$ 13. $2\frac{3}{16}$ 14. $4\frac{2}{7}$

Set 45 **Change to a mixed number in simplest form.**

1. 1.5   2. 2.15   3. 4.2   4. 3.75   5. 2.04   6. 4.375
7. 8.35   8. 1.64   9. 3.6   10. 4.13   11. 6.42   12. 2.075

Set 46 Change to a mixed number.

1. $\dfrac{7}{5}$ 2. $\dfrac{7}{2}$ 3. $\dfrac{8}{3}$ 4. $\dfrac{9}{4}$ 5. $\dfrac{7}{6}$ 6. $\dfrac{17}{2}$ 7. $\dfrac{17}{3}$

8. $\dfrac{17}{4}$ 9. $\dfrac{17}{5}$ 10. $\dfrac{17}{6}$ 11. $\dfrac{17}{7}$ 12. $\dfrac{17}{8}$ 13. $\dfrac{17}{9}$ 14. $\dfrac{17}{10}$

Set 47 Add.

1. $5\dfrac{1}{5}$ $+2\dfrac{1}{5}$

2. $8\dfrac{1}{2}$ $+3\dfrac{1}{4}$

3. $9\dfrac{1}{2}$ $+1\dfrac{1}{2}$

4. $7\dfrac{1}{4}$ $+5\dfrac{3}{8}$

5. $8\dfrac{1}{3}$ $+4\dfrac{1}{4}$

6. $9\dfrac{1}{4}$ $+3\dfrac{1}{8}$

7. $15\dfrac{2}{3}$ $+8\dfrac{2}{3}$

8. 14 $+9\dfrac{3}{8}$

9. $13\dfrac{3}{4}$ $+6\dfrac{2}{5}$

10. $11\dfrac{1}{3}$ $+5\dfrac{1}{6}$

11. $14\dfrac{2}{3}$ $+7\dfrac{5}{9}$

12. $18\dfrac{3}{8}$ $+6\dfrac{7}{8}$

13. $23\dfrac{2}{9}$ $+15\dfrac{1}{3}$

14. $24\dfrac{1}{2}$ $+12\dfrac{3}{5}$

15. $32\dfrac{3}{4}$ $+14\dfrac{1}{2}$

16. $46\dfrac{2}{3}$ $+21\dfrac{3}{4}$

17. $40\dfrac{1}{4}$ $+35\dfrac{1}{8}$

18. $38\dfrac{3}{4}$ $+27\dfrac{5}{8}$

Set 48 Subtract.

1. $8\dfrac{2}{3}$ $-3\dfrac{1}{3}$

2. $9\dfrac{1}{2}$ $-4\dfrac{1}{2}$

3. $7\dfrac{3}{4}$ $-6\dfrac{1}{2}$

4. $8\dfrac{5}{9}$ $-6\dfrac{2}{9}$

5. $9\dfrac{3}{5}$ $-4\dfrac{1}{5}$

6. 8 $-3\dfrac{1}{2}$

7. $14\dfrac{1}{3}$ $-5\dfrac{2}{3}$

8. $15\dfrac{1}{8}$ $-6\dfrac{3}{4}$

9. $19\dfrac{3}{5}$ $-6\dfrac{7}{10}$

10. $18\dfrac{1}{2}$ $-5\dfrac{3}{4}$

11. 26 $-8\dfrac{3}{5}$

12. $27\dfrac{1}{4}$ $-6\dfrac{3}{5}$

13. $24\dfrac{4}{9}$ $-17\dfrac{2}{3}$

14. 36 $-15\dfrac{5}{8}$

15. $35\dfrac{1}{6}$ $-17\dfrac{1}{8}$

16. 25 $-14\dfrac{2}{3}$

17. $28\dfrac{1}{3}$ $-14\dfrac{1}{2}$

18. $27\dfrac{2}{3}$ $-18\dfrac{3}{4}$

Set 49 Give each product in simplest form.

1. $\dfrac{1}{2} \times \dfrac{1}{4}$ 2. $\dfrac{4}{7} \times \dfrac{2}{5}$ 3. $\dfrac{2}{3} \times \dfrac{3}{4}$ 4. $\dfrac{5}{8} \times \dfrac{0}{6}$ 5. $\dfrac{5}{9} \times \dfrac{3}{10}$ 6. $\dfrac{3}{5} \times \dfrac{3}{5}$

7. $\dfrac{1}{7} \times \dfrac{1}{8}$ 8. $\dfrac{1}{2} \times \dfrac{3}{8}$ 9. $\dfrac{6}{4} \times \dfrac{2}{2}$ 10. $\dfrac{3}{4} \times \dfrac{8}{3}$ 11. $\dfrac{3}{4} \times \dfrac{6}{7}$ 12. $\dfrac{5}{9} \times \dfrac{2}{3}$

13. $\dfrac{3}{4} \times \dfrac{12}{2}$ 14. $\dfrac{3}{4} \times \dfrac{5}{3}$ 15. $\dfrac{5}{8} \times \dfrac{7}{5}$ 16. $\dfrac{2}{5} \times \dfrac{3}{4}$ 17. $\dfrac{2}{5} \times \dfrac{3}{5}$ 18. $\dfrac{7}{3} \times \dfrac{8}{3}$

Set 50   Give each quotient in simplest form.

1. $\frac{1}{2} \div \frac{2}{3}$ 2. $\frac{4}{9} \div \frac{2}{3}$ 3. $\frac{3}{2} \div \frac{3}{4}$ 4. $\frac{3}{4} \div \frac{5}{8}$ 5. $\frac{9}{5} \div \frac{3}{8}$ 6. $\frac{3}{10} \div \frac{2}{5}$

7. $\frac{5}{6} \div \frac{1}{2}$ 8. $\frac{1}{8} \div \frac{9}{5}$ 9. $\frac{1}{5} \div \frac{5}{4}$ 10. $\frac{7}{4} \div \frac{3}{4}$ 11. $\frac{2}{3} \div \frac{2}{3}$ 12. $\frac{7}{8} \div \frac{5}{4}$

13. $\frac{3}{5} \div \frac{3}{10}$ 14. $\frac{5}{6} \div \frac{5}{8}$ 15. $\frac{3}{4} \div \frac{2}{2}$ 16. $\frac{3}{4} \div \frac{7}{7}$ 17. $\frac{3}{10} \div \frac{7}{10}$ 18. $\frac{9}{2} \div \frac{3}{4}$

19. $\frac{3}{10} \div \frac{1}{5}$ 20. $\frac{1}{2} \div \frac{7}{2}$ 21. $\frac{4}{5} \div \frac{2}{3}$ 22. $\frac{8}{7} \div \frac{3}{2}$ 23. $\frac{9}{5} \div \frac{2}{5}$ 24. $\frac{5}{8} \div \frac{10}{2}$

Set 51   Solve.

1. $\frac{1}{3} \times 81 = n$ 2. $\frac{2}{3} \times 90 = n$ 3. $\frac{3}{4} \times 20 = n$ 4. $\frac{3}{2} \times 44 = n$

5. $\frac{7}{8} \times 56 = n$ 6. $\frac{5}{3} \times 45 = n$ 7. $\frac{3}{5} \times 45 = n$ 8. $\frac{5}{8} \times 64 = n$

9. $\frac{1}{8} n = 12$ 10. $\frac{3}{4} n = 24$ 11. $\frac{3}{2} n = 9$ 12. $\frac{5}{8} n = 40$

13. $\frac{5}{2} n = 10$ 14. $\frac{4}{3} n = 24$ 15. $\frac{4}{5} n = 40$ 16. $\frac{3}{8} n = 21$

Set 52   Multiply.

1. $2\frac{1}{3} \times 7$ 2. $5 \times 6\frac{1}{3}$ 3. $3 \times 4\frac{1}{2}$ 4. $5\frac{1}{4} \times 5$ 5. $2\frac{1}{5} \times 6$

6. $1\frac{1}{4} \times 2\frac{1}{5}$ 7. $1\frac{1}{4} \times 1\frac{3}{8}$ 8. $4\frac{1}{4} \times 3\frac{3}{4}$ 9. $3\frac{1}{3} \times 3\frac{1}{4}$ 10. $2\frac{1}{2} \times 2\frac{2}{3}$

11. $4\frac{2}{3} \times 1\frac{3}{4}$ 12. $1\frac{1}{6} \times 1\frac{3}{4}$ 13. $3\frac{1}{2} \times 4\frac{2}{3}$ 14. $2\frac{1}{4} \times 2\frac{1}{9}$ 15. $3\frac{1}{4} \times 2\frac{3}{8}$

16. $2\frac{3}{4} \times 2\frac{1}{4}$ 17. $2\frac{3}{4} \times 1\frac{1}{5}$ 18. $2\frac{1}{5} \times 3\frac{1}{3}$ 19. $1\frac{1}{2} \times 1\frac{1}{2}$ 20. $2\frac{1}{2} \times 3\frac{2}{3}$

Set 53   Divide.

1. $1\frac{1}{2} \div 1\frac{1}{2}$ 2. $2\frac{2}{9} \div 1$ 3. $3\frac{1}{2} \div 1\frac{3}{4}$ 4. $3\frac{3}{4} \div 3$ 5. $9\frac{1}{2} \div 3\frac{1}{2}$

6. $7\frac{2}{3} \div 4$ 7. $5 \div 1\frac{1}{2}$ 8. $0 \div 5\frac{1}{2}$ 9. $7\frac{1}{3} \div 2\frac{1}{4}$ 10. $2\frac{7}{8} \div 7\frac{2}{3}$

11. $6\frac{2}{3} \div 8\frac{3}{4}$ 12. $8\frac{1}{4} \div 4\frac{2}{3}$ 13. $3 \div 6\frac{2}{3}$ 14. $6\frac{3}{5} \div 8\frac{2}{3}$ 15. $6\frac{1}{3} \div 7\frac{1}{5}$

16. $9\frac{1}{3} \div 2\frac{3}{5}$ 17. $4\frac{5}{8} \div 6\frac{3}{4}$ 18. $5\frac{1}{4} \div 5\frac{4}{5}$ 19. $8\frac{1}{2} \div 2\frac{1}{8}$ 20. $4\frac{1}{2} \div 3\frac{1}{6}$

Set 54   Give the area.

1.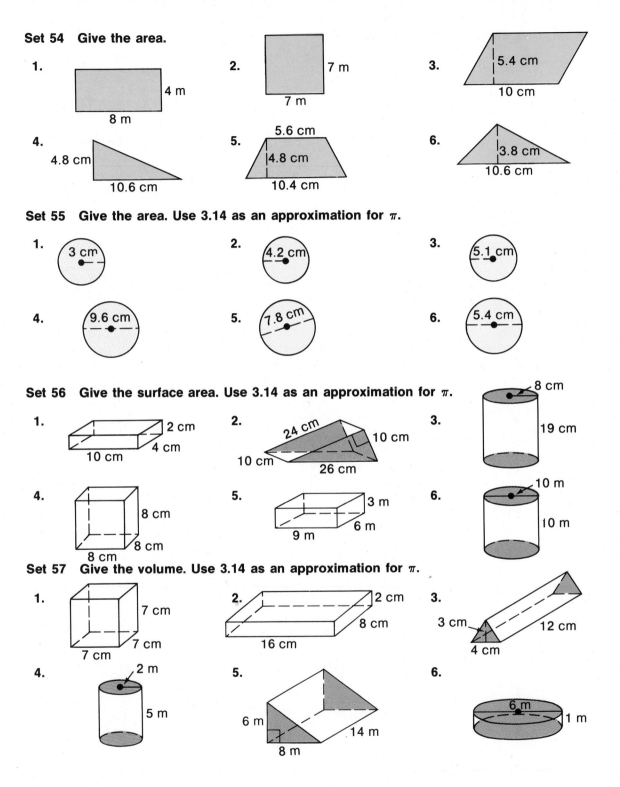
4 m
8 m

2.
7 m
7 m

3.
5.4 cm
10 cm

4.
4.8 cm
10.6 cm

5.
5.6 cm
4.8 cm
10.4 cm

6.
3.8 cm
10.6 cm

Set 55   Give the area. Use 3.14 as an approximation for π.

1.
3 cm

2.
4.2 cm

3.
5.1 cm

4.
9.6 cm

5.
7.8 cm

6.
5.4 cm

Set 56   Give the surface area. Use 3.14 as an approximation for π.

1.
2 cm
4 cm
10 cm

2.
24 cm
10 cm
10 cm
26 cm

3.
8 cm
19 cm

4.
8 cm
8 cm
8 cm

5.
3 m
6 m
9 m

6.
10 m
10 m

Set 57   Give the volume. Use 3.14 as an approximation for π.

1.
7 cm
7 cm
7 cm

2.
2 cm
8 cm
16 cm

3.
3 cm
4 cm
12 cm

4.
2 m
5 m

5.
6 m
8 m
14 m

6.
6 m
1 m

Set 58   Give the volume. Use 3.14 as an approximation for π.

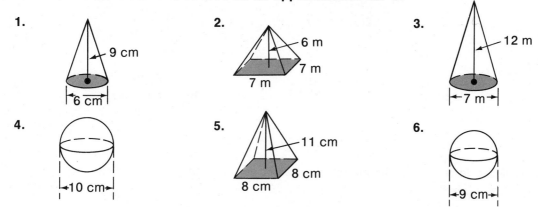

1. 9 cm / 6 cm
2. 6 m / 7 m / 7 m
3. 12 m / 7 m
4. 10 cm
5. 11 cm / 8 cm / 8 cm
6. 9 cm

Set 59   Find each area. Use 3.14 as an approximation for π.

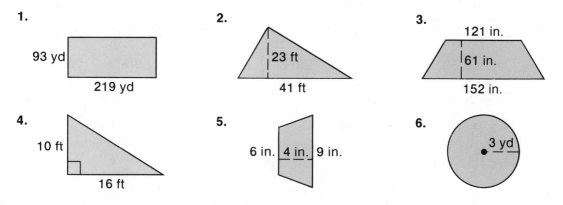

1. 93 yd / 219 yd
2. 23 ft / 41 ft
3. 121 in. / 61 in. / 152 in.
4. 10 ft / 16 ft
5. 6 in. 4 in. 9 in.
6. 3 yd

Set 60   Find each volume. Use 3.14 as an approximation for π.

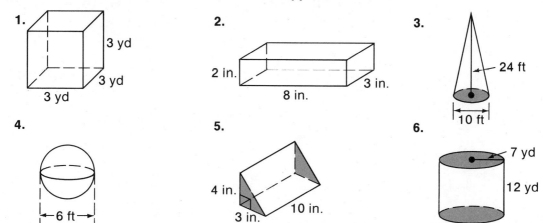

1. 3 yd / 3 yd / 3 yd
2. 2 in. / 8 in. / 3 in.
3. 24 ft / 10 ft
4. 6 ft
5. 4 in. / 3 in. / 10 in.
6. 7 yd / 12 yd

Set 61 Solve each proportion.

1. $\frac{2}{4} = \frac{x}{2}$
2. $\frac{5}{6} = \frac{a}{12}$
3. $\frac{f}{9} = \frac{4}{3}$
4. $\frac{5}{6} = \frac{11}{a}$
5. $\frac{8}{3} = \frac{13}{d}$

6. $\frac{3}{2} = \frac{5}{f}$
7. $\frac{g}{12} = \frac{1}{4}$
8. $\frac{h}{2} = \frac{9}{4}$
9. $\frac{c}{11} = \frac{3}{8}$
10. $\frac{7}{8} = \frac{w}{4}$

11. $\frac{z}{14} = \frac{7}{4}$
12. $\frac{20}{24} = \frac{k}{12}$
13. $\frac{6}{7} = \frac{9}{b}$
14. $\frac{a}{18} = \frac{5}{4}$
15. $\frac{3}{y} = \frac{4}{7}$

16. $\frac{5}{9} = \frac{8}{g}$
17. $\frac{19}{j} = \frac{9}{5}$
18. $\frac{5}{9} = \frac{k}{5}$
19. $\frac{9}{4} = \frac{9}{w}$
20. $\frac{13}{x} = \frac{3}{5}$

Set 62 Change to a fraction or mixed number in simplest form.

1. 10%   2. 20%   3. 30%   4. 40%   5. 50%   6. 60%   7. 70%

8. 80%   9. 85%   10. 90%   11. 250%   12. 175%   13. $66\frac{2}{3}$%   14. $16\frac{2}{3}$%

15. 1%   16. $\frac{1}{2}$%   17. $\frac{1}{4}$%   18. $87\frac{1}{2}$%   19. $83\frac{1}{3}$%   20. $12\frac{1}{2}$%   21. $11\frac{1}{9}$%

22. 6.5%   23. 18.5%   24. 5.25%   25. 0.6%   26. 5.8%   27. 9.6%   28. 32.25%

Set 63 Change to a percent.

1. $\frac{1}{4}$ 2. $\frac{2}{4}$ 3. $\frac{3}{4}$ 4. $\frac{4}{4}$ 5. $\frac{5}{4}$ 6. $\frac{6}{4}$ 7. $\frac{1}{3}$ 8. $\frac{2}{3}$

9. $\frac{3}{3}$ 10. $\frac{4}{3}$ 11. $\frac{1}{8}$ 12. $\frac{3}{8}$ 13. $\frac{5}{8}$ 14. $\frac{7}{8}$ 15. $\frac{1}{6}$ 16. $\frac{5}{6}$

17. $\frac{1}{5}$ 18. $\frac{2}{5}$ 19. $\frac{3}{5}$ 20. $\frac{4}{5}$ 21. $\frac{5}{5}$ 22. $\frac{6}{5}$ 23. $\frac{7}{5}$ 24. $\frac{8}{5}$

25. $\frac{5}{12}$ 26. $\frac{5}{24}$ 27. $\frac{19}{24}$ 28. $\frac{7}{12}$ 29. $\frac{5}{32}$ 30. $\frac{21}{32}$ 31. $\frac{25}{16}$ 32. $\frac{35}{24}$

Set 64 Change to a percent.

1. 0.8   2. 1.46   3. 2.7   4. 0.06   5. 0.24   6. $0.62\frac{1}{2}$

7. 0.75   8. 1.05   9. 0.003   10. 0.024   11. $0.08\frac{1}{3}$ 12. $0.41\frac{2}{3}$

Set 65 Change to a decimal.

1. 15%   2. 130%   3. 2.6%   4. 18.3%   5. 40%   6. $66\frac{2}{3}$%

7. $55\frac{5}{9}$%   8. 32.5%   9. 275%   10. $188\frac{2}{5}$%   11. 3%   12. $83\frac{1}{3}$%

Set 66 Solve.

1. 75% of 164 = n
2. 50% of 386 = n
3. 35% of 146 = n
4. $12\frac{1}{2}$% of 136 = n
5. 100% of 48 = n
6. 40% of 437 = n
7. $33\frac{1}{3}$% of 132 = n
8. 6% of 80 = n
9. 150% of 27 = n
10. 300% of 48 = n
11. 40% of 380 = n
12. 30% of 480 = n
13. 8% of 500 = n
14. 20% of 125 = n
15. $83\frac{1}{3}$% of 42 = n
16. 500% of 17 = n
17. $62\frac{1}{2}$% of 264 = n
18. 10% of 521 = n

Set 67 Solve.

1. 10% of n = 6
2. 50% of n = 18
3. 200% of n = 38
4. 150% of n = 120
5. 5% of n = 8
6. 25% of n = 18
7. $37\frac{1}{2}$% of n = 27
8. 175% of n = 42
9. $33\frac{1}{3}$% of n = 30
10. 1% of n = 5
11. 20% of n = 6
12. 60% of n = 141
13. $12\frac{1}{2}$% of n = 42
14. $83\frac{1}{3}$% of n = 56
15. $16\frac{2}{3}$% of n = 27
16. $87\frac{1}{2}$% of n = 35
17. 40% of n = 48
18. $133\frac{1}{3}$% of n = 128

Set 68 Solve.

1. n% of 8 = 4
2. n% of 32 = 8
3. n% of 18 = 6
4. n% of 16 = 6
5. n% of 24 = 15
6. n% of 18 = 12
7. n% of 12 = 18
8. n% of 12 = 15
9. n% of 24 = 21
10. n% of 15 = 25
11. n% of 36 = 24
12. n% of 75 = 60
13. n% of 18 = 42
14. n% of 48 = 32
15. n% of 75 = 100
16. n% of 100 = 75
17. n% of 80 = 120
18. n% of 120 = 80

Set 69 The regular price is given. Compute the sale price.

1. $4.80
   20% off
2. $6.64
   50% off
3. $8.00
   25% off
4. $9.60
   40% off
5. $5.35
   40% off
6. $6.29
   30% off
7. $9.60
   $33\frac{1}{3}$% off
8. $10.46
   28% off
9. $20.48
   35% off
10. $35.63
    $37\frac{1}{2}$% off
11. $18.32
    45% off
12. $43.49
    75% off

Set 70 Complete.

	Principal	Yearly Rate	Time	Interest
1.	$1000	$12\frac{1}{2}\%$	3 months	?
2.	$450	15%	8 months	?
3.	$100	16%	1 year	?
4.	$300	14%	2 years	?
5.	$3600	$13\frac{1}{2}\%$	18 months	?
6.	$8000	$14\frac{3}{4}\%$	$1\frac{3}{4}$ years	?
7.	$150	18%	$1\frac{1}{2}$ years	?
8.	$600	12%	9 months	?

Set 71 Complete.

	Cash price	Installment plan	Installment price	Difference between installment price and cash price
1.	$150	$50 down and $9 a month for 12 mo.		
2.	$200	$50 down and $19.44 a month for 12 mo.		
3.	$240	$80 down and $14.40 a month for 12 mo.		
4.	$300	$75 down and $39.19 a month for 6 mo.		
5.	$360	$72 down and $34.40 a month for 9 mo.		
6.	$420	$105 down and $41.74 a month for 8 mo.		

Set 72   < or >?

1. $^+8$ ● $^+7$
2. $^-8$ ● $^+7$
3. $^-8$ ● $^-7$
4. $^+8$ ● $^-7$
5. $^+19$ ● $^-18$
6. $^+16$ ● $^+15$
7. $^-19$ ● $^-18$
8. $^-15$ ● $^+14$
9. $^-14$ ● $^+16$
10. $^+9$ ● $^-12$
11. $^-16$ ● $^-15$
12. 0 ● $^-16$
13. $^+1.8$ ● $^+1.9$
14. $^+3.2$ ● $^+3.3$
15. $^-1.6$ ● $^-1.5$
16. $^+1.8$ ● $^-1.8$
17. $\frac{^-2}{3}$ ● $\frac{^+3}{4}$
18. $\frac{^+2}{3}$ ● $\frac{^-3}{4}$
19. $\frac{^-5}{2}$ ● $\frac{^+2}{5}$
20. 0 ● $\frac{^-3}{5}$

Set 73   Add.

1. $^-5 + ^-6$
2. $^-8 + 0$
3. $^-5 + ^+9$
4. $^+9 + ^+5$
5. $0 + ^+9$
6. $^-6 + ^-6$
7. $^-5 + ^-9$
8. $^+3 + ^+9$
9. $^-9 + ^+13$
10. $^+8 + ^-9$
11. $^-3 + ^-11$
12. $^+11 + ^-15$
13. $^+14 + ^-14$
14. $^+9 + ^+7$
15. $^-10 + ^-1$
16. $\frac{^+9}{4} + \frac{^+11}{8}$
17. $\frac{^-5}{3} + \frac{^+12}{5}$
18. $0 + 0$
19. $\frac{^+16}{5} + \frac{^-16}{3}$
20. $\frac{^-8}{3} + \frac{^+15}{2}$

Set 74   Subtract.

1. $^+7 - ^-5$
2. $^+7 - 0$
3. $^+6 - ^-4$
4. $^+4 - ^+6$
5. $^+12 - ^+5$
6. $^-3 - ^+9$
7. $^-5 - ^-3$
8. $0 - ^+6$
9. $^-8 - ^-2$
10. $^+8 - ^+3$
11. $^+0.4 - ^-0.6$
12. $^-1.9 - ^-0.4$
13. $^-2.4 - ^+1.1$
14. $^+2.3 - ^+0.8$
15. $^-0.1 - ^-5.6$
16. $\frac{^+6}{5} - \frac{^-14}{3}$
17. $\frac{^+13}{4} - \frac{^-6}{5}$
18. $\frac{^+4}{3} - \frac{^-6}{5}$
19. $\frac{^-8}{3} - \frac{^-7}{2}$
20. $\frac{^+7}{4} - \frac{^-15}{3}$

Set 75   Multiply.

1. $^-6 \times ^+6$
2. $^-8 \times ^-8$
3. $^+7 \times ^-3$
4. $^+5 \times ^+5$
5. $^-4 \times ^+3$
6. $^-9 \times ^+9$
7. $^-3 \times ^-9$
8. $^-9 \times ^-8$
9. $^-9 \times ^+5$
10. $^+4 \times ^+6$
11. $^+0.9 \times ^-7$
12. $^+0.8 \times ^-0.9$
13. $^-2.8 \times ^-0.4$
14. $^+3.7 \times ^+7$
15. $^+7.8 \times ^+0.9$
16. $\frac{^+9}{5} \times \frac{^+6}{5}$
17. $\frac{^-8}{3} \times \frac{^+6}{4}$
18. $\frac{^-4}{3} \times \frac{^+6}{5}$
19. $\frac{^-6}{3} \times \frac{^-9}{2}$
20. $\frac{^-8}{6} \times \frac{^-12}{4}$

Set 76   Divide.

1. $^-27 \div ^-3$
2. $^-32 \div ^+8$
3. $^+24 \div ^-6$
4. $^+24 \div ^+6$
5. $^+32 \div ^+8$
6. $0 \div ^-7$
7. $^-36 \div ^-6$
8. $^-35 \div ^+7$
9. $^-45 \div ^-9$
10. $^+48 \div ^-6$
11. $^+4.9 \div ^-7$
12. $\frac{^+3}{4} \div \frac{^+1}{4}$
13. $\frac{^-3}{5} \div \frac{^+1}{5}$
14. $^-21 \div ^+3$
15. $^+63 \div ^-9$
16. $^+4.32 \div ^-9$
17. $^-48 \div ^-8$
18. $^-4.5 \div ^-1.5$
19. $^+72 \div ^-9$
20. $^+81 \div ^+9$

Set 77 Solve.

1. $x + {}^-8 = 6$	2. $y + 9 = {}^-11$	3. $w + {}^-4 = {}^-8$	4. $z + 6 = 5$
5. $z + {}^-15 = {}^-4$	6. $w + {}^-8 = {}^-8$	7. $y + 12 = 11$	8. $z + 9 = 19$
9. $x - {}^-3 = {}^-5$	10. $y - 6 = {}^-9$	11. $x - {}^-8 = 6$	12. $w - 5 = 7$
13. $z - {}^-15 = 12$	14. $w - {}^-18 = {}^-11$	15. $y - 19 = 10$	16. $x - 16 = {}^-15$
17. $y + 18 = {}^-12$	18. $x - {}^-21 = 17$	19. $z + 16 = {}^-20$	20. $w - {}^-14 = 16$

Set 78 Solve.

1. $3x = {}^-27$	2. $4w = 28$	3. ${}^-2y = {}^-32$	4. ${}^-5x = 30$
5. ${}^-6w = 15$	6. $8x = {}^-7$	7. $10z = {}^-16$	8. ${}^-12y = 8$
9. $\frac{x}{{}^-2} = 5$	10. $\frac{z}{{}^-5} = 3$	11. $\frac{w}{6} = 4$	12. $\frac{y}{9} = 6$
13. $\frac{y}{{}^-12} = 10$	14. $\frac{x}{18} = 11$	15. $\frac{z}{{}^-16} = {}^-12$	16. $\frac{w}{20} = {}^-12$
17. $9x = {}^-52$	18. $\frac{w}{{}^-6} = {}^-17$	19. ${}^-11y = 64$	20. $\frac{z}{19} = {}^-11$

Set 79 Solve.

1. ${}^-2x + 6 = 3$	2. $4y + 5 = 6$	3. ${}^-2y - 8 = {}^-8$	4. $8x - {}^-4 = 9$
5. $5w + {}^-4 = {}^-5$	6. ${}^-3x - 7 = 0$	7. $8w + {}^-9 = 2$	8. ${}^-6y - 8 = 2$
9. $\frac{w}{5} + 10 = {}^-6$	10. $\frac{x}{3} + 19 = 5$	11. $\frac{y}{4} - {}^-13 = 7$	12. $\frac{z}{6} - {}^-16 = {}^-5$
13. $\frac{y}{{}^-9} - 3 = 4$	14. $\frac{z}{8} + {}^-8 = {}^-9$	15. $\frac{w}{{}^-5} - 6 = {}^-4$	16. $\frac{x}{8} + 9 = 8$
17. $5y + {}^-2 = {}^-5$	18. ${}^-7x - {}^-4 = 15$	19. $\frac{w}{{}^-3} + 7 = 11$	20. $\frac{z}{4} - {}^-10 = 12$

Set 80 Draw a pair of axes on graph paper. Locate these points. Label each with its letter.

1. $A{:}(0, 4)$	2. $W{:}(3, 0)$	3. $R{:}(1, 5)$	4. $T{:}(5, 1)$	5. $D{:}(5, 8)$	6. $G{:}(6, 0)$
7. $J{:}(3, 5)$	8. $K{:}(2, 7)$	9. $B{:}(3, 5)$	10. $V{:}(6, 3)$	11. $U{:}(7, 2)$	12. $X{:}(5, 4)$
13. $F{:}(1, 2)$	14. $C{:}(4, 2)$	15. $S{:}(0, 8)$	16. $E{:}(8, 5)$	17. $Z{:}(7, 6)$	18. $H{:}(8, 1)$

Set 81 Give the coordinates.

1. Point *A*
2. Point *B*
3. Point *C*
4. Point *D*
5. Point *E*
6. Point *F*
7. Point *G*
8. Point *H*
9. Point *I*
10. Point *J*
11. Point *K*
12. Point *L*

second coordinate axis

first coordinate axis

Set 82 First tell how many outcomes. Then tell whether they are equally likely.

1. Toss die with sides numbered 1, 2, 3, 4. Look at the bottom number.

2. Toss die with sides numbered 1–6. Look at the top number.

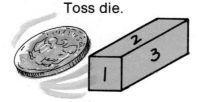

3. Spin this spinner. Look at the color where the arrow lands.

4. Toss coin. Toss die.

5. Toss coin. Toss die.

6. Toss die. Spin spinner.

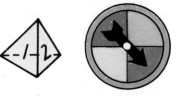

Set 83 Give each probability.

Event:
Toss a cube with sides numbered 1–6.

1. *P*(1)
2. *P*(even number)
3. *P*(2)
4. *P*(not 2)
5. *P*(odd number)
6. *P*(prime number)
7. *P*(less than 2)
8. *P*(greater than 3)
9. *P*(1 or 3)
10. *P*(1 and 3)

Set 84 **Give each probability.**

Event:
Toss a cube with
sides numbered 1–6.
Toss the cube again.

1. P(3 and then 4)
2. P(even number and then even number)
3. P(1 and then odd number)
4. P(prime number and then composite number)
5. P(2 and then not 3)
6. P(not prime number and then not prime number)

Set 85 **Give the odds.**

Event:
Spin this spinner.

1. Odds in favor of 6   2. Odds against 6
3. Odds in favor of 5   4. Odds against 5
5. Odds in favor of even number
6. Odds against even number
7. Odds in favor of a number less than 2
8. Odds in favor of a prime number

Set 86 **Give the range, mean, median, and mode.**

1. 3, 5, 8, 8, 10, 11, 14
2. 5, 6, 9, 9, 11, 12
3. 32, 38, 45, 49, 50
4. 26, 32, 34, 41, 42, 42, 46
5. 68, 69, 70, 71, 72
6. 39, 43, 56, 57, 65
7. 45, 45, 45, 45, 45, 45
8. 83, 86, 86, 89, 90, 91

Set 87 **The two figures in each exercise are similar. Find the missing length.**

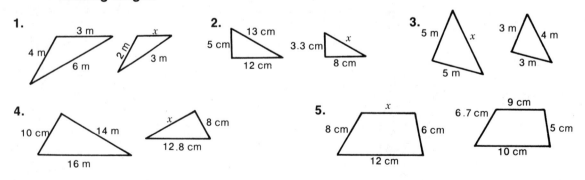

Set 88 Find the missing lengths to the nearest 0.1 meter. Use the table of tangents.

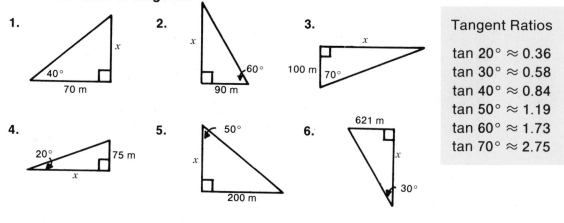

Tangent Ratios

$\tan 20° \approx 0.36$
$\tan 30° \approx 0.58$
$\tan 40° \approx 0.84$
$\tan 50° \approx 1.19$
$\tan 60° \approx 1.73$
$\tan 70° \approx 2.75$

Set 89 Simplify.

1. $\sqrt{25}$ 2. $\sqrt{441}$ 3. $\sqrt{100}$ 4. $\sqrt{900}$ 5. $\sqrt{784}$ 6. $\sqrt{1600}$

7. $\sqrt{1.96}$ 8. $\sqrt{5.29}$ 9. $\sqrt{1.44}$ 10. $\sqrt{10.89}$ 11. $\sqrt{16.81}$ 12. $\sqrt{0.49}$

Set 90 Use the divide-and-average method.
Give an approximation to the nearest tenth.

1. $\sqrt{50}$ 2. $\sqrt{60}$ 3. $\sqrt{85}$ 4. $\sqrt{90}$ 5. $\sqrt{110}$ 6. $\sqrt{150}$

7. $\sqrt{312}$ 8. $\sqrt{456}$ 9. $\sqrt{512}$ 10. $\sqrt{675}$ 11. $\sqrt{860}$ 12. $\sqrt{958}$

Set 91 Find the missing lengths to the nearest 0.1 meter.

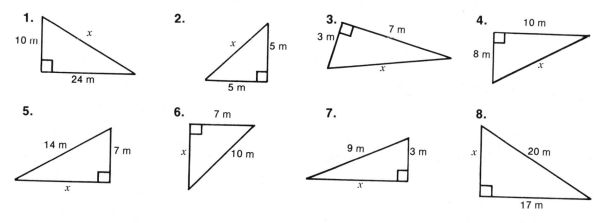

Extra Problem Solving

Airplanes that fly beyond the speed of sound usually have their speeds given in *Mach* numbers. The Mach number is the quotient

Speed of plane ÷ Speed of sound at plane's altitude

This means that the Mach number tells how many times the speed of sound a plane is flying.

Set 1

1. Suppose that a plane flies at a speed of 2000 km per hour at an altitude where the speed of sound is 1000 km per hour. What is the Mach number?

2. Suppose that a plane is flying at a speed of Mach 1.5 at an altitude where the speed of sound is 1140 km per hour. How fast is the plane flying?

3. The speed of sound near sea level is 1190 km per hour. How many kilometers per hour is a plane near sea level flying if its speed is Mach 2.1?

4. At 14,000 m the speed of sound is 1060 km per hour. What is the speed in kilometers per hour of a plane at 14,000 m if its speed is Mach 1.3?

Set 2

1. The first supersonic flight was by Charles Yeager on October 14, 1947. He flew a Bell XS-1 rocket plane at Mach 1.015 at an altitude of 12,800 m. This speed is 1079 kilometers per hour. What is the speed of sound at 12,800 m?

2. In 1962 the Russians held the jet speed record at 2680.99 km per hour. In 1976 a U.S. Air Force jet raised the record to 3529.56 km per hour. How much faster was that?

3. The Wright Brothers made their first flight on December 17, 1903. The longest flight, by Wilbur Wright, was 260 m long and lasted 59 seconds. What was the speed in kilometers per hour?

4. Speeds greater than Mach 5 are called *hypersonic*. On June 27, 1962, J. A. Walker flew an X-15 rocket plane at a speed of Mach 6.06, or 6696 km per hour. The plane was designed to fly at Mach 8 at that altitude. What is that speed in kilometers per hour?

Set 3

The altitude record for a jet plane is 37.65 km.

1. The altitude record for a rocket plane was set in 1962 by Robert White of the U.S. His altitude was about 2.55 times the altitude record for a jet plane (set in 1977). What is the altitude record for a rocket plane?

2. The altitude record for a glider was set in 1961 by Paul Bikle of the U.S. His altitude was 4723 m less than half of the altitude record for a jet plane. What is the altitude record for a glider?

3. The altitude record for a jet plane is about 1.09 times the altitude record for a balloon. What is the altitude record for a balloon?

4. The altitude record for a turboprop plane is 15,549 meters. How many kilometers is that?

Set 4

The distance record for a jet plane is 20,168.78 km.

1. The distance record for a piston-engine plane is 2086.79 km less than the distance record for a jet plane (set in 1962). What is the distance record for a piston-engine plane?

2. The distance record for a glider was set in 1972 by Hans Grosse of West Germany. The distance record for a jet plane is about 14 times this distance. How far did Grosse sail his glider?

3. The distance record for a helicopter is 3561.546 km. How much more is the distance record for a jet plane?

4. Charles A. Lindbergh was the first to fly alone across the Atlantic Ocean. He flew 5810 km in 33.5 hours. What was his average speed in km per hour?

Set 5

1. An off-road vehicle has a tank that holds 22.2 gallons of gas. The vehicle can average 14.4 miles per gallon on the highway. How far can it travel on a tank of gas?

2. An off-road motorcycle has a 3.3-gallon gas tank. It can travel 90 miles on a full tank. How many miles per gallon does it get?

3. A motorbike can go 319 miles on a tank of gas. This distance is 29 miles farther than twice the distance it can go on a gallon of gas. How far can it go on a gallon of gas?

4. Carol drove 825 miles. Her car averaged 27.2 miles per gallon. Gas cost her $1.429 per gallon. How much did she spend on gas for her trip?

5. Calvin filled the tank of his car with 17.2 gallons of gas. He drove 460.3 miles and then refilled the tank with 16.4 gallons. How many miles per gallon did his car average?

Set 6

1. A Japanese 4-wheel-drive vehicle weighed 1701 pounds, 932 pounds of which was on the front axle. How many pounds of weight were on the rear axle?

2. The length of a Japanese car is 152 inches. The width is 60 inches. Its width is what fraction of its length?

3. A Japanese car can turn in a circle with a 33-foot diameter. What distance does the car travel in that circle?

4. Jim had tires with 30-inch diameters on his truck. How far would the truck move as the tires revolved once?

5. How many revolutions of the tires would there be in a mile of driving? (See exercise 4.)

Set 7

1. Ken ordered a fiberglass top for his 1980 jeep for $700. There was a $28 sales tax, a $75 crating charge, and a $37.50 shipping charge. How much did the top cost in all?

2. Terry ordered a 3-inch roll bar for $199.95 and a power winch for $229.95. He had to pay a $23.64 sales tax and a $25 shipping charge. How much did his order cost him?

3. Dan drove his pickup 263.2 miles on 17.2 gallons of gas. Then he added a device that was supposed to increase his mileage (miles per gallon). He drove 299.9 miles on 16.3 gallons of gas. What was the increase in mileage?

4. An auto part was made from $\frac{3}{40}$-inch-thick steel. This was $\frac{1}{40}$ inch thicker than the steel usually used. What was the usual thickness of the steel?

5. Jed ordered special oversized wheels and tires for his truck. Each wheel and tire cost $189.95. How much did a set of 5 wheels and tires cost him?

2. The entry fee for a 125-mile off-road race was $150. Then $\frac{7}{10}$ of the entry fees was returned to the drivers as prize money. What was the prize money if 38 drivers entered the race?

4. A land speed of 608 miles per hour was attained by the driver of a four-wheeled vehicle in 1965. The course was a mile long. About how many seconds did it take the driver to pass through the course?

Set 8

1. The winner of the 1979 Baja International covered the 403 miles in 7 hours and 39 minutes. What was the average speed in miles per hour?

3. In the Indianapolis 500 a driver drove one lap of the 2.5-mile track at an average speed of 184.56 miles per hour. How many seconds did it take to drive that lap?

5. In a race, the winner was 6 seconds ahead of the second-place finisher. If the vehicles were traveling at 60 mph at the finish, how many feet was the winner ahead of the second-place finisher?

Set 9

Technology has produced many benefits.

1. Living standards are higher because of technology—and people live longer. Today people can expect to live to the age of 72 years. In 1900 few people lived past $\frac{2}{3}$ of that. What is $\frac{2}{3}$ of 72 years?

2. In 1850 a stagecoach was fast ground transportation—9 miles per hour. Today an electric rail line in Japan has trains that travel about $14\frac{1}{2}$ times as fast. How fast do the trains travel?

3. Today, Hovercraft in England travel on water at 75 miles per hour. This is $3\frac{3}{4}$ times the best speeds of the clipper ships that sailed the seas in 1850. How fast could the clipper ships sail?

4. Of course, there was no air travel at all in 1850. Today a Boeing 747 can fly 600 miles per hour and the supersonic *Concorde* can fly $2\frac{11}{12}$ times as fast. How fast is the *Concorde*?

Set 10

Technology also has some bad side effects.

1. In the mid-1970's, 3 billion tons of solid waste were produced in the U.S. in a year. If the population was 210 million, what was the average number of pounds of solid waste produced per person?

2. A little over $\frac{3}{5}$ of the solid waste was mineral (mine waste, etc.). How much mineral waste was there in a year? (See exercise 1.)

3. 150 million tons of the solid waste was municipal waste (bottles, papers, etc.). What fraction of the solid waste was municipal waste? (See exercise 1.)

4. Technology has increased the use of fuels that cannot be replaced. 100,000 kilowatt hours of energy are generated in the U.S. per person per year. What is the total amount of energy generated in the U.S. in a year? (See exercise 1.)

Set 11

1. At the Athlete's Foot Shop, jogging shoes sell for $34.95 a pair. Soccer shoes cost $1\frac{1}{3}$ times as much. How much do soccer shoes cost?

2. A pair of tennis shoes costs $\frac{3}{4}$ of what the soccer shoes cost. How much do the tennis shoes cost? (See exercise 1.)

3. A sporting goods store was having a sale. The most expensive tennis racket regularly cost $225 plus $26.50 for stringing. The racket was on sale for $195 including stringing. How much is saved by buying the racket at the sale?

4. Hal bought 2 pairs of sweat socks for $2.95 each plus a sales tax of $\frac{1}{20}$ of the total. How much change did he get from a $10 bill?

2. Jim bought a racket-ball racket for $24.98 and a can of balls for $1.98. He also paid a $1.48 sales tax. How much change did he get from 2 $20 bills?

4. A sporting goods store received a shipment of skis. The ratio of the wholesale price to the retail price was the same for each pair of skis. One pair of skis was marked up from a wholesale price of $90 to a retail price of $210. What was the retail price on skis that cost $105 wholesale?

Set 12

1. This ad appeared in a newspaper:

Cross-country Ski Package
—only $87
cross-country skis $69.95 value
boots $19.95 value
ski poles $8.75 value

How much is saved by buying the package?

3. Hockey skates were priced at $45.50 on sale. They had been reduced to $\frac{7}{10}$ of the regular price. What was the regular price?

5. A pair of roller skates was marked up $60 from wholesale to retail and then marked down $13.50 on sale. The sale price was $121.50. What was the wholesale price?

Set 13

1. A Senegal parrot was priced at $200 and a male canary (guaranteed to sing) was priced at $44.99. How much cheaper was the canary?

2. Suppose that the two birds were each reduced $\frac{1}{4}$ in price. How much cheaper than the parrot would the canary be? (See exercise 1.)

3. For someone who wanted an unusual pet, a pet shop had a Mexican red-leg tarantula. It cost $\frac{1}{8}$ as much as the Senegal parrot. How much did the tarantula cost? (See exercise 1.)

4. A 3-foot-long boa constrictor cost $99.99, while a baby boa cost $\frac{3}{5}$ as much. What was the price of the baby boa?

5. A Florida king snake cost 1¢ less than $\frac{1}{2}$ of what the large boa cost. How much did the king snake cost? (See exercise 4.)

Set 14

To get enough oxygen, fish need some water surface exposed to the air.

Kind of fish	Minimum water surface needed
swordtail	8 in.²
barb	20 in.²
angelfish	25 in.²

1. How many swordtails can live in an aquarium with a 10-inch by 20-inch water surface?

2. How many barbs can live in an aquarium with a 10-inch by 20-inch water surface?

3. How much water surface is needed in an aquarium to keep 2 angelfish, 10 swordtails, and 6 barbs?

4. Bill has an aquarium with a 20-inch by 40-inch water surface. He wants to keep an equal number of swordtails and barbs in it. How many of each kind should he get?

Set 15

1. A 20-gallon aquarium with all accessories was priced at $48.95. During a sale it was 20% off. What was the sale price?

2. Fancy fantail red guppies cost $2.99 a pair. How many guppies could you get with the money you would save by buying the aquarium on sale? (See exercise 1.)

3. Jim bought an aquarium regularly priced at $35.00. It was on sale for 25% off. There was a 5% sales tax in his state. How much did he pay in all?

4. Carol bought these fish for her aquarium:

1 gold-veil angel	$14.99
2 red-tail sharks	$3.99 each
6 green swordtails	$.79 each

   She had to pay a 5% sales tax too. How much change did she get from 2 $20 bills?

Set 16

1. A dachshund was reduced in price from $250 to $149. What was the percent of reduction?

2. A miniature schnauzer was reduced $101 to a sale price of $199. What was the percent of reduction?

3. Did the dachshund or the schnauzer have the greater price reduction? Which had the greater percent of reduction? (See exercises 1 and 2.)

4. A medium-sized dog eats $1\frac{1}{2}$ cups (1 c = 8 oz) of a dog food each day. The dog food is sold in 20-pound bags. How long would a bag of the food last a medium-sized dog?

5. A collie was priced at $280 before a 30% reduction. What was the sale price?

6. A German shepherd was priced at $240 after a $33\frac{1}{3}$% reduction. What was the original price?

Set 17

1. In a men's downhill ski race the maximum vertical drop of the course is 1000 m. For women the maximum is 30% less than for men. What is the maximum vertical drop in a downhill race for women?

2. The highway speed limit for cars is 88 km per hour. Downhill racers have exceeded that by 16%. What speed is attained by downhill racers?

3. The maximum vertical drop in a men's slalom race is 122% of the maximum vertical drop in a women's slalom race. The drop for women is 180 m. What is it for men?

4. The maximum vertical drop in a women's giant slalom is 10% less than that for men, which is 500 m. What is the maximum drop for women?

5. There are 3 standard cross-country ski races for men. One is 30 km, one is 50% shorter, and one is $233\frac{1}{3}$% longer than the shortest race. What are the lengths of the 3 races?

Set 18

1. Jenny took beginning downhill ski lessons using the Graduated Length Method. The first skis that she used were 0.9 m long. When she had completed her lessons, she was using skis that were 89% longer. How long were those last skis?

2. Jenny bought this equipment:

skis	$125
bindings	$48
boots	$95
poles	$15

   How much did she pay in all if there was a 5.5% sales tax on the equipment?

3. Jenny could pay $15 per hour for ski lessons. She could also buy a booklet of tickets for 8 one-hour lessons for $100. What was the percent of savings on a lesson by using the tickets?

4. John bought cross-country ski equipment for $89 and used it an average of 30 days per year for 2 years. He skied for a couple of hours each time in a park 3 blocks from his home. What was the average daily cost of his skiing?

Set 19

1. Carol could buy skis, boots, bindings, and ski poles for $227, or she could rent the equipment for just under 4% of that. How many times would Carol have to use her ski equipment to make it cheaper to buy than to rent?

2. Carol bought the ski equipment and used it for 2 years. She averaged 20 days of skiing each year. A lift ticket cost her $14 each day, food cost her $3.75 each day, and round-trip transportation cost her $5 each day. What was the average daily expense related to skiing? (See exercise 1.)

3. Kevin wants to buy cross-country ski equipment that costs $129. He can buy it on the installment plan for $30 down and $22 per month for 5 months. How much extra does the installment plan cost?

4. Marna works in a ski shop and gets a 15% discount. How much would she pay for cross-country ski equipment that is regularly priced at $145.95?

Set 20

1. Experts can ski cross-country at a rate of 16 km per hour. How long would it take an expert to ski 70 km?

2. The fastest that long-distance runners can run a marathon is about 42.2 km in 2 hours 10 minutes. How much faster is this running rate than the skiing rate? (See exercise 1.)

3. Years ago John Thompson, carrying mail, skied between two cities 140 km apart. Without mail, he could ski at an average rate of 9 km per hour. When he carried 45 kg of mail, his rate was reduced by 40%. How long did one trip take when Thompson was loaded with mail?

4. In a biathlon an athlete skis 20 km. He stops to shoot 5 times at each of 4 targets. He is penalized 2 minutes for each shot that he misses. What is the time of an athlete who skis the course in 83 minutes but misses 3 shots?

5. A man raced in a biathlon. His penalty time for missing shots was 5.4% of his skiing time. His total time was 78 minutes. How many shots did he miss? (See exercise 4.)

427

Set 21

1. In a recent year 81.8 million kilograms of freshwater fish were caught by U.S. commercial fishermen. This was only 3% of the total fish caught commercially. How many kilograms of saltwater fish were caught that year?

2. In the same year 240.9 million kilograms of fish were caught in waters in and around New England. What percent of the total catch was caught in New England? (See exercise 1.)

3. The total fish catch for the world in 1972 was 65.5 billion kilograms. This was a 150% increase from 1945. What was the catch in 1945?

4. With proper management it is predicted that the total catch can be increased to 350% of the 1972 catch. What will be the total catch if this does occur? (See exercise 3.)

5. For 10 years the total yearly U.S. catch was 23 billion kg. But its share of the total world's catch dropped from 13% to 4%. Explain how this could happen.

Set 22

1. Jerry bought a spin-casting rod and reel for $38.95, a tackle box for $4.49, and 6 lures for $1.89 each. There was a 5.5% sales tax on the fishing equipment. How much did he pay in all?

2. One day Jerry caught 3 walleye weighing 1.7 kg, 2.2 kg, and 0.9 kg. His 3 fish together were 58% lighter than the record walleye. How much did the record walleye weigh?

3. Jerry spent 18% of his savings for a boat and 12% of his savings for an outboard motor. This left him with $1200 in savings. How much did the boat cost?

4. After a year Jerry bought a cottage on his favorite fishing lake for $18,000. He paid 20% down and obtained a 9.5% loan for the rest. How much interest did he pay in the first month of his loan?

Glossary

acute angle An angle that measures between 0° and 90°.

addend A number used in an addition problem.

adding 0 property The sum of any number and 0 is the number.

$$29 + 0 = 29$$

adjacent angles Two angles that have a common side between them and a common vertex.

∠1 and ∠2 are adjacent angles.

angle A figure formed by two rays with the same endpoint.

arc Part of a circle.

area The number of unit squares that it takes to cover a region.

associative property of addition Changing the grouping of the addends does not change the sum.

$$(9 + 4) + 6 = 9 + (4 + 6)$$

associative property of multiplication Changing the grouping of the factors does not change the product.

$$(7 \times 25) \times 4 = 7 \times (25 \times 4)$$

average The sum of all the numbers divided by the number of numbers.

axes Two perpendicular lines used as a reference for graphing ordered pairs.

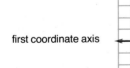

second coordinate axis

first coordinate axis

The horizontal line is the first coordinate axis and the vertical line is the second coordinate axis.

base (of an exponent) The number that is raised to a power.

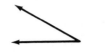

base → 2³ ← power

BASIC A language that a computer understands. It consists of specific symbols such as + and specific words such as PRINT.

basic counting principle. If a first event has *m* outcomes and a second event has *n* outcomes, then the first event followed by the second event has *m* × *n* outcomes.

bisect To cut into halves.

This segment is bisected.

This angle is bisected.

budget A plan for using your money.

canceling Dividing both the numerator and the denominator by a common factor before multiplying fractions.

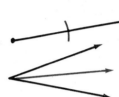

Celsius temperature scale (°C) The metric temperature scale, in which 0°C is the freezing point of water and 100°C is the boiling point of water.

centimeter A metric unit of length.
1 centimeter = 0.01 meter.

circle A curved plane figure with all points a given distance from the center.

circumference The distance around a circle.

commission The part of the total sales that goes to the salesperson.

common denominator A common denominator for $\frac{1}{2}$ and $\frac{1}{3}$ is 6, because $\frac{1}{2} = \frac{3}{6}$ and $\frac{1}{3} = \frac{2}{6}$. A common denominator is a common multiple of the denominators of two fractions.

common factor   2 is a common factor of 4 and 6, because 2 is a factor of both 4 and 6.

common multiple   30 is a common multiple of 5 and 6, because it is a multiple of both 5 and 6.

commutative property of addition   Changing the order of the addends does not change the sum.

$$23 + 89 = 89 + 23$$

cummutative property of multiplication   Changing the order of the factors does not change the product.

$$19 \times 54 = 54 \times 19$$

compass   An instrument used to draw circles.

complex fraction   A fraction in which either the numerator or the denominator or both are fractions.

$$\frac{\frac{6}{7}}{\frac{2}{3}} \qquad \frac{8}{\frac{3}{4}} \qquad \frac{\frac{5}{2}}{6}$$

composite number   A whole number other than 0 that has more than two factors.

compound interest   Interest that is added to the principal at regular intervals. This makes the principal grow and earn more and more interest.

computer program   A detailed set of instructions given to a computer.

cone   A three-dimensional figure with one flat face (known as the base) that is a circle and with one other face that is curved.

congruent figures   Figures that have the same size and shape.

construct   Draw a figure without measuring. Use only a compass and a straightedge.

conversion fraction   A fraction equivalent to 1 that is multiplied by a measurement to convert the measurement from one unit to another unit.

$$2 \,\cancel{ft} \times \frac{12 \text{ in.}}{1 \,\cancel{ft}} = 24 \text{ in.}$$

coordinates   An ordered pair of numbers that locates a point on a grid.

corresponding parts   In congruent figures, the congruent angles and the congruent sides are corresponding parts. In similar figures, the congruent angles and the proportional sides are corresponding parts.

cube   A rectangular prism whose six faces are squares.

cube number   The third power of a whole number.

$$64 = 4^3$$

customary system   The system of measurement that uses foot, quart, pound, and Fahrenheit temperature.

cylinder   A solid figure that has two circular bases that are the same size and are in parallel planes. It has one curved face.

data   Numerical pieces of information.

decagon   A polygon with ten sides.

decimal or decimal fraction   A number written in our place-value system with a decimal point before the tenths place.

decimeter   A metric unit of length.
1 decimeter = 0.1 meter.

degree   A unit for measuring angles. This is a 1° (1-degree) angle.

dekameter   A metric unit of length.
1 dekameter = 10 meters.

denominator   In the fraction $\frac{2}{3}$, the denominator is 3.

dependent events   Two events such that the outcome of the first affects the outcome of the second—for instance, draw a first and a second card without replacing the first card.

diameter The distance across a circle through its center. The length of the diameter is twice the length of the radius.

difference The answer to a subtraction problem.

digits The basic symbols used to write numerals in a place-value system. In our base-ten system the digits are 0, 1, 2, 3, 4, 5, 6, 7, 8, and 9.

discount An amount subtracted from the regular price of an item.

distributive property of multiplication A product can be written as the sum of two products.

$$3 \times (10 + 2) = (3 \times 10) + (3 \times 2)$$

divide-and-average method A method for finding square roots that uses division and averaging.

dividend The number that is divided.

$$3\overline{)18} \qquad 18 \div 3 = 6$$
dividend

divisible One number is divisible by another number if there is no remainder after division. 84 is divisible by 2, since $84 \div 2$ leaves no remainder.

divisor The number that one divides by.

$$4\overline{)36} \qquad 36 \div 4 = 9$$
divisor

down payment The first amount paid when buying on an installment plan.

equally likely outcomes Outcomes such that each has the same chance of occurring.

equation A sentence with an equal sign, such as $3 \times 9 = 27$.

equilateral triangle A triangle with 3 lines of symmetry and 3 congruent sides.

equivalent fractions Fractions that name the same number. $\frac{1}{2}$, $\frac{2}{4}$, and $\frac{3}{6}$ are equivalent fractions.

error of measurement The difference between the true measurement and the recorded measurement.

estimate To use rounded numbers to check whether an answer is correct. To estimate $47 + 32$, you would add $50 + 30$. The sum should be about 80.

even number Zero and the multiples of 2.

expanded numeral A numeral used to show the place value of each digit in a standard numeral.

$$248 = 200 + 40 + 8$$

exponent An exponent tells how many times a number is used as a factor.

exponent

$$2^3 = 2 \times 2 \times 2$$

3 factors

factors Numbers used in a multiplication problem.

$$8 \leftarrow \text{factor}$$
$$\times 6 \leftarrow \text{factor}$$
$$48 \leftarrow \text{product}$$

Fahrenheit temperature scale (°F) The customary temperature scale, in which 32°F is the freezing point of water and 212°F is the boiling point of water.

finance charge Buying an item on an installment plan costs more than paying cash. The difference is called the finance charge.

flow chart A general plan written before writing a program that gives step-by-step directions.

formula A general way of expressing a relationship using symbols.

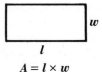

$$A = l \times w$$

fraction A numeral for part of a group or for part of a region. $\frac{1}{2}$, $\frac{4}{6}$, and $\frac{6}{5}$ are fractions.

frequency distribution A table showing the number of times different events occur.

function A set of number pairs of which no two first numbers are the same.

Function rule
$n \rightarrow n + 3$
$(0, 3)$
$(1, 4)$
$(2, 5)$

gram A metric unit of weight (mass).
$$1 \text{ gram} = 0.001 \text{ kilogram}.$$

graph   A picture used to show numerical information. A graph can be a bar graph, a picture graph, a circle graph, or a line graph.

greatest common factor (GCF)   The greatest number that is a factor of each of two or more numbers.

4 is the GCF of 8 and 12.

greatest possible error   Half of the unit used in making the measurement.

hectometer   A metric unit of length.
                     1 hectometer = 100 meters.

heptagon   A polygon with seven sides.

hexagon   A polygon with six sides.

histogram   A special kind of bar graph that is used to show frequency.

hypotenuse   The side of a right triangle that is opposite the right angle. It is the longest side of a right triangle.

independent events   Events such that the outcome of the first does not affect the outcome of the second.

Toss a coin.   Roll a die.

indirect measurement   A measurement that is computed from other measurements rather than measured directly.

inequality   A mathematical sentence that contains a symbol such as =, <, >, ≥, or ≤.

$$3 + 6 < 11$$
$$2r + 5 \geq 6$$

installment buying   A way of buying expensive items. You pay part of the cost (the down payment) when you get the item and then agree to pay a certain amount each month for a certain number of months.

integers   The numbers..., ⁻5, ⁻4, ⁻3, ⁻2, ⁻1, 0, ⁺1, ⁺2, ⁺3, ⁺4, ⁺5,....

interest   The amount a borrower pays for using the money.

intersecting lines   Lines that meet at only one point.

intersecting segments (or rays)   Segments (or rays) that are parts of intersecting lines.

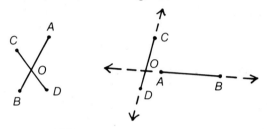

$\overline{AB}$ intersects $\overline{CD}$ at point O.

isosceles trapezoid   A trapezoid with 1 line of symmetry through opposite sides and 2 congruent sides.

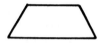

isosceles triangle   A triangle with 1 line of symmetry and 2 congruent sides.

kilogram   A metric unit of weight.
                   1 kilogram = 1000 grams.

kilometer   A metric unit of length.
                   1 kilometer = 1000 meters.

kite   A quadrilateral with a line of symmetry through opposite vertices and 2 pairs of congruent sides.

congruent   congruent

least common denominator   The least common multiple of the denominators of two or more fractions.

least common multiple   The least (smallest) common multiple of two or more numbers.
The least common multiple of 6 and 15 is 30.

leg of a right triangle
Either of the two shorter sides of a right triangle.

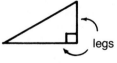

legs

line of symmetry   If a figure can be folded along a line so the two halves of the figure match, the fold line is a line of symmetry.

line of symmetry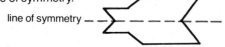

liter   A metric unit of volume.

lowest terms   A fraction is in lowest terms if the greatest common factor of the numerator and the denominator is 1.

mean   The average of all the numbers.

median   If there is an odd number of numbers, the median is the number in the middle. If there is an even number of numbers, the median is the average of the two numbers.

meter   A metric unit of length.
$$1 \text{ meter} = 100 \text{ centimeters}.$$

metric system   An international system of measurement that uses meter, liter, gram, and Celsius temperature.

midpoint   The point that bisects a segment.

midpoint

milligram   A metric unit of weight (mass).
$$1 \text{ milligram} = 0.001 \text{ gram}.$$

milliliter   A metric unit of volume.
$$1 \text{ milliliter} = 0.001 \text{ liter}.$$

millimeter   A metric unit of length.
$$1 \text{ millimeter} = 0.001 \text{ meter}.$$

mixed decimal   A number that has a decimal part and a fraction part. $0.25\frac{1}{2}$ is a mixed decimal.

mixed number   A number that has a whole-number part and a fraction part. $2\frac{3}{4}$ is a mixed number.

mode   The number that occurs most often.

multiple   A product. 4, 8, 12, 16, 20, and so on, are multiples of 4.

multiplying by 1 property   The product of any number and 1 is the number.
$$8 \times 1 = 8$$

negative number   A number that is less than 0.

nonagon   A polygon with nine sides.

number line   A line with its points labeled with numbers.

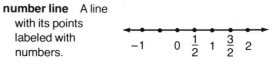

numeral   A name or symbol for a number. Numerals for ten: 10, 2 × 5, 12 − 2, X

numerator   In the fraction $\frac{2}{3}$, the numerator is 2.

obtuse angle   An angle that measures between 90° and 180°.

octagon   A polygon with eight sides.

odd number   A whole number that is not even. The numbers 1, 3, 5, 7, 9, 11, and so on, are odd.

odds   The ratio of the number of ways that an outcome can occur to the number of ways that the outcome cannot occur.

opposites   Two numbers are opposites if their sum is 0.
$$^-3 + {}^+3 = 0$$
opposites

ordered pair   A pair of numbers that give the coordinates of a point on a grid.

origin   The point where axes intersect.

outcome   A possible result.

parallel lines   Lines in a plane that do not intersect.

parallelogram   A quadrilateral with a point of symmetry and opposite sides parallel.

pentagon   A polygon with five sides.

percent (%)   *Percent* means "per hundred." 5% (5 percent) equals $\frac{5}{100}$.

perimeter The distance around a figure. The sum of the lengths of the sides.

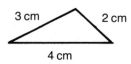

The perimeter is 9 cm.

perpendicular bisector The perpendicular bisector of a segment is the line that is perpendicular to the segment at the midpoint of the segment.

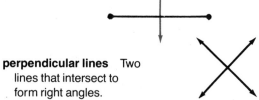

perpendicular lines Two lines that intersect to form right angles.

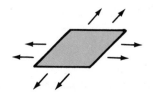

pi The number that is the ratio of the circumference of a circle to its diameter. It is represented by the Greek letter π and is approximately equal to 3.14.

place value A system for writing numbers in which the value of a digit is determined by its position.

plane A flat surface that extends endlessly in all directions.

point of symmetry If a figure fits itself after a half-turn about a point, the point is a point of symmetry of the figure.

point of symmetry

polygon A plane figure made up of segments.

polygons   not polygons

positive number A number greater than 0.

power An exponent. The number that tells how many times a number is used as a factor.

2^3 ← power

prime factorization Expression of a composite number as a product of prime numbers. The prime factorization of 18 is $2 \times 3 \times 3$.

prime number A whole number that has exactly two factors. 2, 3, 5, 7, 11, 13, and so on, are prime numbers.

principal An amount of money borrowed or deposited in an account.

prism A solid that has two bases that are the same size and shape and are in parallel planes. The other faces are all rectangles.

probability The ratio of the number of favorable outcomes to the total number of outcomes.

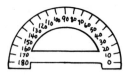

probability of picking black $= \dfrac{3}{5}$

product The answer to a multiplication problem.

proportion An equation stating that two ratios are equal. $\dfrac{5}{8} = \dfrac{30}{48}$

protractor An instrument used to measure angles.

pyramid A solid figure with a face (known as the base) that is any polygon and with all other faces, which are triangles, sharing a common vertex.

quadrilateral A polygon with four sides.

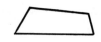

quotient The answer to a division problem.

radius The distance from the center of a circle to the circle. The radius is equal to one half the diameter.

range The difference between the least and the greatest numbers.

rate A comparison by division of two quantities.

$$\frac{87 \text{ kilometers}}{2 \text{ hours}}$$

ratio A comparison of two quantities by division. Below, the ratio of squares to circles is 4 to 2, 4:2, or $\frac{4}{2}$.

ray A part of a line that has one endpoint. This is ray *AB*.

reciprocal Two numbers are reciprocals when their product is 1.

$$\frac{3}{4} \times \frac{4}{3} = 1$$

reciprocals

rectangle A parallelogram with a point of symmetry, a line of symmetry through opposite sides, and four right angles.

rectangular prism A prism whose six faces are rectangles.

regular polygon A polygon that has all of its sides congruent and all of its angles congruent.

relative error The ratio of the greatest possible error of measurement to the actual measurement.

remainder In a division problem, the number that is "left over." When it is added to the product of the divisor and quotient, the sum is the dividend.

$$\begin{array}{r} 3 \\ 8)\overline{29} \\ -24 \\ \hline 5 \end{array} \leftarrow \text{remainder}$$

repeating decimal A decimal in which a digit or a group of digits repeats forever.

0.3333...   1.47474747...

rhombus A parallelogram with a point of symmetry, a line of symmetry through opposite vertices, and four congruent sides.

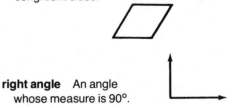

right angle An angle whose measure is 90°.

right triangle A triangle that has a 90° angle.

round a number To replace a number by another one that is easier to use. You round a number to the nearest ten by choosing the nearest multiple of 10. (5 is rounded up.)

13 → 10   27 → 30   45 → 50

You round a number to the nearest hundred by choosing the nearest multiple of 100.

487 → 500   1238 → 1200   550 → 600

Rule of Pythagoras The square of the hypotenuse of a right triangle is equal to the sum of the squares of the legs.

$$a^2 + b^2 = c^2$$

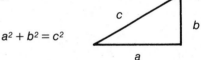

sales tax A tax paid when you make a purchase.

sample A small group, chosen from a larger group, that is examined carefully in order to make predictions about the larger group.

sample space The set of all possible outcomes of an event.

scale drawing A drawing of an object such that the ratio of a unit of length on the drawing to a unit of length on the object is fixed.

scalene triangle A triangle with no lines of symmetry and no congruent sides.

scientific notation A notation for writing a number as the product of a number between 1 and 10 and a power of ten.

$$186.3 = 1.863 \times 10^2$$

435

segment   A part of a line that has two endpoints.

side of a plane figure   One of the segments that make up a figure.

← side

similar figures   Two figures that have the same shape.

simple interest   Interest that is computed by using the formula $I = prt$, where p is principal, r is rate, and t is time.

solution   A number that makes an equation or inequality true.

solve   Find all the numbers that make an equation or inequality true.

sphere   A curved space figure with all points a given distance from the center.

square   A rectangle with a point of symmetry, four lines of symmetry, and four congruent sides.

square number   The second power of a whole number.

$$16 = 4^2$$

square root   The number that can be squared to get a given number.

$$\sqrt{49} = 7$$

statistics   A branch of mathematics that studies numerical facts as a basis for drawing general conclusions and making predictions.

substitute   Replace a variable with a numeral.

$$7a + 3$$
$$7 \cdot 6 + 3$$

sum   The answer to an addition problem.

supplementary angles   Two angles are supplementary if the sum of their measures is 180°.

surface area   The sum of the areas of all the surfaces of a solid figure.

tangent ratio   The ratio of the side opposite the given acute angle to the side adjacent to the given acute angle.

$$\tan 30° = \frac{a}{b}$$

terminating decimal   A decimal fraction, such as 0.5 or 1.47, which is not a repeating decimal.

terms (of a fraction)   The numerator and denominator of a fraction.

$\frac{3}{4}$ terms

transversal   A line that intersects two lines.

trapezoid   A quadrilateral with two parallel sides.

tree diagram   A diagram that shows all the possible outcomes of an event.

triangle   A polygon with three sides.

triangular prism   A prism with two triangular faces in parallel planes.

unbiased   A sample of a given population is unbiased when each member of the population has an equally likely chance of being chosen for the sample.

unit price   The cost per unit (weight, volume, etc.) of an item.

variable   A symbol, usually a letter, that holds the place for a number.

$$8x + 19 = 23$$

vertex   The point at the "corner" of an angle, plane figure, or solid figure.
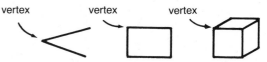
vertex   vertex   vertex

vertical angles   Angles that are formed by two intersecting lines. They have a common vertex but no common side.

volume   The measure of the space inside a solid figure.

whole number   Any of the numbers 0, 1, 2, 3, 4, and so on.

Symbols

$<$	is less than	$\overline{AB}$	segment AB
$>$	is greater than	$\overrightarrow{AB}$	ray AB
$=$	is equal to	$\triangle$	triangle
$\approx$	is approximately equal to	$\parallel$	is parallel to
π	pi	$\perp$	is perpendicular to
$\circ$	degree	$\leftrightarrow$	corresponds to
$'$	foot	$\cong$	is congruent to
$''$	inch	$^+5$	positive 5
$0.\overline{37}$	0.373737	$^-5$	negative 5
$a:b$	the ratio of a to b	$P(2)$	the probability of the outcome 2
$\neq$	is not equal to	$\sim$	is similar to
$\%$	percent	$\tan 30°$	tangent of 30°
$\angle$	angle	$\sqrt{}$	square root

Formulas

$P = 2(l + w)$	Perimeter of a rectangle	$V = lwh$	Volume of a rectangular prism
$C = \pi d$	Circumference of a circle	$V = Bh$	Volume of a prism
$A = lw$	Area of a rectangle	$V = \frac{1}{3}Bh$	Volume of a pyramid
$A = s^2$	Area of a square	$V = \frac{4}{3}\pi r^3$	Volume of a sphere
$A = bh$	Area of a parallelogram	$I = prt$	Interest
$A = \frac{1}{2}bh$	Area of a triangle	$F = \frac{9}{5}C + 32$	Temperature conversion to Fahrenheit
$A = \frac{1}{2}(b_1 + b_2)h$	Area of a trapezoid	$C = \frac{5}{9}(F - 32)$	Temperature conversion to Celsius
$A = \pi r^2$	Area of a circle	$a^2 + b^2 = c^2$	Rule of Pythagoras

Index

Degrees of angle measurement, 241, 261, 353, 370, 371
Degrees of temperature, 45, 69, 103, 309
Dekameter, 90, 93
Denominator, 118–120, 122–124, 126, 128, 130, 132, 134, 144, 184, 200, 218, 220
  common, least common, 122–124, 126, 130, 134
Density, 191
Dependent and independent events, 342, 343
Deposit, 288, 289, 292, 293
Diagonal, 383
Diameter, 45, 91, 98, 99, 105, 113, 123, 173, 175, 181–183, 189, 193
Difference, 26, 27, 126, 127, 134, 139, 307, 333, 354, 412
Discount, 239, 280, 281
Distance formula, 68, 69
Distributive property, 62
Divide-and-average method, 379, 382, 417
Dividend (division), 34
  (stock), 278, 279, 295
Divisibility rules, 60, 61
Division
  by decimals, 34, 35, 379, 382
  of a decimal by a whole number, 32, 42, 43, 115
  equations, 74, 75, 318, 319, 322
  and fractions, 118–121, 130, 148, 149, 150, 226, 407
  of mixed numbers, 156, 157, 161, 407
  related to multiplication, 92, 147–149, 313, 318
  of positive and negative numbers, 312–315, 322, 413
  by powers of 10, 40–43, 92, 93
  with units of measure, 110, 111, 403
  of whole numbers, 14, 60, 61, 398
  zeros in, 32, 40
Divisor, 14, 34, 40, 382
Down payment, 227, 286, 287, 297, 384, 412

Equally likely outcomes, 338–340, 344, 415
Equal ratios, 196–198
Equations
  addition and subtraction, 72, 73, 316, 317, 322, 402, 414
  decimal, 141, 202
  fraction, 152, 153, 407
  multiplication and division, 74, 75, 198, 202, 318, 319, 322, 402, 414
  and percent, 224–229, 231, 236
  in problem solving, 72–83, 141, 153
  two-step, 78–81, 320–322, 402, 414
  writing, 72–76, 78–80, 82, 141, 153, 225, 317, 319, 320, 323
Equilateral triangle, 260, 261, 267, 371, 383
Equivalent decimals, 120–123
Equivalent fractions, 118–124, 126, 128, 141, 156, 196, 200, 220
Error of measurement, 94, 95, 97, 115

Estimating
  in addition and subtraction, 26, 31, 36
  measurements, 91, 103, 113, 201
  in multiplication and division, 28, 31, 34, 36, 156, 348
  with percents, 232, 233
  probabilities, 348, 349
Even numbers, 55, 61, 267, 341, 347, 354, 355, 415, 416
Event, 338, 339, 342, 343, 346, 347, 415, 416
Exemption, 278, 279
Expanded numeral, 41
Exponent, 42–45, 51, 56, 57
Expressions, 64–67, 72, 74, 76, 78, 80, 82

Face, 174
Factor(s), 42, 54–59, 62, 85, 87, 144
  common, greatest common (GCF), 58, 59, 119, 144, 401
Factorization, 56–58, 85, 401
Factor tree, 56
Fahrenheit, 309
Flow chart, 70, 71, 104, 105, 290, 291
Foot, 106, 107, 110, 111, 403
Formulas, 68, 69, 98, 166–172, 176–181, 284, 309
Fractions
  adding and subtracting, 124–127, 131, 132, 134, 150, 405
  canceling, 144, 145
  comparing, 122, 123, 404
  complex, 149, 219
  to decimals, 120, 121, 129, 234, 236, 404
  dividing, 148–150, 156, 407
  equations, 152, 153, 407
  equivalent, 118–124, 126, 128, 141, 156, 196, 200, 220, 404
  and mixed numbers, 129–132, 154, 156, 406
  multiplying, 144–150, 154, 224, 406
  of a number, 152, 153
  and percent, 218–221, 223–225, 229–231, 236, 410
  as ratios, 196, 197
  reciprocal of, 146, 147
  of a region or set, 118, 151, 377
  whole numbers to, 128–131
Frequency distribution, 356, 357

Geometry, 246–271
Gram, 102, 103, 191, 197, 213, 282, 403
Graph, 33, 63, 161, 221, 241, 283, 324–331, 350–353, 356–359, 414
Greater than, 4, 22, 24, 25, 40, 55, 71, 121–123, 130, 146, 279, 303, 308, 311, 335, 347, 404, 413
Greater than or equal to, 71, 335
Greatest common factor, 58, 59, 119
Greatest possible error, 94, 95, 97, 115
Grouping properties, 62
Grouping symbols, 31, 36, 64, 65, 104, 170, 314

3 4 5 6 7 8 9 0

699 ∕ 481
609
699